P9-DGF-085

All about

small gas engines

HOW TO FIX
ALL KINDS OF 2-CYCLE,
AND 4-CYCLE ENGINES

By Jud Purvis
Editorial Consultant, Motor Service Magazine
Member, Society of Automotive Engineers

THE GOODHEART-WILLCOX COMPANY, INC.
Publishers

 Printed in U. S. A. Library of Congress Catalog Card No. 63-22385.

LPIU 122-L

INTRODUCTION

ALL ABOUT SMALL GAS ENGINES Tells and Shows how small Two-Cycle, and Four-Cycle Gas Engines are constructed; how they operate, what goes wrong; how to service and repair them.

With a casual study of Operating Principles, plus some attention to the Service Sections of this book, ANYONE can learn enough about small gas engines to get out of trouble, and stay out of trouble by avoiding conditions that cause trouble.

ALL ABOUT SMALL GAS ENGINES is intended too, as a basic text for those who desire to learn about automobile engines. Much of the basic information given here is applicable to automobile engines. In working with small gas engines, such as used on lawn mowers, chain saws, power plants, outboards, etc., but little shop space, and a minimum number of tools are required. After mastering basic engine fundamentals, the student interested in learning the automotive service business can then go on to the additional subjects of automobile brakes, transmissions, wheel suspensions and other automobile units.

In selecting material for this book, and deciding how to present the material so it would be of most benefit to the reader, the author and publisher have drawn liberally on their successful experience with MOTOR SERVICE'S AUTOMOTIVE ENCYCLOPEDIA. We feel sure ALL ABOUT SMALL GAS ENGINES will be a valuable Instruction Tool wherever it is used.

CONTENTS

CONTENTS

Small gasoline engines are usually complete units having built in fuel and ignition systems and a rope or spring device to facilitate starting.

SMALL GAS ENGINES

Small gasoline engines are made in a wide variety and used for a great many purposes.

The principal difference in these small engines is whether they operate on the two-stroke cycle or the four-stroke cycle. Both are carefully explained in this book. Either of the two basic types may be air-cooled or water-cooled. The differences are important. Eithertype -- air-cooled or water-cooled may have one, two or more cylinders. However all gasoline engines have much in common.

It is essential to have a thorough understanding of the basic principles upon which all of them operate. Otherwise a person might be familiar with one particular type of engine and all but helpless when another type is encountered.

One modern dictionary defines an engine as: "Any mechanism or machine designed to convert energy into mechanical work; a steam engine, internal combustion engine, etc. . ." A steam engine is an EXTERNAL combustion engine as the fuel is burned outside of the engine proper. See Fig. A-1. An INTERNAL combustion engine burns the fuel inside the engine cylinder to produce expansion which is turned into power. Heat of course is a form of energy.

FUEL

The fuel used in most internal combustion engines is gasoline. Other fuels include methanol, benzol, alcohol, alcohol-gasoline blends and liquefied petroleum gas.

Gasoline is a colorless liquid and a relatively light liquid. Color in the form of synthetic dyes is often added for commercial reasons. Originally it was produced from crude petroleum by what is known as fractional distillation.

The gasoline in use today differs considerably from the original product, both in characteristics and method of manufacture, Fig. A-2.

ENGINE DESIGN

When an engineer starts to design an internal combustion engine, he has a number of decisions to make. Of course the purpose for which the engine is to be used will dictate some of the decisions.

One of the very first decisions is whether the engine is to be cooled by water or air.

Any air cooled engine needs some sort of air circulation through the heat radiation fins which are a part of, or attached to the cylinder head and

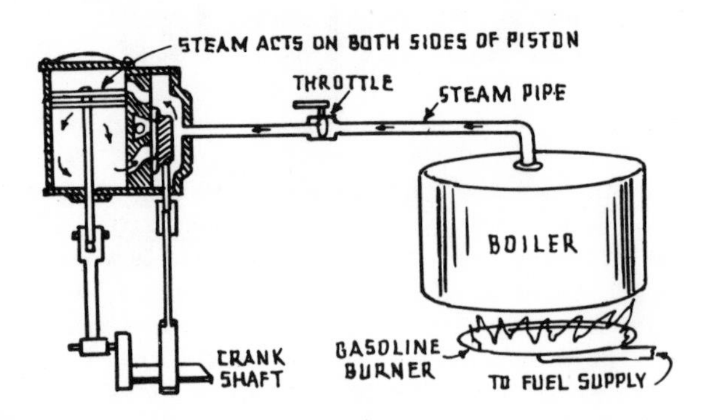

A-1. In an external combustion engine, the fuel is burned outside of the power generating cylinder.

walls. These fins have more radiation surface on the head where the heat is more intense than on the lower cylinder wall which runs cooler. It is often desirable to use a fan or blower to force the air circulation around these fins.

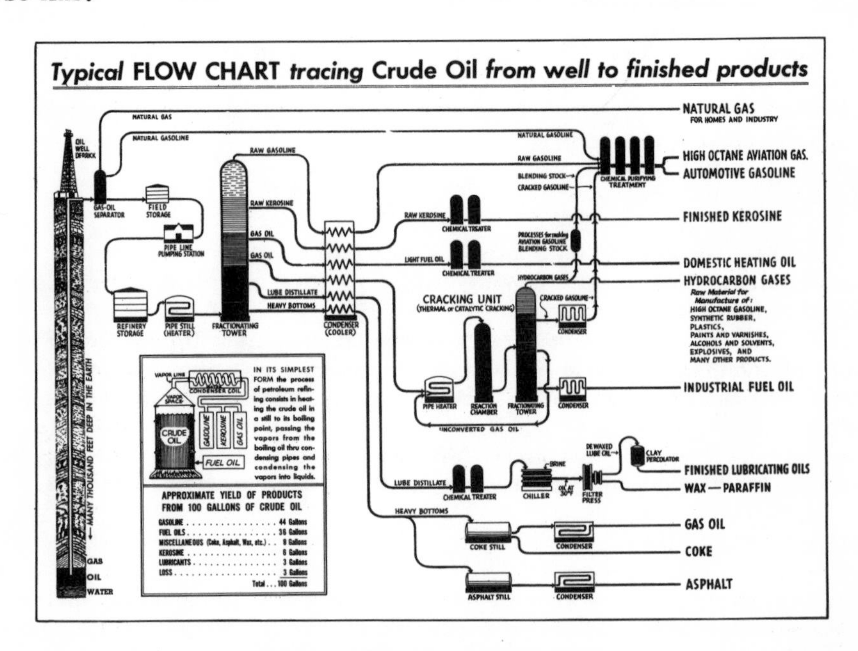

APPROXIMATE YIELD OF PRODUCTS FROM 100 GALLONS OF CRUDE OIL

GASOLINE	44 Gallons
FUEL OILS	36 Gallons
MISCELLANEOUS (Coke, Asphalt, Wax, etc.)	8 Gallons
KEROSINE	6 Gallons
LUBRICANTS	3 Gallons
LOSS	3 Gallons
Total	100 Gallons

A-2. A modern gasoline refinery.

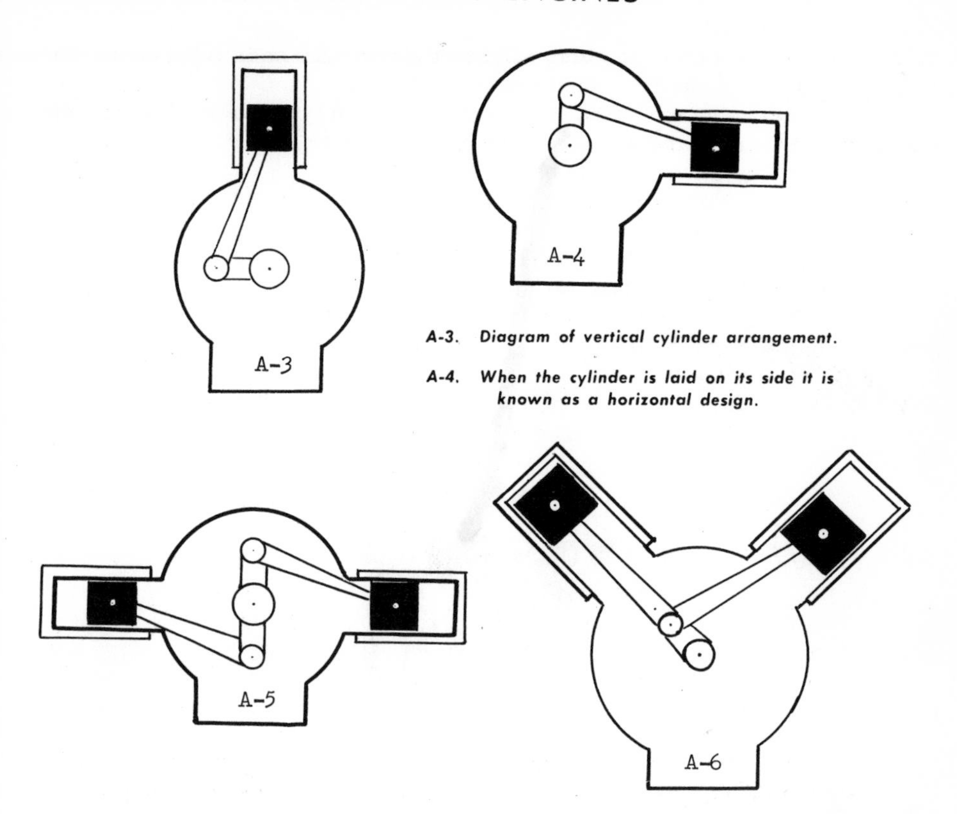

A-3. Diagram of vertical cylinder arrangement.

A-4. When the cylinder is laid on its side it is known as a horizontal design.

A-5. When cylinders are on each side of the crankcase, the engine is known as of the opposed type.

A-6. Where the cylinders are located in two banks at an angle with each other, the engine is called a V-type.

Another primary decision is the arrangement of the cylinders. They can be arranged vertically, horizontally, angularly or opposed. Each is illustrated in diagrammatical form in Figs. A-3 to A-6.

It will also be necessary to decide the size of the cylinders and the number to be used. The diameter of the cylinder can range from less than one inch, as in a model airplane engine, to several feet, as in a ship Diesel. The number of cylinders is almost infinite and single engines have been built having almost all numbers of cylinders from 1 to 28.

Still another decision must be made before the engineer can even start his design. He must decide whether the engine is to be of the two stroke cycle type or operate on the four stroke cycle principle. Both are entirely successful. If the two cycle is selected there will be an explosion in each cylinder every time the piston gets to the end of the outward stroke. In other words, a power impulse will occur each revolution of the crankshaft. In the four cycle (also called the Otto cycle after the name of the designer), there will be one power impulse in each cylinder for each two revolutions of the engine crankshaft.

In any internal combustion engine of the piston type, there is a definite series of events that must occur in sequence. They are:

A) Fill the cylinder with an explosive mixture.
B) Compress this mixture into a smaller space.
C) Ignite the mixture or cause it to explode.
D) Utilize the explosive or expansive force for power production.
E) Remove the burned out mixture from the cylinder.

This series of events must be repeated over and over in the same sequence automatically in each cylinder if the engine is to run.

The first requisite is to fill the cylinder with an explosive mixture. If gasoline is the fuel, it must be mixed with the proper proportion of air.

A-7. Method of introducing the explosive mixture into a four stroke cycle engine through the open inlet valve.

Gasoline itself will not burn. It must be mixed with air in the proportion of 10 to 15 parts of air to each part of gasoline in order to operate in a gasoline engine. Such a mixture is compounded automatically and continuously by a device known as a carburetor described elsewhere in this book.

If the fuel is to be fuel oil such as in a Diesel engine, the oil is injected into the cylinders under high pressure. In some Diesel engines, the heat of the compression is used to ignite the fuel in the cylinders, but in gasoline engines an electrical spark is utilized. The method of creating and timing this spark is described in the electrical section of this book.

FOUR CYCLE OPERATION

The explosive mixture from the carburetor is drawn into the cylinder by a vacuum created when this piston is pulled toward the crankshaft. The

A-8. With both valves closed and the piston traveling into the cylinder, the mixture is compressed.

mixture is conducted from the carburetor through a pipe known as a manifold and is regulated by the opening and closing of a valve. These valves will be studied in detail later. The path of the mixture is shown in Fig. A-7. After it reaches the cylinder the mixture must be compressed in order to increase the power of the explosion.

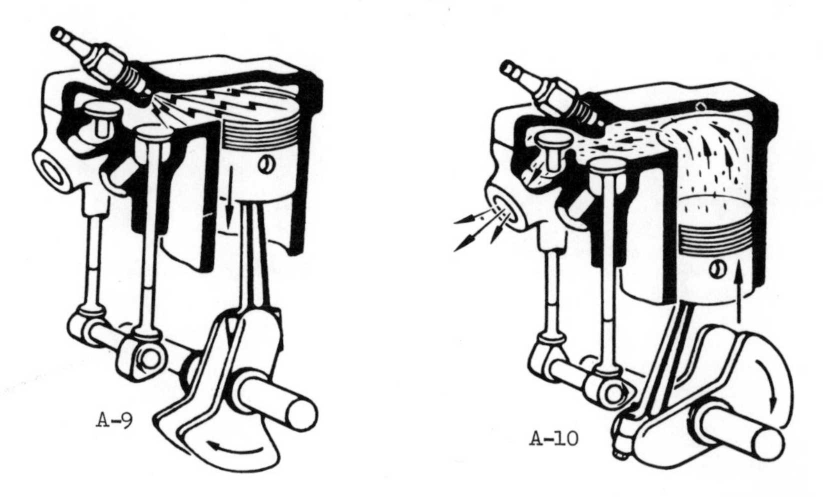

A-9. At the end of the compression cycle, an electrical spark ignites the mixture causing it to burn and expand forcing the piston outward to generate power.

A-10. The exhaust valve opens as the piston again starts into the cylinder to expel the burned gas.

When the piston gets to the end of the stroke, or first cycle and starts in the opposite direction, see Fig. A-8, the valve is closed. As the cylinder is then sealed, the piston as it moves away from the crankshaft compresses the mixture into a fraction of the space it originally occupied to complete the second cycle as shown in Fig. A-9. The crankshaft has now made one complete revolution.

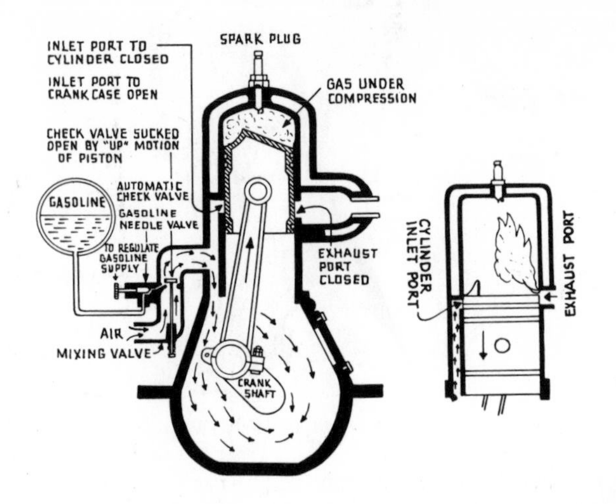

A-11. The path of the explosive mixture in a two stroke cycle engine is shown here.

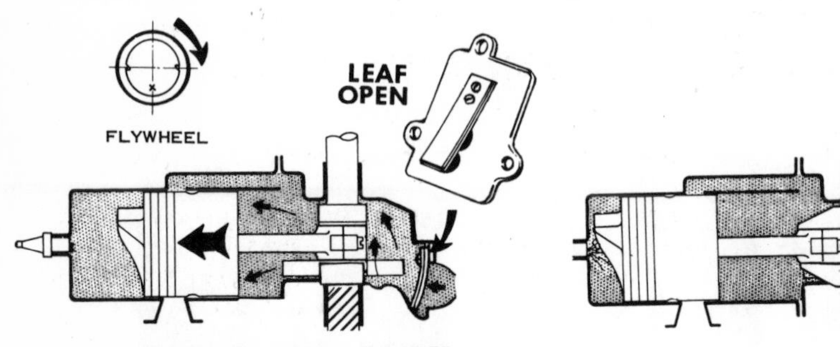

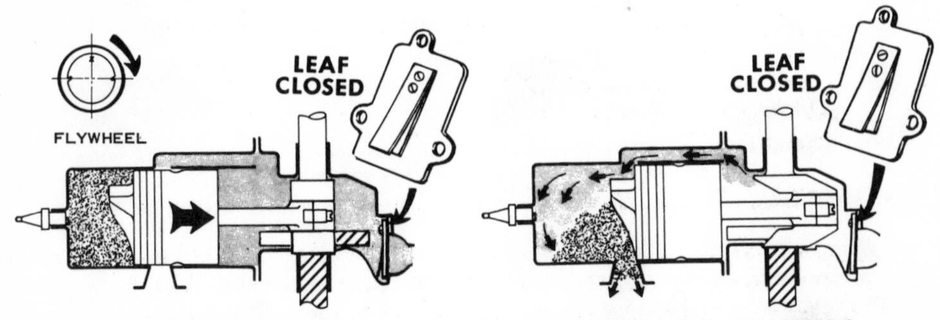

A-12. Diagram of 2-stroke cycle operating principle—leaf valve.

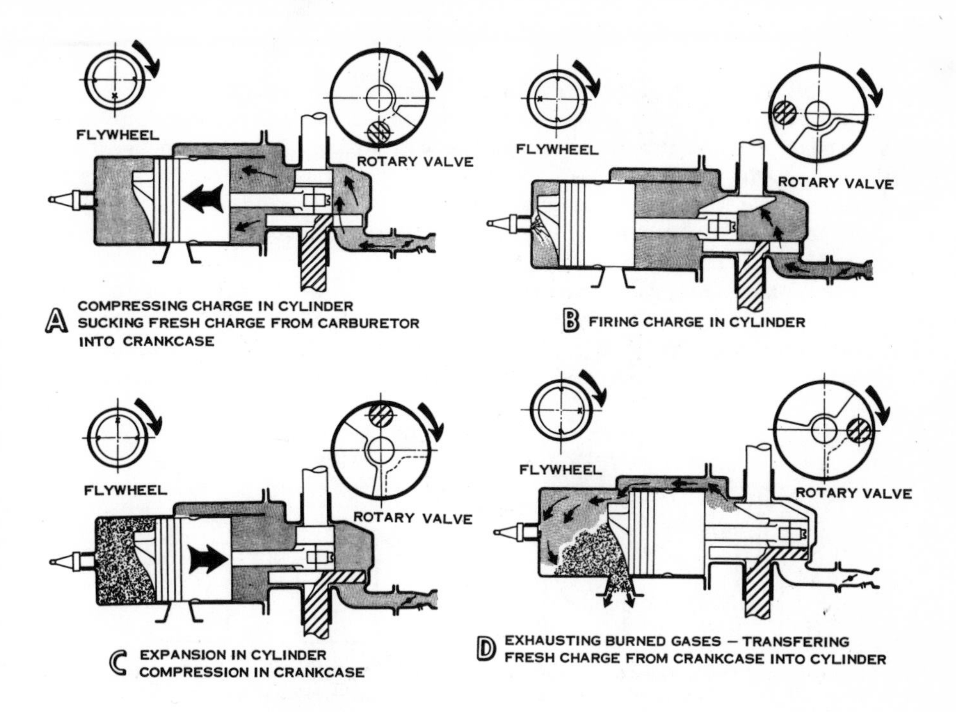

A-13. Diagram of two-stroke cycle operating principle—rotary valve.

At the peak of compression, an electrical spark is caused to occur within the cylinder serving to ignite the mixture. As the burning gas expands, it forces the piston toward the crankshaft and thus creates power to turn the shaft. As the piston reaches the end of its travel, the third cycle is complete.

It now becomes necessary to remove the burned gas from the cylinder preparatory to filling it with a fresh charge. To accomplish this another valve is opened in the cylinder as the piston again reverses its direction. As the piston moves away from the crankshaft to complete the fourth cycle, it pushes the burned gas out through the valve into an exhaust pipe, see Fig. A-10.

Thus the four strokes or cycles of induction, compression, explosion and exhaust are completed while the crankshaft makes two complete revolutions.

TWO CYCLE ENGINES

In the two cycle engine, the piston takes over some of the valve function in order to obtain a power stroke each revolution of the crankshaft. This involves the use of ports in the cylinders as shown in Fig. A-11. These ports are covered and uncovered by the movement of the piston and thus act as a valve in controlling the filling and emptying of the cylinder.

With the type of port shown in Figs. A-12 and A-13, the gasoline and air mixture enters the engine crankcase through an automatic valve. It is drawn into the crankcase when the piston moves away from the crankshaft which creates a slight vacuum in the crankcase. Then when the piston reverses at the end of the stroke, it creates a slight pressure in the crankcase while the piston is moving into the crankcase. When the piston reaches the end of its stroke, it uncovers the port and allows the mixture to enter the cylinder from the crankcase.

At the same time, the burning exhaust gas is still expanding and goes out the exhaust port on the other side of the cylinder. It must be understood that both inlet and exhaust ports are covered by the piston except for a short time at the extreme end of the stroke. A deflector is placed on top

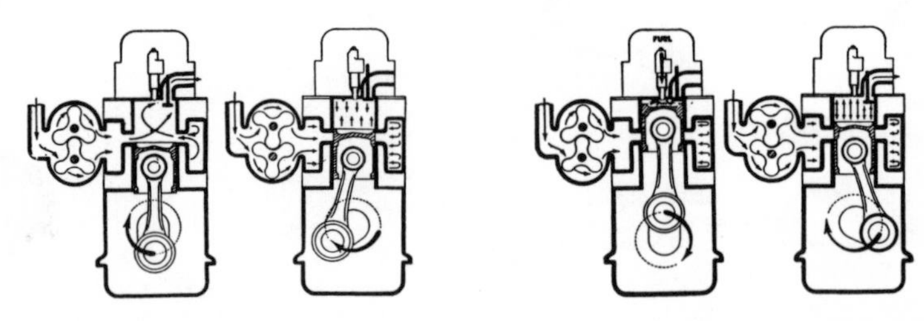

A-14. In this type of two cycle engine, exhaust valves are used and a blower is utilized to push air into the cylinder through inlet ports, while the piston is used to push the exhaust gas out thorugh exhaust valves.

of the piston on the inlet side to divert the fresh mixture up into the cylinder while the exhaust is leaving the cylinder on the opposite side.

Alternate phases of vacuum and compression in the crankcase can be avoided by using a blower or supercharger to push air into the cylinder as illustrated in Fig. A-14. In this particular design, a row of ports around the bottom of the cylinder serves for the inlet. In this case the piston acts as an inlet valve and a cam operated exhaust valve is placed in the cylinder head. In this type of design, used as a Diesel, the blower pumps air into the cylinder and the fuel is pumped in under pressure.

CYLINDER DESIGN

After the basic features of the engine are decided, there are still many possible variations in design to be determined. One important matter is the shape of the cylinder which is determined by the location of the valves. There are four general designs known as: T-Head, L-Head, F-Head and I-Head.

The T-Head as shown in Fig. A-15 has one or more inlet valves on one side of the cylinder and the exhaust valve or valves on the opposite side. This design was widely used in early days when the cylinders were individual or cast in pairs.

The L-Head as shown in Fig. A-16 has both inlet and exhaust valves on the same side of the cylinder. This was the predominant design for

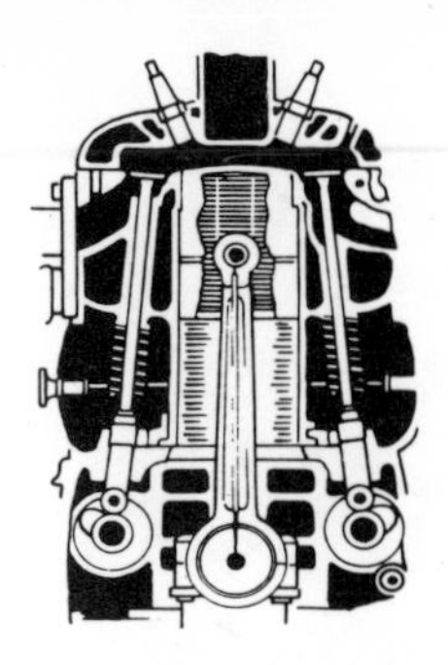

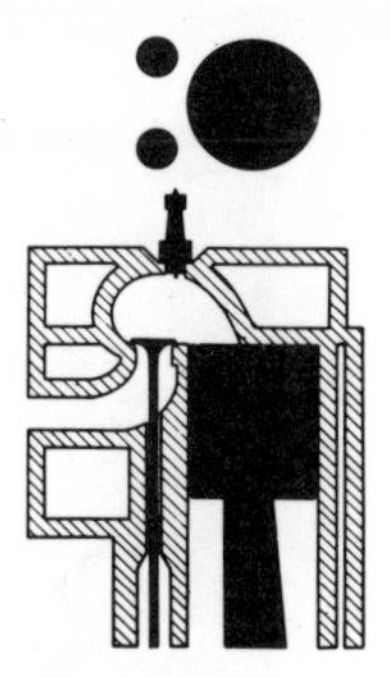

A-15. Location of the valves in the cylinder in the manner here shown is known as the T-head design.

A-16. If both valves are on the same side of the cylinder, it is known as the L-head design.

many years, particularly since cylinders were cast in block form with detachable cylinder heads.

The F-Head shown in Fig. A-17 has never been used extensively, but some excellent engines have been built in this form. The inlet valve is in the head of the block and the exhaust valve located at one side of the cylinder. This is a combination of the L-Head and I-Head design. Also see Fig. A-18.

The I-Head or valve-in-head or overhead valve engine is now the predominant design. This engine has both inlet and exhaust valves located in the head over the piston as shown in Fig. A-18. This design was used in some of the very early engines and continued in use by a few important makers.

Each of the four designs have certain advantages and disadvantages. The same can be said of sleeve valves, rotary valves and other designs.

A-17. One valve at the side and another valve in the end of the cylinder is known as the F-head construction.

A-18. Where both valves are located in the end of the cylinder, the engine is known as an I-head, valve-in-head or overhead valve design.

Changing conditions serve to emphasize some particular advantage or disadvantage at different times and thus influence engine design.

CYLINDER SIZE

Before deciding on the cylinder size and the number of cylinders, the

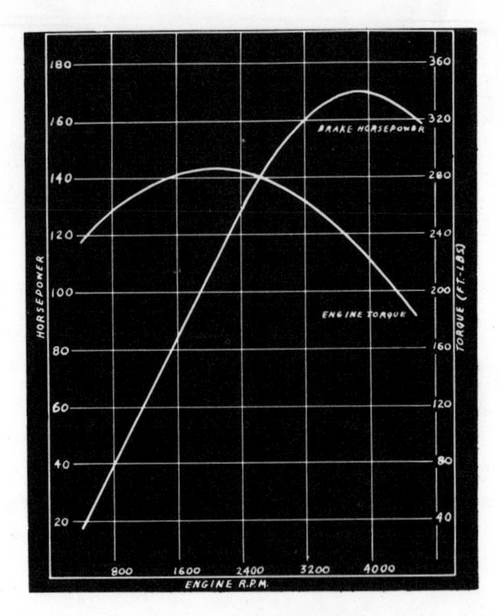

A-19. It will be noted that the developed or brake horsepower of an engine increases very rapidly as the speed of the engine is increased. It will also be noted that engine torque and horsepower are not the same thing and that the torque reaches its maximum at a speed somewhat below that at which maximum horsepower is obtained. This will be explained later in this text.

engineer will need to know how much power is wanted. For example, if the need is for 20 hp. (horsepower) it can be developed by a one cylinder engine having a cylinder of sufficient size. Or the same power can be developed by a 4 cylinder engine having much smaller cylinders. If the engine is to run steadily at comparatively slow speed, the choice might be one or two cylinders. Such an engine would not lend itself to rapid acceleration or high speed operation.

The smaller cylinders would have smaller pistons, rods, etc. . ., and as the reciprocating parts are thus much lighter, the engine can be run at higher rotational speed for a gain in power. As an example of the power obtained by an increase in speed, study the horsepower curve of a typical engine shown in Fig. A-19.

Of course it must be remembered that many improvements have been made in engine design in the past years. Actually, we today obtain about four times the power from a given size engine that we did thirty years ago. This is due to a great number of improvements which have been made.

Of course the bore of the engine is not the sole determining factor in the amount of power that an engine will produce. Neither is the speed at which the engine is operated the determining factor. Many things need to be taken into consideration and will be covered in detail as this text progresses. The tremendous increase in horsepower has been due to a long period of testing and experimenting and huge sums of money have been expended to improve the power output of engines.

It may be seen from the foregoing that the engineer in designing his engine today has many possibilities to consider in order to obtain the size engine that will be needed. To summarize, he can build an engine with large bore, low compression, small valves and operate it at slow speed. Or to go in the other direction, he can use multiple cylinders of smaller size, lighter reciprocating parts which will improve the acceleraion and flexibility, use larger valves and higher compression to obtain more efficient inlet and egress of the mixture in the cylinders, and increase the speed of rotation to obtain the desired results.

HORSEPOWER

RATED HORSEPOWER

This matter of horsepower rating is sometimes confusing as there are several measurements ordinarily used. One is the rated horsepower which is used primarily for licensing purposes. The rated horsepower designation has been with us since the very early days of inefficient engines. At that time some measurement of engine size was desirable and a formula was developed which was felt to be usable for all engines. This consisted of taking the bore in inches multiplied by itself, multiplied again by the number of cylinders and divided by 2.5. While it was a crude measure and served its purpose at the time, it is now misleading.

DEVELOPED OR BRAKE HORSEPOWER

For example refer to an automobile engine: the 1920 Ford four cylinder engine having a bore of 3 3/4 in. and a stroke of 4 in. was rated at 22 1/2 hp. by this formula, but it actually only developed about 20 hp. at 1600 r.p.m. The 1920 Mercer was also a four cylinder engine having a bore of 3 3/4 in. and a stroke of 6 3/4 in. As the bore of both cylinders was identical, each engine was rated at 22 1/2 hp. Actually, the Mercer would develop three or four times as much power as the Ford engine.

This great increase in power was due to the difference in stroke. The longer stroke drew more mixture into the cylinder and provided a longer power stroke. The difference in the two engines is indicated by the cubic inch displacement figures. In the case of the Ford, it was 176.7 and in the Mercer it was 298.2.

PISTON DISPLACEMENT

The cubic inch displacement is a much more reliable figure for indicating the potential power output of the engine. Piston displacement is the number of cubic inches of space displaced by the pistons as they move in the cylinder away from the crankshaft. The cubic inch displacement of an engine can be obtained mathematically from the dimensions.

The area of the piston head is obtained by squaring the bore (the inside diameter of the cylinder times the inside diameter of the cylinder) and multiplying this figure by .7854. This gives the area of one piston. This figure multiplied by the stroke (the length of the distance the piston travels in the cylinder) in inches gives the displacement of one piston. The displacement of one piston in cubic inches multiplied by the number of cylinders will provide the piston displacement of the engine.

POWER MEASUREMENT

Power is defined as the rate or speed of doing work. Work is the action of force through a distance. As an example: lifting 10 pounds to a height of four feet performs 40 foot-pounds (ft. lbs.) of work. Lifting 20 pounds two feet would be an equal amount of work. Another factor is the time required to accomplish the work. If we lift the 10 pounds four feet in two minutes our power would be 20 ft. lbs. per minute (10 pounds times 4 feet, or 40 ft. lbs., divided by two minutes would be 20).

One horsepower is defined as the amount of power required to lift 33,000 lbs. one foot in one minute. The developed or brake horsepower of

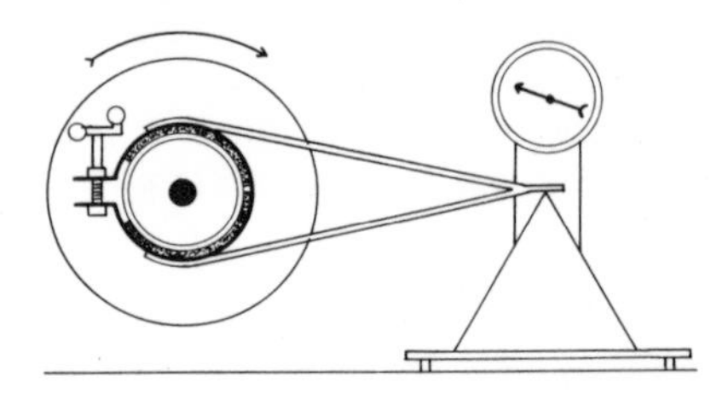

A-20. A brake band mounted on a pulley attached to the engine crankshaft arranged as shown herewith, provides a means of weighing or measuring the amount of power produced by an engine.

an engine is the actual power delivered by the engine. The horsepower is measured by means of either a dynamometer, or what is known as a Prony brake.

In order to set up a "measuring stick" or unit of measurement an engineer named Watt found that a strong horse could hoist 366 lbs. of coal up a mineshaft at the rate of one foot per second. In 60 seconds, or one minute, the horse would have raised the 366 lbs. 60 feet. This would be equivalent to raising 21,960 lbs. one foot in one minute. Mr. Watt added 50 per cent to this figure and decided that one horsepower would represent the power required to raise 33,000 lbs. one foot in one minute. Similarly the same amount of work would be performed if the horse were to lift one pound 33,000 feet in one minute.

PRONY BRAKE

One method of determining the amount of power produced by an engine is the Prony brake test. A pulley is mounted on the engine crankshaft and a brake band applied to the pulley. A lever is attached to the brake band and the other end of the lever rests on a platform scale. See Fig. A-20.

With the engine running, the brake band is tightened which causes the lever to press on the scale. The tighter the band is adjusted, the more pressure will be indicated on the scale. The speed of the engine, the size of the pulley, the length of the lever and the weight or force indicated on the scale can then be used to calculate the developed horsepower.

DYNAMOMETERS

Another instrument for measuring the developed horsepower is known as a dynamometer. This device consists of a resistance creating device, such as an electric armature revolving within a magnetized field. Or a paddle wheel revolving in a fluid may be used to absorb the energy. The engine is connected to the dynamometer and drives it while suitable gauges register the amount of power produced.

INDICATED HORSEPOWER

There is still another power measurement known as indicated horsepower. This is an engineering measurement and is seldom used outside the factory or laboratory. It is a measurement of the force delivered by the expanding gas to the piston inside the cylinder. It does not take into consideration the friction losses within the engine. The indicated horsepower is useful to the engineer who is dealing with compression pressure, expansion pressure and mean effective pressure.

COMPRESSION PRESSURE

Compression pressure is the pressure existing in the combustion chamber when the piston is at the limit of its travel into the cylinder on the compression stroke. The mechanical condition of the engine and the compression ratio, which will be taken up herein, will cause this pressure to vary and there is no set figure for it.

The expansion (or explosion) pressure is at a peak immediately after the mixture is fired in the cylinder. This pressure is of course much greater than the compression pressure, but diminishes as the power stroke proceeds.

The mean effective pressure is an engineering term used to describe the power producing pressures minus the opposing pressures. In other words it is the average effective pressure. In a four cycle engine there is only one power stroke out of every four strokes. The intake, compression and exhaust strokes offer resistance to the power stroke. Also all these pressures vary from one end of the stroke to the other. By averaging up the pressures on all the strokes and subtracting the three pressures that hinder from the one that helps, we will have the mean effective pressure which is a measure of the engine efficiency.

TORQUE

Another measure of engine efficiency in addition to developed horsepower is the torque rating. It is necessary to distinguish between horsepower - which is power - and torque - which is turning effort. The two do not coincide as may be seen by reference to Fig. A-19. This shows that horsepower rises rapidly with the speed up to 3800 r.p.m. on this particular engine and then falls off.

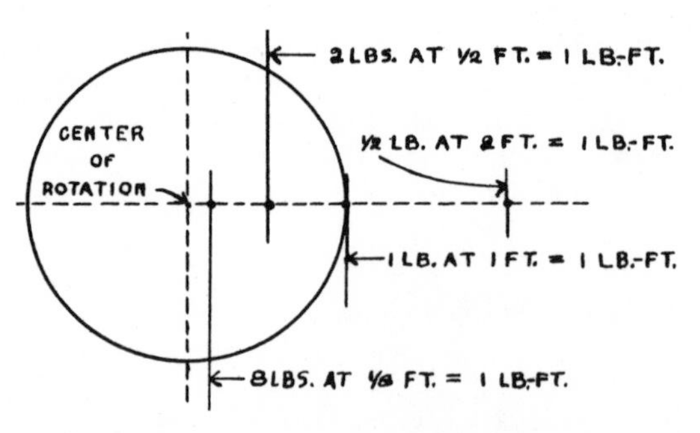

A-21. The amount of torque obtainable from a source of power is proportional to the distance from the center of rotation at which it is applied.

Torque, however, is not so much a function of speed and in fact after a short rise starts to fall off. This falling off of torque as the speed increases above a certain point is caused by the inability of the engine to obtain as full a charge of gas as at lower speed. This will be given fuller consideration later in this text.

Torque is measured in foot-pounds. This means that a foot-pound consists of one pound of effort exerted at a distance of one foot from the center

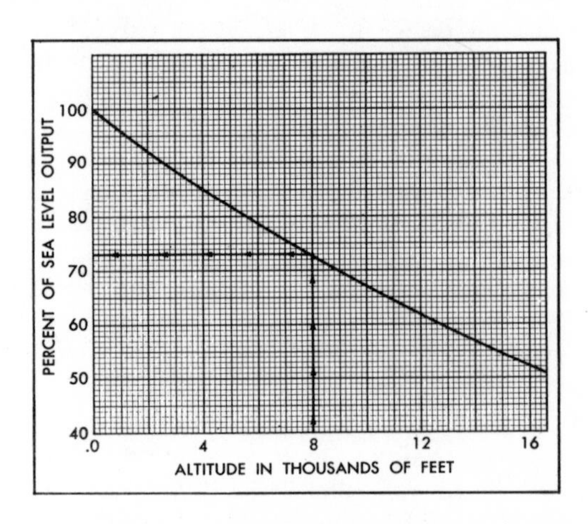

A-22. This table indicates that the power output of an engine decreases rapidly as the altitude increases.

of rotation. Likewise, a pressure of one-half pound at two feet, or two pounds at one-half foot would be the same thing or one foot-pound. See Fig. A-21.

Reference to Fig. A-19 indicates that this particular engine develops its maximum torque of 285 ft. lbs. at 1800 r.p.m. In other words, this would be a force of 285 lbs. at a distance of one foot from the center of the shaft rotation. Likewise it would be a force of one pound at a distance of 285 ft. from the center of the shaft.

VOLUMETRIC EFFICIENCY

The particular engine represented by the curves in Fig. A-19 develops maximum torque at 1800 r.p.m. which simply means that the engine 'breathes' best or has the highest volumetric efficiency at that speed. A maximum amount of explosive gas is being drawn in and utilized to best advantages. At high speeds, less mixture is being drawn in for several reasons: the amount of time available for filling the cylinder is less and the inertia of the gas as well as the friction of the gas flow is increased.

Furthermore, the atmospheric pressure and the temperature of the gas will influence the quantity of mixture drawn into the cylinders. When thinking of gases, VOLUME and QUANTITY should not be confused. The quantity of a gas is measured best by weight. Either a small quantity or a large quantity of gas will completely occupy the volume of a closed vessel such as a bottle or an engine cylinder. Pressure, temperature and volume all enter into the quantity of gas in a container.

Gas is a fluid and therefore it has inertia which slows down its acceleration. Also being a fluid, it develops friction in the carburetor, intake manifold, as it passes through the valves, etc. . . All of this tends to restrict the quantity of gas that will be drawn into the cylinder as the speed of the engine increases.

Furthermore, air weighs less when heated and expanded so the quantity is thus decreased. Also the atmospheric pressure will vary with the altitude and barometric pressure so there will be less pressure at high altitude to push the gas into the cylinders, see Fig. A-22.

SUPERCHARGERS

The better the engine "breathes" - or the higher the volumetric efficiency - the more power the engine will produce. That is why superchargers are so effective in increasing engine power. Superchargers or "blowers" are simply air pumps used to force air or gas into the cylinders. They have been used extensively on racing engines and to a limited extent on passenger cars and trucks. See Fig. A-14.

COMPRESSION RATIO

Generally speaking, the more the gas is compressed in the cylinder the

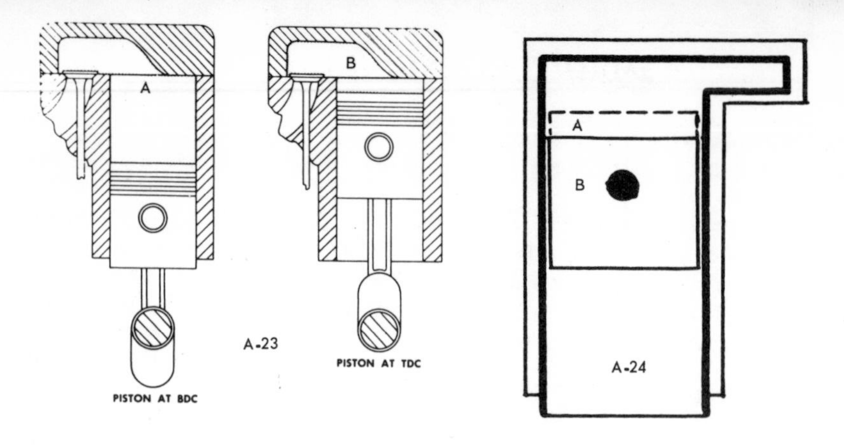

A-23. Dividing the volume A by the volume B gives the compression ratio.

A-24. Compression of an engine can be increased by installing what are known as "altitude pistons" which are longer above the piston pin as shown at A and B.

more power will be created by the burning and expansion of the gas. There are limiting factors as will be explained herein. The design of the engine controls the degree of compression and the degree is known as the "compression ratio" of the engine.

When the piston in the cylinder is at the end of its stroke nearest the crankshaft, it is said to be at "bottom dead center" (b.d.c.). If the engine were of the inverted type it would actually be at "top dead center" (t.d.c.), but as most engines are of the vertical type the term t.d.c. always means the end of the stroke where the piston is farthest from the crankshaft.

With the piston at b.d.c. there is a certain volume of space in the cylinder and combustion chamber above the piston. See Fig. A-23. As the piston moves toward t.d.c. this volume is decreased and the gas within it compressed. If the volume is compressed into one-fourth of the space the compression ratio would be 4 to 1. If compressed into one-sixth of the original space it would be 6 to 1.

Obviously the bore of the cylinder and the size of the combustion chamber will determine the volume within the cylinder. Also the distance the piston travels in one stroke will determine the degree to which the volume is compressed. Piston travel is determined by the stroke of the crankshaft journal to which the piston is attached by the connecting rod.

ALTERING COMPRESSION RATIO

The compression ratio in a given size engine can then be changed by altering the length of the stroke or the volume of the combustion chamber. It is impractical to reshape the original crankshaft, so the usual method is to install a different crankshaft. It is possible to change the stroke slightly by regrinding the crank throws off center. This is often done in building engines for racing purposes.

Perhaps the easiest method of lowering the compression ratio of an engine is to install a thicker cylinder head gasket (or two gaskets). This of course moves the cylinder head away from the block and the compression ratio is lowered by the increase in volume. To increase the compression the cylinder head is often milled or "shaved" off on the gasket face to bring the cylinder head closer to the block.

Another method of altering the compression ratio of an engine consists of adding or subtracting metal in the combustion chamber or on the piston. Thus if metal were to be ground out of the cylinder head the compression ratio would be lowered. If metal was added by welding or otherwise the compression ratio would be raised.

The same result could be obtained by adding to or subtracting from the length of the piston ABOVE THE PISTON PIN. See Fig. A-24. Thus engines operating at high altitudes where the air is "thinner" are often equipped with longer or "altitude pistons."

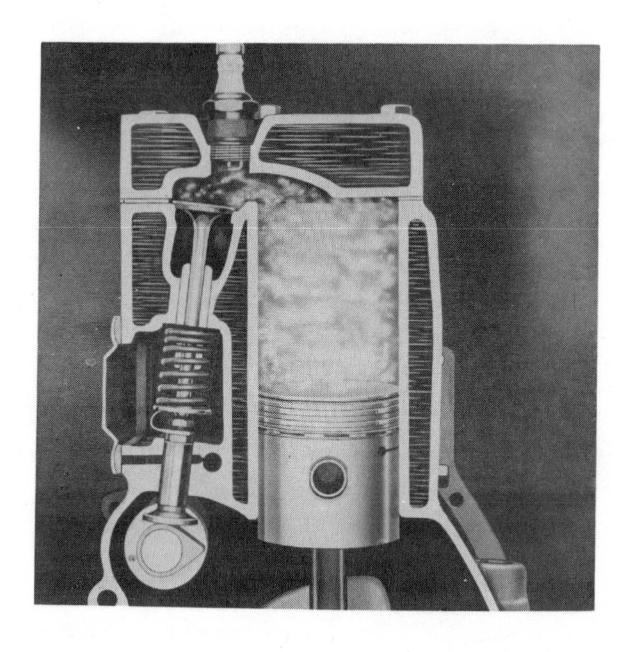

A-25. The combustion chamber of an engine includes all the space above the piston wherein the gas burns and expands to create power.

It will be apparent from the foregoing that almost every design feature and individual part of an engine has something to do with its efficiency. For example, the amount of air entering the engine will be controlled by the density of the atmosphere, the size of the opening in the air cleaner and carburetor, the size and shape of the inlet manifold and the volume that can get through the inlet valves.

All these things affect the amount of combustible mixture that enters the cylinders. Then the efficiency of the combustion will depend upon the degree of compression prior to ignition, the temperature of the engine and gas, the time in the cycle at which the explosion occurs and the ability of the engine to dispose of the burned gas.

Finally, the ability of the engine to utilize the burning and expansion of the gas in creating power will depend upon the friction losses in the engine, the thermal losses and the mechanical conditions such as leakage from worn out or improperly fitted parts.

The foregoing is an incomplete listing of all the things that enter into the efficiency with which the heat in fuel is converted into usable power. All of the factors will be fully considered in succeeding chapters of this book.

COMBUSTION CHAMBER

The combustion chamber is the space within the cylinder above the piston where the burning of the gas occurs. See Fig. A-25. Since the early days, research has continued and is still continuing perhaps at a more rapid pace than ever before on the design characteristics of the combus-

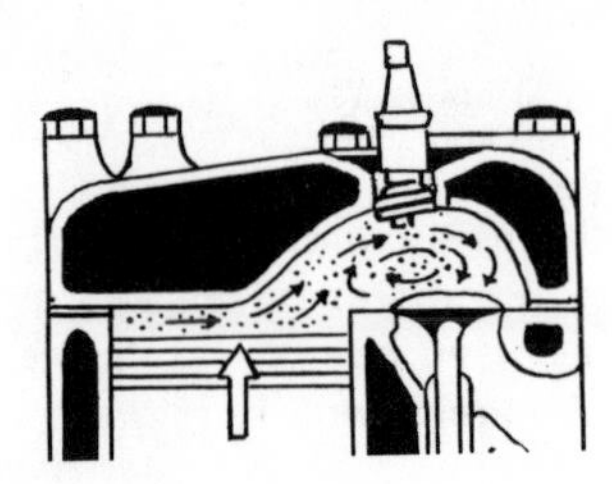

A-26. The shape of the combustion chamber has much to do with the proper mixing of the gasoline and air to obtain maximum benefit from the combustion.

tion chamber itself. This is not an engineering text, but is intended as a service text. We will therefore not get into combustion chamber design any deeper than is necessary for our purpose.

The trend in design has been, and is, to concentrate as much of the expansive force as possible directly on the head of the piston and avoid dissipation of the expansion force in directions that do not produce power. It may be readily seen by reference to Figs. A-15, A-16, A-17 and A-18 that the I-Head engine comes nearer to accomplishing this objective than any of the others.

Another trend is toward the creation and control of turbulence or movement of the air and gasoline mixture within the cylinder to create a more uniform and better mixture of the gasoline and air. One design was developed by an engineer named Ricardo and was used extensively for many years. The principle of this design is shown in Fig. A-26. In the case of extremely high compression engines, some very involved designs have included pre-combustion chambers and specific dams or obstructions built within the combustion chamber.

It has been recognized for many years that the more the explosive mixture is compressed within the cylinder before it is ignited, the more power will be developed by the explosion stroke. A limiting factor other than the strength of the engine parts is imposed, however, by the characteristics of the fuel used. One of these characteristics is the tendency of the fuel to "ping" or "knock" as the compression pressure is raised. Much research and study has been expended on this phenomenon. This knocking, known as detonation, is attributed to irregular and too rapid expansion or explosion of the gasoline and air mixture. The noise comes from vibration of the walls of the combustion chamber.

As a means of overcoming this detonation, ingredients such as tetraethylead (Ethyl fluid or "leaded" gasoline) have been added to the gasoline which serve to slow down the rate of combustion and place an expanding rather than an explosive force on the piston. It has also been found that the shape of the piston and combustion chamber and the action of the gas as it enters the cylinder and is being compressed has a considerable effect upon the ability of the mixture to resist detonation.

The degree of compression employed in an engine is known as the compression ratio and is expressed numerically. In the early days, automobile engines operated on 3 to 1 or 4 to 1 compression ratio. The compression ratio has been increased gradually and will probably continue to increase until it approaches Diesel practice.

It is common practice to build Diesel engines having 16 to 1 or 18 to 1 compression ratio as they run on oil rather than gasoline. It is also common

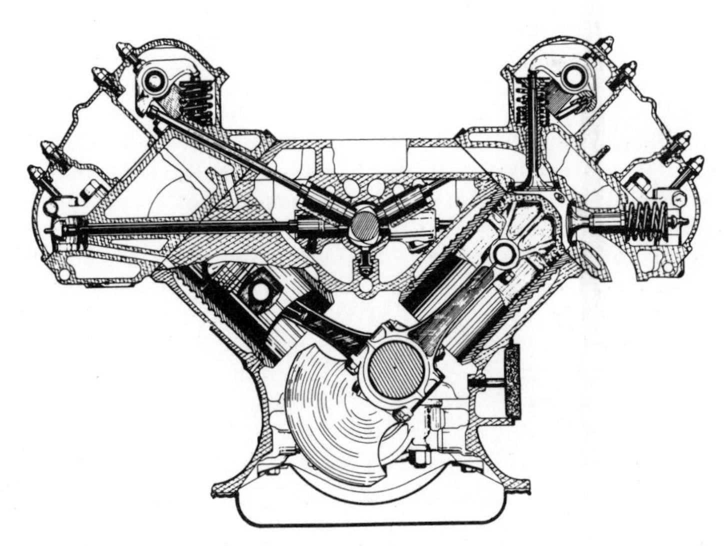

A-27. In this V-type overhead valve engine, the entire engine casting is made of aluminum with cast iron sleeves inserted as a wearing surface for the pistons and rings and steel alloy inserts provided for the valve seats.

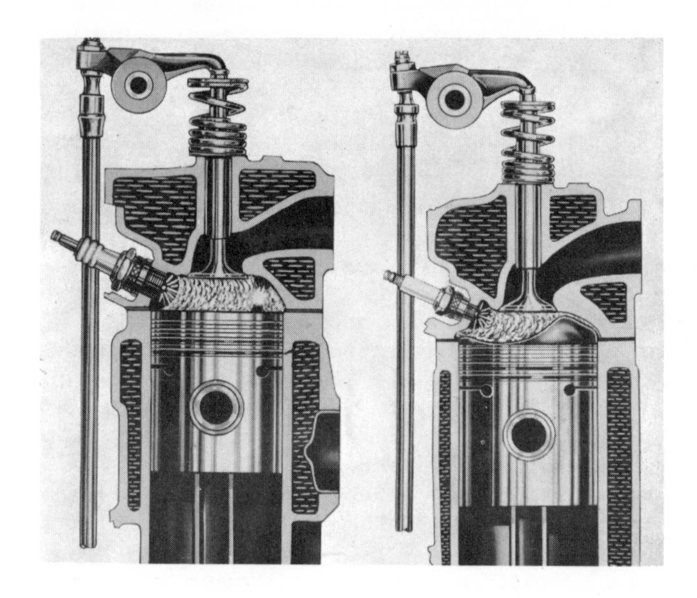

A-28. The shape of the piston head has almost as much to do with the combustion chamber as the contour of the cylinder head.

practice to build racing engines with 15 to 1 and 16 to 1 compression ratio, but these engines are operated on special fuels and under unusual conditions.

In general, however, it is felt that the higher the compression ratio can be raised without incurring too severe penalties from detonation, the more power will be coaxed out of each gallon of gasoline. The anti-knock rating, or detonation resisting ability of gasoline is gradually being increased as refining methods improve. Improvement in gasoline of course permits the use of higher compression.

The material of which the combustion chamber is made and the efficiency of the cooling system also has a distinct bearing on the compression ratio that can be used in a given engine. For example, aluminum pistons and aluminum cylinder heads can operate at higher compression ratios than could cast iron or steel. One reason for this is perhaps that the heat of combustion is dissipated more rapidly to the cooling water due to the superior heat conducting ability of aluminum.

A special type of aluminum is used for the cylinder and crankcase casting of many air cooled small engines. In this case, the piston rings bear directly on the aluminum cylinder wall and the heat dissipating advantages of aluminum are obtained. Also it is entirely practical to make the cylinder casting including the water jacket out of aluminum and insert a cast iron cylinder sleeve or barrel inside the aluminum. An aluminum cylinder block with cast iron sleeves in combination with an aluminum cylinder head and aluminum pistons provides excellent heat dissipation and anti-detonation qualities. See Fig. A-27.

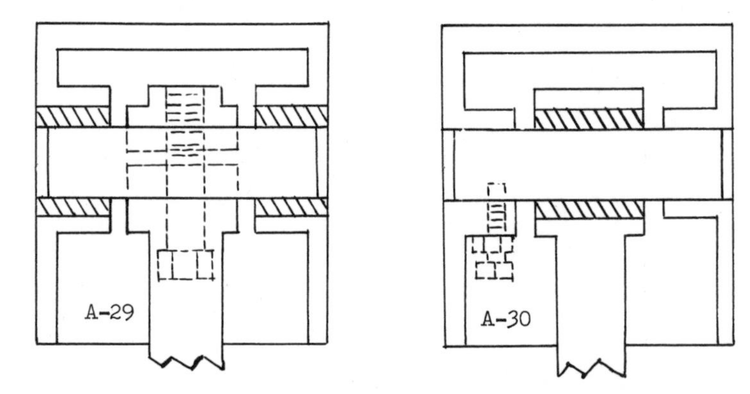

***A-29.** Where the piston pin is anchored in the connecting rod, there is a bearing in each of the piston bosses.*

***A-30.** Where the pin is anchored in the piston, the bearing is located in the upper end of the connecting rod.*

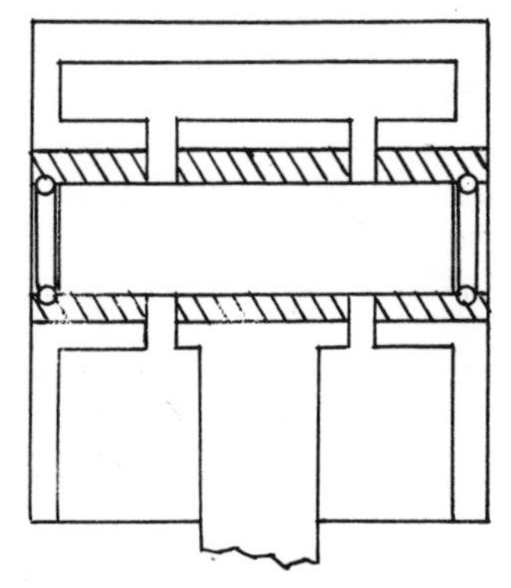

***A-31.** Where the pin is held in place by means of snap-rings or plugs, the pin floats in both connecting rod and piston bosses.*

Conventional pistons for internal combustion engines are shaped like a bucket, but many variations in the specific design are possible. This will be gone into in detail in another part of this text. In general, however, they are made of cast iron or aluminum, carry three or four piston rings and may be flat, concave or convex on the outer surface of the closed end. See Fig. A-28.

The piston pin (sometimes called wrist pin) may turn in the piston and be anchored in the upper end of the connecting rod. It may be anchored in the piston and turn in the upper end of the rod or it may be anchored in neither and turn in both as shown in Figs. A-29, A-30 and A-31.

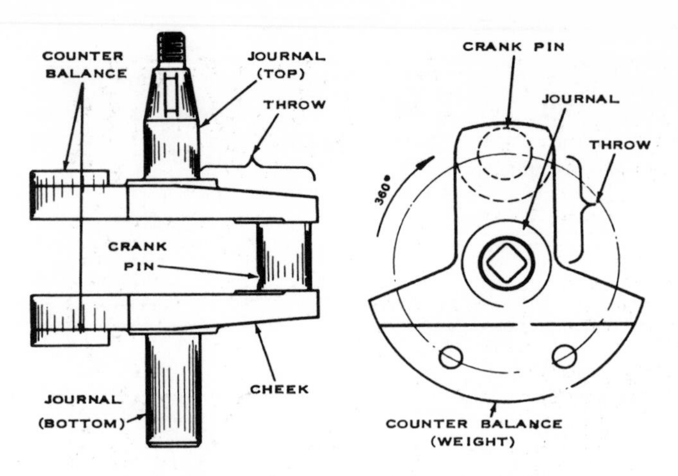

A-32. Single throw crankshaft as used in single cylinder engine.

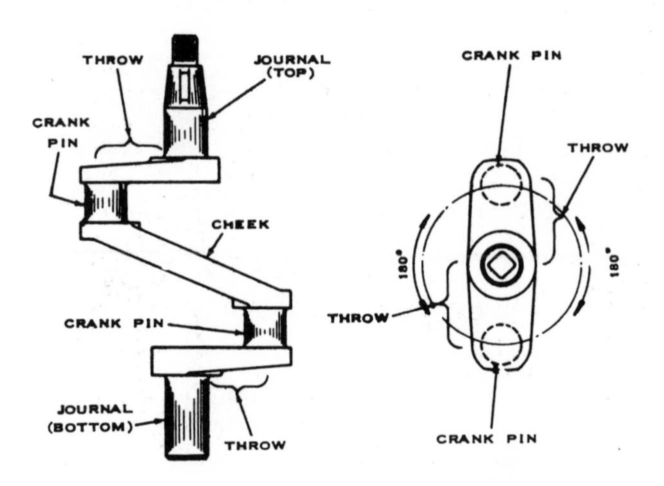

A-33. Two throw crankshaft as used for opposed two cylinder engines.

CRANKSHAFTS

While engine crankshafts are in general quite similar there is latitude for variation depending on the design of the engine. A single cylinder engine will have one throw on the crankshaft as shown in Fig. A-32.

A two cylinder opposed (one cylinder on each side of the crankshaft) engine of the four cycle type will have two throws spaced 180 deg. apart. The cylinders will fire alternately. See Fig. A-33.

The same crankshaft and cylinder location will be used for a two cycle opposed engine having two cylinders, but both cylinders will fire at the same time. See Fig. A-34.

A similar crankshaft will be used for a two cycle, two cylinder, alternate firing engine, but in this case the cylinders will both be on the

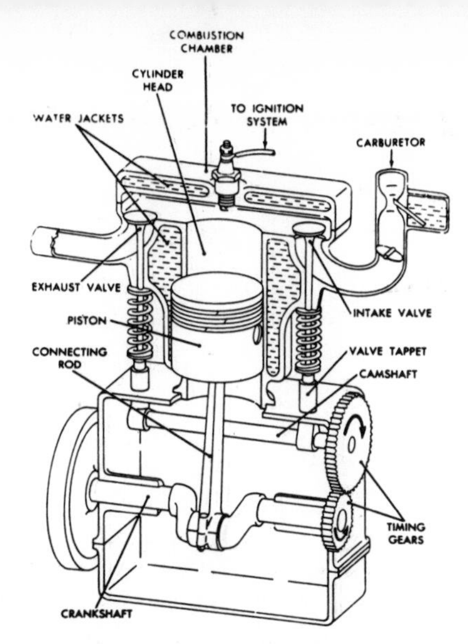

A-42. In the T-head engine design a camshaft is located on each side of the crankshaft.

haust valve must then open and permit these hot gases to flow between it and the cylinder block. It may be readily seen that the exhaust valve may attain a temperature in excess of 1,000 degs. under these conditions. The valve cannot readily be cooled directly by the cooling water in the engine and the only cooling comes from contact with the valve guides and with the cylinder block during the short space of time it is in contact with the valve seat. How short this space of time is may be realized if thought is given to the speed at which the engine operates.

If a four cycle engine is operating 2,000 r.p.m., that means that any one cylinder will fire 1,000 times in that minute and that every time the cylinder fires, the exhaust valve must open to let the burned gas out. Obviously, if the valve is lifted off of its seat 1,000 times each minute, it will not remain in contact with the cylinder block long enough at any one time for much of the heat to flow out of it.

The inlet valve has a somewhat easier task as it is not exposed to the burning gas while it is off its seat. The inlet valve is also cooled by the incoming gas mixture which is at about atmospheric temperature.

Exhaust valves are therefore made of heat resistant alloy steel and are quite often partially filled with mineral salts to help them get rid of some of the heat. See Fig. A-40. It is desirable to keep the weight of the valve and valve operating mechanism as low as possible because they reciprocate at high speed and any excess weight is undesirable. Very strong springs are required to close the valve quickly and hold it tightly on the seat. The valve seat is often also made of heat resistant alloy in the form of an insert which is set into the cylinder block under the exhaust valve. See Fig. A-41.

In the L-Head engine where the valves are located at one side of the cylinder, it is customary to place the camshaft directly under the valves and operate the valves by short push rods. See Fig. A-25. In the case of the

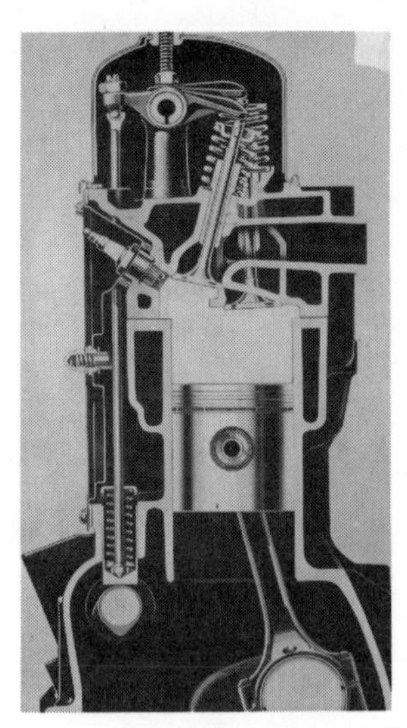

A-43. The reciprocating parts of overhead valves are kept as light as possible.

L-Head engine, one camshaft with a cam for each valve is used. In the case of a T-Head engine, two camshafts are used, one for the inlet valves and one for the exhaust valves. See Fig. A-42.

In the I-Head or overhead valve engine, a single camshaft is usual with a cam for each valve, but in this case a long push rod is used to operate a rocker arm which operates the valve. See Fig. A-43. As the rocker arm, valve and push rod all reciprocate, this represents considerable weight per valve. This has been overcome in some cases by mounting the camshaft or camshafts directly on top of the overhead valves above the engine. This is a satisfactory method, but brings in complications of cost and accurate timing. See Fig. A-44.

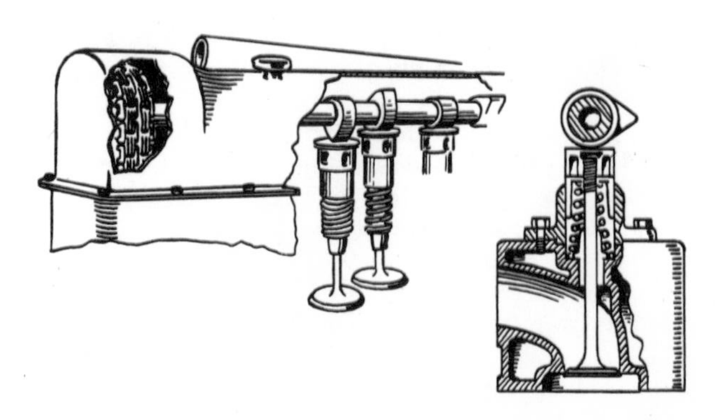

A-44. The camshaft is sometimes placed directly on the overhead valves and operated by either gears or chains.

On the F-Head engine, a single camshaft is ordinarily used, one valve being operated directly by means of a short push rod and the other valve being operated by a long push rod and a rocker arm.

As the valves must be very accurately opened and closed with relation to the piston travel, they are operated either with gears or metal chains. When the gear or chain wears, the valve will not be opened and closed at the exact instant desired and a loss in engine efficiency will be incurred. For this reason, it is usual to avoid long chains or multiple gears in the camshaft drive arrangement.

The extreme accuracy with which it is desired to open and close the valves may be realized when thought is given to the speed at which the valve parts of an engine operate. This timing becomes more and more important as engine speeds are increased. This is the reason for what is known as

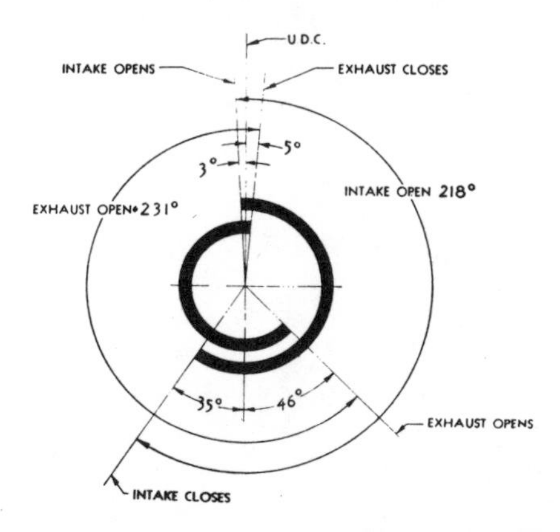

A-45. This diagram illustrates the overlap or time during which both valves are open in the same cylinder. This is necessary in a high speed engine to compensate for the inertia of the gas moving into and out of the cylinders.

valve "overlap." Valve overlap means that the intake and exhaust valves may both be open at the same time in any one cylinder. This, however, is to compensate for the time required by the air or gas to flow through the manifolds.

Theoretically, of course, the inlet valve should open at the time the piston starts down in the cylinder and should close at the instant the piston starts up in the cylinder on the compression stroke. Both valves should remain closed during compression and explosion and the exhaust valve would then open at the end of the power stroke and close at the end of the exhaust stroke. Such would be a satisfactory cycle for a slow speed engine. A valve timing diagram for a typical high speed engine is shown in Fig. A-45.

It will be noted that the inlet valve opens 3 degs. before t.d.c. while the exhaust valve does not close until 5 degs. after t.d.c. Therefore both inlet and exhaust valves are open during 8 degs. of crankshaft rotation.

Damaged threads can often be repaired by the insertion of a special Heli-Coil insert.

CYLINDERS, CRANK & CAMSHAFTS, BEARINGS, PISTONS, VALVES

ENGINE CYLINDERS

The engine crankcase and cylinder block or blocks are often cast in one piece. Even when the cylinders, cylinder heads or cylinder sleeves are separate pieces, the crankcase is still the largest single part in the engine and practically all of the engine parts are attached to it directly or indirectly.

Sometimes the crankcase is an aluminum casting and the iron cylinder block casting is bolted to it. Also the entire engine block and crankcase may be an aluminum alloy casting. At other times, the crankcase and cylinder block may be two separate iron castings and the cylinder head bolted to the cylinder block. In addition, the cylinder heads are sometimes made of aluminum and bolted to the iron cylinder block.

The crankcase of course has the crankshaft and camshaft attached to it and with the oil pan, which goes on the lower surface of the crankcase, forms an oil tight housing in which the rotating parts of the engine operate. The cylinder block of course contains the pistons, which are attached to the connecting rods and crankshaft and in four cycle engines also contains the valves, valve seats and operating mechanism.

Cast iron is the predominant material for engine blocks for several reasons: It is comparatively inexpensive; it forms easily in commercial sand casting procedures; it is quite rigid in comparison to its weight; it is easily machined and possesses excellent wearing characteristics. Engines have been produced almost entirely of steel; steel tubing being used for the cylinders and steel stampings for the balance of the assembly. These parts were welded together to form an engine.

The making of the cylinder block is a high example of the foundry art because of the intricate coring required for the water jackets and other internal passages. The castings are made as nearly to the finished dimensions as possible for three reasons:

A) To avoid excessive machining.

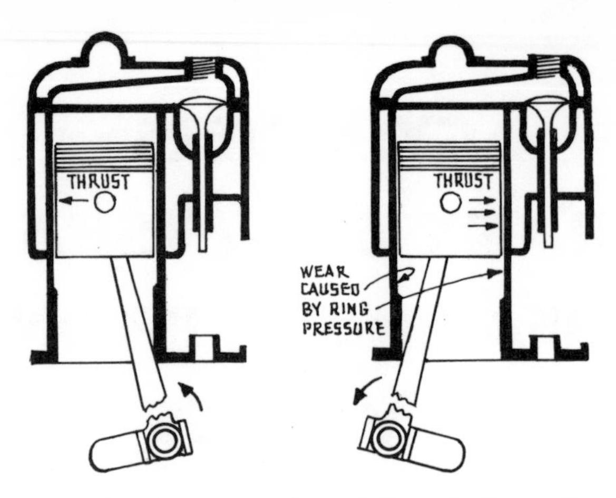

B-1. The side thrust on the piston is greater on the explosion stroke than on the compression stroke due to the greater pressures on the piston head.

B) To have the finer grain of the cast iron near the wearing surfaces.

C) To minimize warpage as much as possible.

The reason for A) of course is obvious as any machining operation costs money and for competitive reasons, engines must be built as efficiently and at as low cost as possible.

Concerning B) it is characteristic of sand castings that the grain of material at the outside of the casting will be finer than the grain in the middle of the casting. As the finer grain machines more readily and produces a better wearing surface, it is particularly desirable to avoid excess machining of the cylinder bores which would cut away the finer outside and cut into the coarser inside of the casting.

C) becomes important in today's production methods. In the early days of the Industry the cylinder blocks were cast and then stacked up like cordwood and allowed to season for several months in order that internal stresses might be relieved and any warpage might occur before machining. As the casting varies in thickness, it does not cool uniformly and internal stresses are created. Some of the most expensive engines were allowed to season, then machined to approximate size and allowed to season some more before final finishing.

Today a piece of pig iron goes through the foundry and the machine shop and becomes a finished engine in a few days. Of course casting methods and foundry practice have improved and some normalizing of the raw castings can be done by heat treatment.

CYLINDER BLOCK WARPAGE

Some warpage does occur in cylinder blocks, but much has been done in the way of design to minimize the effects of the warpage by causing it to occur in such directions that it does not cause the cylinder bores to warp considerably or become excessively out-of-round. Distortion occurs from incorrect placing of the metal masses around the cylinder, from expansion and contraction due to the heat of operation, or from excessive mechanical stresses placed upon it, such as unequal tightening of bolts, etc. . . This warpage can occur in several directions. The cylinder head attachment surface can warp or twist, the cylinder bore may warp longitudinally or become out-of-round, the crankshaft or camshaft bearing bores may be warped out of line, etc.

WATER JACKETS

As it is desirable to avoid distortion of the cylinder walls in order that they may remain round and true in operation, it is necessary to have the cylinder walls as nearly as possible the same thickness. If the casting cores shift, the cylinder wall is thinner on one side than on the other and some minor distortion may occur. It is also felt to be good practice to have the water jackets extend as nearly as possible the full length of the cylinders. It is not always practical to attain these ideals and many successful engines have been built with water jackets less then the full length of the cylinders and in fact, many successful engines are running with no water jackets between adjacent cylinders.

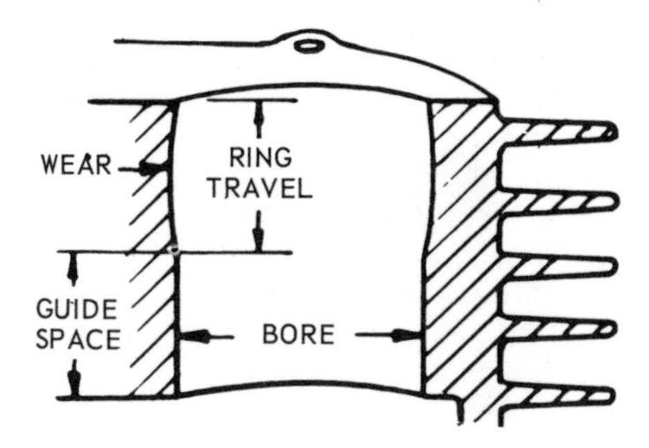

B-2. Cylinder wear is greatest in the top of the cylinder because of the abrasive dust that enters the combustion chamber with the air and also because this area of the cylinder is exposed to the greatest amount of heat. Lower bore has better lubrication and less dirt to contend with and therefore wears more slowly.

It is of such paramount importance that the cylinders be round and true that they are machined and finished to an accuracy of a fraction of a thousandth of an inch. This is in order that the piston and rings which are finished with equal accuracy will have a true mating surface; otherwise, the compression may leak between the cylinders and pistons on the power and compression strokes and oil might leak between the piston and cylinder wall on the suction stroke.

CYLINDER WALL WEAR

Cylinder walls do wear regardless of how carefully they are designed or finished. This is due to the side thrust on the piston in the cylinder, see

Fig. B-1, and the pressure of the piston rings against the cylinder walls. There must be some pressure on these rings to prevent them from leaking compression and oil. This wear occurs mostly in the area covered by the piston rings as they travel up and down in the cylinder. The cylinders wear to a taper as shown in Fig. B-2. The cylinders also wear out-of-round because of the side thrust of the pistons which is due to the angular relationship between the connecting rod and crankshaft. Pressures exerted on the piston are much greater on the power stroke than on any other of the three strokes. As a consequence, the cylinder wears most on the power thrust side and becomes out-of-round.

Reference to Fig. B-2 indicates that the wear at the top of the ring travel is greater than at the bottom. This tapered wear is caused by two facts:

A) The cylinder and piston are hotter and exposed to more grit at the top than at the bottom and therefore wear is accelerated.

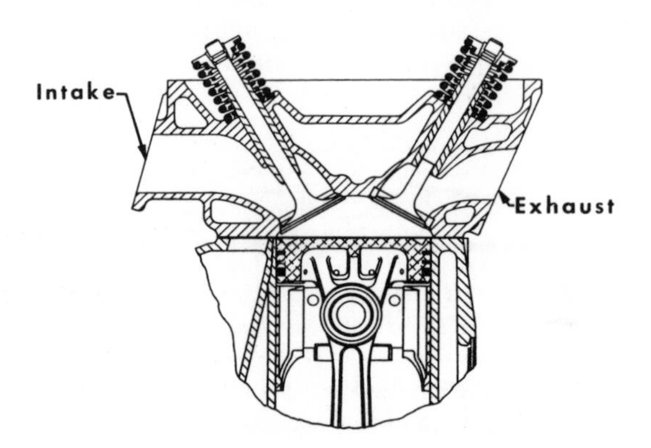

B-3. In the overhead valve design, the cylinder block casting is simpler, but the cylinder head is more complicated as the inlet and exhaust passages must be placed therein.

B) There is more oil at the bottom ring and in the bottom of the cylinder than in the top which tends of course to reduce friction and wear.

This cylinder and ring wear will be given additional consideration later in this text.

In the L-Head engine the valve ports and gas passages are built in the cylinder block. In the I-Head engine these passages are built in the detachable cylinder head. This serves to simplify the valve-in-head cylinder block casting to a certain extent. See Fig. B-3.

COMBUSTION CHAMBER DESIGN

As previously stated, a great amount of engineering effort and experimentation with engines of various designs has resulted in continuous im-

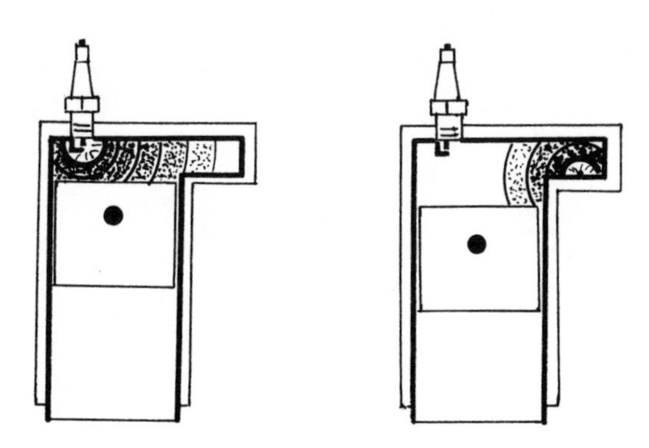

B-4. The explosive mixture in the cylinder should burn progressively away from the spark plug as shown at the left. If ignition occurs before the spark plug ignites it, a second and conflicting flame front will be set up as shown at the right.

provement in combustion chamber design. An engineer by the name of Ricardo found that it was desirable to produce turbulence of the mixture in the cylinder to promote better distribution of the gasoline in the air or in other words, to provide a more thorough mixing of the gasoline and air. He did this by designing the combustion chamber so that the incoming mixture had a swirling action.

Unless there is turbulence or agitation of the mixture, the gasoline has a tendency to separate from the air in certain parts of the combustion chamber and not burn at the same rate as in the rest of the chamber. This causes detonation or knocking.

Further experimentation has resulted in altering the shape of the piston heads and the combustion chamber to produce additional turbulence and consequent better mixing of the gasoline and air. Also the portion of the combustion chamber most distant from the spark plug in an L-Head engine is usually smaller to avoid stagnation of the mixture. Another reason for this is that the surface area is large in proportion to the volume of burning mixture and the heat is transferred faster to avoid a temperature high enough to cause preignition.

DETONATION

By proper design, it is possible to reduce the knocking or detonating characteristics of an engine and thus we might say that the designer can build mechanical octanes into the engine. Gasoline is said to have a certain octane rating which is an indication of its tendency to cause detonation as explained previously.

Detonation is called by several names: Carbon knock, spark knock, timing knock and perhaps others. In any case, it is an uncontrolled burning and expansion. The so-called explosion of the gasoline and air mixture in the cylinder of an engine is actually a controlled burning that is so rapid that it is often referred to as an explosion. It is desirable that the burning action proceed from the point of ignition, which is the spark plug, through the cylinder in a constantly widening flame front. See Fig. B-4. When detonation occurs, this flame front is disrupted.

In order to understand this, we must give consideration to a characteristic of all gases. When they are compressed, heat is liberated; when they are allowed to expand they cool with great rapidity. That is the theory upon which refrigeration is based. Now of course as we compress the mixture in the cylinder, the temperature of the mixture rises. If an explosive mixture is sufficiently compressed, enough heat will be generated to cause it to ignite.

The spark in the cylinder is of course timed to occur at, or near, top center and the burning fuel produces an expansive force on the descending

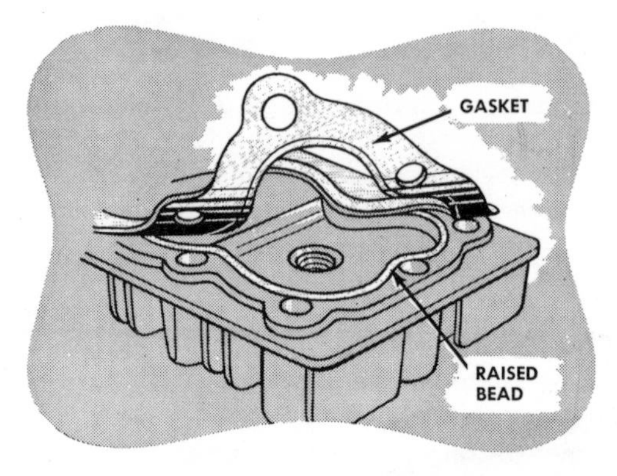

B-5. Cylinder head gaskets must be capable of deforming enough to compensate for any inequalities in the surface of the cylinder or cylinder head, yet must be strong enough to withstand the heat and pressure existing in the cylinder.

piston. Now if the mixture ignites from the heat of compression before the spark occurs or in other words preignites, there is a tendency to drive the piston back down in the cylinder before it gets to the top of the stroke. This of course will cause the piston and combustion chamber walls to vibrate and create the sound that is known as knocking.

Anything that is done to decrease the volume of the combustion chamber, such as an accumulation of carbon, will aggravate this tendency to preignite. Other causes are local "hot-spots." This might be the thin edge of an exhaust valve which often operates at red heat under normal conditions, or an overheated electrode of a spark plug. It might be the thin edge of a flake of carbon, a sharp edge on a cylinder head gasket, etc. . . Preignition is also aggravated by poor cooling water circulation which allows a small portion of the combustion chamber to become much hotter than the surrounding area.

Likewise, an accumulation of carbon on the inside of the combustion chamber acts as an insulator to slow down the transfer of heat from the burning mixture to the cooling water. This of course increases temperatures in the cylinder. Similarly a coating of carbon on the piston head reduces the cooling action of the oil being sprayed on the underside of the piston.

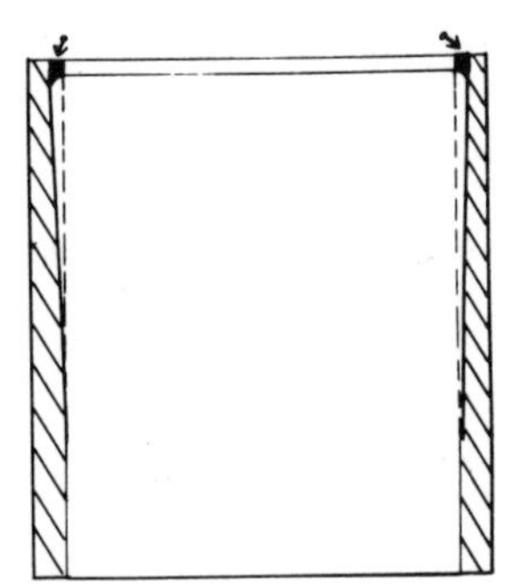

B-6. As the piston rings do not ordinarily travel to the extreme end of the cylinder bore, a shoulder will be left beyond the point of wear in the cylinder.

CYLINDER HEAD GASKETS

The cylinder head is of course bolted to the cylinder block and a gasket is placed between the head and block to maintain a watertight and gastight seal. These gaskets are ordinarily made like a sandwich, two thin plates of soft metal with a reinforced asbestos filling between them. See Fig. B-5. As the water must circulate between the head and block, holes are punched in this gasket to coincide with the matched openings in the block and head. If a poorly made gasket is used, or an improper model gasket used, the flow of cooling water between the head and block will be restricted and hot-spots are liable to result.

It is therefore important to make sure that the correct gasket is used and that it is correctly installed in order that no restriction or closing of the water circulation holes will occur.

INSPECTION AND REPAIR

When an engine is dismantled for repair work, it is necessary to inspect the cylinder block and cylinder head thoroughly to discover any defects that need to be remedied.

As previously mentioned, the cylinder bores wear in tapered form and also often out-of-round. It is desirable to measure the amount of wear and decide whether or not reconditioning is necessary. If the cylinder walls are worn to such an extent that there is a considerable ridge near the top of the cylinder as shown in Fig. B-6, it will be necessary to remove this ridge with a suitable tool in order to remove the pistons and rings without breakage. This will be dealt with more fully in a later chapter devoted to pistons and rings.

It is also desirable to measure the cylinder head surface and the mating cylinder block surface for warpage or damage. These mating surfaces should be flat and true within .020 in. Measurement is made by means of a metal straight edge and feeler gauge strips as shown in Fig. B-7. If the surfaces are warped or damaged, they can be ground flat and true on special equipment made for the purpose.

It is also necessary to inspect the cylinder block and head for cracks. At times, the cylinder wall will crack through to the valve port as shown in Fig. C-27. Repairs are made by drilling and tapping in the crack, screwing in cast iron plugs and machining the surfaces smooth or by welding the cracks shut and refinishing as required.

The valve seats may also be damaged and will require reconditioning or in the case of inserted seats, replacement of the seats. Sometimes these seats are screwed in place and in other cases, they are pressed in place and the edge of the metal block peened over slightly to hold them in place. In either case, they must fit very tightly so that metal-to-metal contact will be intimate enough to offer a full and free flow of heat from the insert to the block and the cooling water. In the case of pressed-in inserts, they are usually broken out and the new inserts shrunk with dry ice to facilitate insertion. This will be covered in more detail in the chapter devoted to valves.

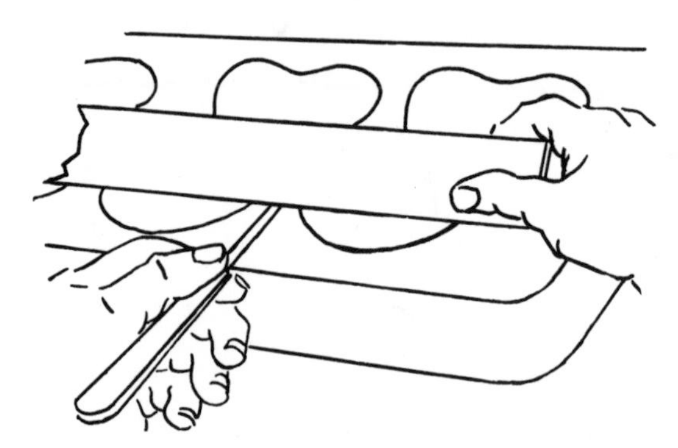

B-7. Flatness of the head and block mating surfaces can be measured with a suitable straight edge and feeler gauges.

It is also desirable to pay considerable attention to the water jackets because an accumulation of lime or sediment at any one point is liable to cause hot-spots, unequal wear due to distortion and perhaps even overheating of the engine. This will be covered more fully in the chapter devoted to cooling systems.

In the case of aluminum heads, it is also desirable to check for corrosion of the metal. Sometimes corrosion of the metal around the water circulation openings will occur from chemicals in the cooling system or even from electrolytic action. If this corrosion is serious enough, it may interfere with the seal of the gasket between head and block and permit water to enter the combustion chamber or compression pressure to escape to the water jacket.

ENGINE CRANKSHAFTS AND CAMSHAFTS

The engine crankshaft is often regarded as the backbone of the engine. It serves to change the reciprocating motion of the piston into rotary motion and handles the entire power output. It revolves in bearings in the

B-8. Typical one cylinder crankshaft as used in West Bend engine.

engine crankcase, must be free to revolve with as little friction as possible, yet must not have any appreciable looseness in the bearings.

For these reasons, the crankshaft is large in diameter, very accurately machined and the bearings, which support it, are of generous size and length. The number of bearings used will depend upon the number of cylinders in the engine and the design of the engine. By locating a main bearing journal between each cylinder, it is possible to use a lighter crankshaft than if two cylinders are placed between each main bearing journal.

MAIN BEARINGS

A one or two cylinder engine of course will usually have two main bearings, a front main bearing and rear main bearing, the rear main bearing always being adjacent to the flywheel. A four cylinder engine normally has three, one at the front, one between cylinders No. 2 and No. 3 and one at the rear.

In the previous chapter we referred to cylinder block and crankcase distortion. This can be serious if the crankcase distorts so as to throw

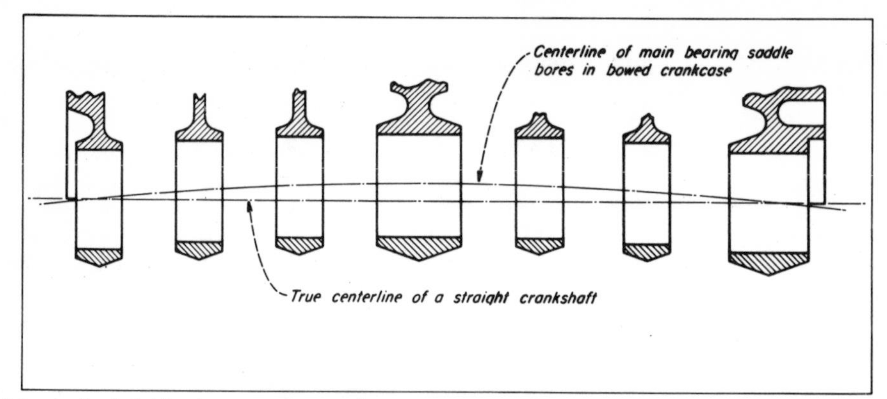

B-9. Lack of rigidity in an engine crankcase may permit the main bearing seats and therefore the bearings to be thrown out of proper alignment.

the engine main bearings out of alignment with each other. An example of this is shown in Fig. B-9.

Crankshafts are usually forged out of one piece of steel. In some cases they are made of cast steel, by a special process. They are usually of one piece, although they are sometimes built up of more than one piece, but in this case each piece must be very carefully and rigidly connected. The bearing journals are all finished in exact alignment one with the other and great care is exercised to see that the journals are absolutely round and not tapered longitudinally. A high degree of accuracy is positively necessary in any work that is done with the engine crankshaft or any of the bearings. This will be covered more fully later in this text.

ENGINE FLYWHEELS

A flywheel is ordinarily mounted near the rear main bearing which is the longest and sometimes the largest of any of the main bearings in order to support the weight of the flywheel. The flywheel of course permits the engine to idle smoothly by carrying the pistons through those parts of the stroke cycle when power is not being produced. The heavier the engine flywheel is, the smoother the engine will idle. However, an excessively heavy flywheel because of its inertia will cause the engine to accelerate and decelerate slowly. For these reasons, heavy duty engines have large and heavy flywheels and high speed engines have light flywheels.

CRANKSHAFT BALANCE

Because of the forces acting on the flywheel and crankshaft and the speed at which they revolve, it is necessary to balance them with great care. They are first balanced statically and then balanced dynamically. To obtain static balance, the weight must be equal in all directions from the center when the crankshaft is at rest. Dynamic balance means balance while the crankshaft is turning. Dynamic balance is attained when the centrifugal forces of rotation are equal in all directions at any point. The balancing operation requires special machinery and involves removal of metal at the heavy points or addition of metal at the light points.

In order to obtain rotating balance, crankshafts are usually equipped with counterweights which are usually forged integrally with the crankshaft, but in some cases have been rigidly bolted to the crankshaft. These counterweights are located on the opposite side of the crankshaft from the connecting rod in order to balance the weight of the rod.

In addition, the connecting rods and pistons are all very carefully balanced one with another so that the rotating mass will have as little vibration as possible.

TORSIONAL VIBRATION

Centrifugal force is one cause of vibration. Inertia forces are another cause. The inertia forces of course come from the connecting rods and pistons which have a certain amount of weight and therefore inertia, and as their direction is reversed twice during each revolution, they must be stopped and started with extreme rapidity. The torsional or twisting vibration is more noticeable in long crankshafts and comes, of course, from the reciprocating movement of the piston being converted to rotary motion.

For example, when the No. 1 cylinder fires, it has a tendency to turn the front end of the crankshaft very rapidly. This force is transferred through the length of the crankshaft to the flywheel which has considerable inertia. The crankshaft then momentarily "winds up" or twists lengthwise to a very small degree, but which is enough to create vibration. Any piece of steel no matter how heavy can be twisted slightly by any torque applied to it. This twisting of the crankshaft depends upon the forces operating in the engine and is more severe at some speeds than at others.

CRITICAL SPEEDS

No matter how carefully the crankshaft and the parts attached to it are balanced, there will be certain speeds at which vibration will occur. These are known as critical speeds and will often cause other parts near them to vibrate also. By means of careful design and balancing, these critical speeds are caused to occur at speeds outside the working speeds of the engine.

In this connection, it is not too difficult to balance rotating parts, but when reciprocating parts are attached to them the problem becomes much more complicated. We have already given consideration to the fact that each one of the heavy piston and connecting rod assemblies must be started, speeded up, slowed down and stopped, twice during each revolution. There are further unbalancing factors that enter into this matter.

OTHER CAUSES OF VIBRATION

For example, the piston does not accelerate and decelerate uniformly during each quarter of a revolution. During the first quarter revolution from t.d.c., the connecting rod moves down a distance equal to the length of the crank throw and also moves away from the center of the cylinder. Both the downward and outward motions cause the piston to travel downward. During the second quarter of a revolution, we have a downward motion again equal to the crank throw, but the end of the rod is now moving back toward the center line of the cylinder which moves the piston up. The result of this is that the actual movement of the piston is less than during the first quarter turn. This is illustrated in Fig. B-10.

It may be seen from the foregoing that all of these forces acting on the crankshaft give it a tremendous job to do and for this reason, too much care cannot be exercised to keep the crankshaft, the bearing journals, the bearings and the engine crankcase in good mechanical condition.

While the crankshaft is very sturdy it does sometimes need attention after long continued use. We have seen that the forces applied to the journal

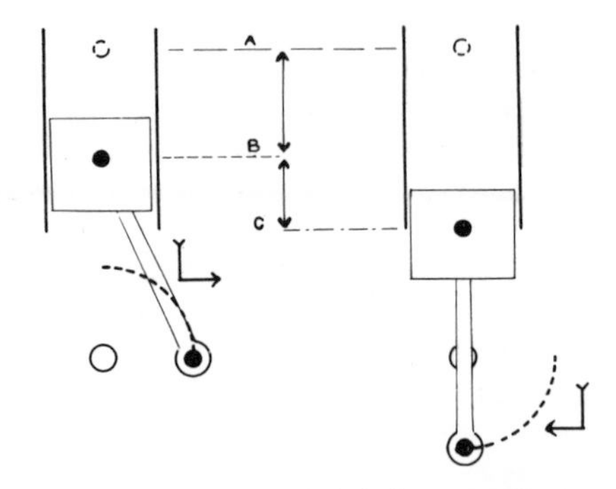

B-10. During the first quarter revolution of the crankshaft from top dead center, the piston moves the distance from A to B. During the second quarter revolution the distance moved by the piston is less as shown from B to C.

are much heavier at some points of rotation than at others. For example, the force of the explosion is several times as strong as the force of the compression stroke. Also the explosion stroke applies the force always at the same spot on the journal. This of course tends to cause a "flat spot" or out-of-round condition on the crankpin journal.

If a connecting rod is bent or out of alignment it will tend to wear the crankpin journal in a tapered fashion - that is, more at one end of the bearing surface than the other end. Also any twisting of the engine crank-case or any excessive vibration of the crankshaft will tend to cause the main crankshaft journal to wear tapered.

Furthermore, if abrasive material gets into the oil the wear may be unequal, more at one bearing or more at some spot on the bearing

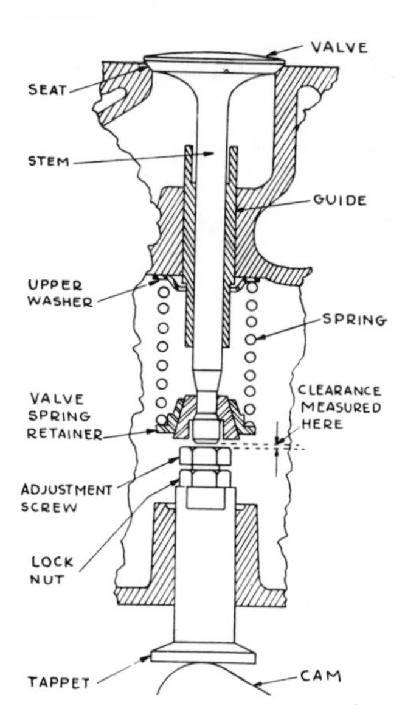

B-11. Typical valve operating parts and layout.

depending on which bearing and where on the bearing the abrasive enters in greatest quantity.

Bearings seldom wear equally for these and other reasons. One bearing may operate with a smaller volume of oil than another for various reasons. This will be discussed in the chapter on lubrication. Likewise one bearing, due to its location in the engine, may operate at a higher temperature than the others. All of these things cause or contribute to unequal wear on the crankshaft journals.

Due to close clearances in the bearings, a sprung crankshaft cannot be tolerated. The main bearings must fit the shaft all around the circumference with only enough clearance for a film of lubricating oil. If the bearing or shaft is scored or other than absolutely round, it cannot be used until it is reconditioned or replaced.

ENGINE CAMSHAFTS

A camshaft in its simplest form is a straight shaft with an eccentric lobe or cam on it. For a one cylinder, four cycle poppet valve engine it would have two cams on it - one for the inlet valve and another for the exhaust valve. These cams would be located at different places around the perimeter of the shaft as the valves need to be opened at different times.

For a multiple cylinder engine there are ordinarily as many cams as there are valves to be operated. See Fig. B-11. In four cycle engines, each valve is opened once every other revolution of the engine crankshaft so therefore the camshaft is geared to run at half the crankshaft speed.

As the camshaft is not subjected to such severe reciprocating forces and runs at slower speed than the crankshaft, it is much smaller and has smaller bearings. The camshaft is usually made of steel and the cams are case hardened to avoid rapid wear on the cam surface.

These cams appear to have a simple shape, but actually the exact shape of the cam is a meticulous job of design. See Fig. B-12. The design is worked out after a painstaking and detailed program of calculation and

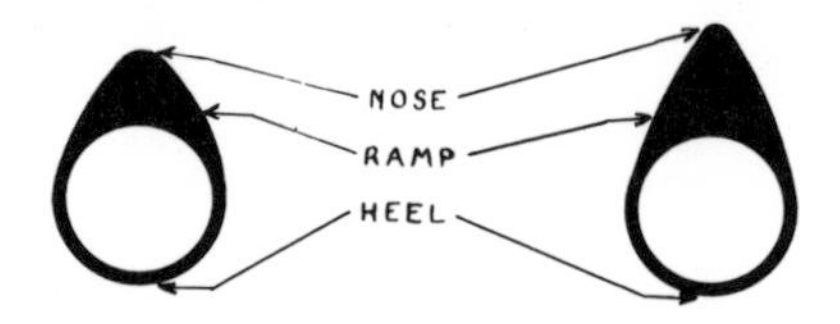

B-12. At left is shown the approximate shape of a cam for a passenger car engine. At the right is shown the high lift type of cam with a long nose and a flat ramp as used in racing engines.

experiment. If the shape of the cams is altered by wear the efficiency of the engine deteriorates with great rapidity. There is much more to the matter than just opening and closing a valve.

This cam is designed to lift the valve at precisely the correct instant of piston travel and hold it open long enough to obtain the most efficient filling and emptying of the cylinder and thus exerts considerable control over the volumetric efficiency of the engine. This will be considered more fully later in this text.

In any engine the ramps on the cams (see Fig. B-12) are designed to open the valve smoothly and gradually. This avoids shock to the valves and valve springs and makes for quietness of operation. The design is usually a compromise between efficiency and quietness of operation.

On racing engines where noise is not so important and utmost efficiency is desired, the cams are often shaped with more abrupt ramps and higher lift. That is, the cam is higher or longer to open the valves wider. Such engines are noisy, idle roughly and wear more quickly.

The location of the cams around the camshaft along with the design of the crankshaft determines the firing order of the engine. At one time the cams were pinned or keyed to the camshaft, but they are now forged in one piece and it is not possible to get them mixed up. When they are worn out of shape, it is necessary to replace the entire camshaft.

As with the crankshaft, it is necessary that the camshaft journals be round and true and that the camshaft be straight and true. There must be no appreciable looseness in the bearings as any radial movement or vibration of the cams would affect the valve operation. It is also customary to provide some adjustment to prevent endwise motion of the camshaft.

If the camshaft is chain driven, it rotates in the same direction as the crankshaft. If the camshaft is driven by a gear meshed with the gear on the crankshaft the camshaft rotation is opposite from the crankshaft. If there is an idler gear interposed between the crankshaft gear and the camshaft gear, the rotation of the camshaft would be the same as the crankshaft.

On the overhead camshaft engine - not to be confused with overhead valve engines - the camshaft is of course located above the cylinder head.

It is often chain driven and the cams bear directly on the end of the valve stems. This construction avoids valve lifters, rocker arms and similar parts. It does permit excellent valve action at high speed as the inertia of reciprocating rods, rocker arms, lifters, etc. ., is eliminated. However, there is cost of construction to consider plus the difficulties of timing lag and noise caused by multiple gears or long chain drives.

ENGINE BEARINGS

Small engines use a wide variety of bearings. Babbitt, ball or roller bearings may be used on the crankshaft for either the main bearings or the connecting rods or both. Either or both ends of the connecting rods may have anti-friction bearings. If ball bearings are used on the big end of the rod, the rod is usually not split, but with babbitt or roller bearings, the rod is often split for ease of assembly.

INTEGRAL BEARINGS

Integral or poured bearings are made by pouring molten babbitt or bearing metal into the bearing seats. The seats are first tinned and the bearing metal adheres permanently until melted out. Also the babbitt metal may be sprayed into the seats from a revolving hollow mandrel.

Babbitt metal is an alloy of tin and other soft metals. For example: 85% tin 7% copper, 7% antimony and 1% lead.

PRECISION BEARINGS

The precision or slip-in type of bearing has become increasingly popular and is now used in engines for both main and connecting rod bearings. The bearing material has also changed considerably and is quite a different alloy from the babbitt metal previously described. Cadmium and silver are mixed with copper, lead and tin to form the alloys now in use. The proportions of the materials used in these alloys vary considerably and their development is the result of much experience and experiment.

Modern precision type bearings consist of a hard shell, perhaps steel or bronze, with a thin lining of anti-friction metal or bearing alloy. They are manufactured to extremely close dimensions and must be handled carefully. When pr̂operly installed they are very durable. When they do wear from continued use, they are discarded and replaced with new bearings.

Fitting and installing them properly involves measurement in fractions of thousandths of an inch. Careless workmanship in fitting cannot be tolerated, as they are not adjustable for wear. We will consider fitting them later in this text.

In order to better understand bearing clearances or fittings, it is necessary to refer briefly to lubrication. Lubrication is dealt with fully in another chapter of this book.

The one most important thing to keep in mind in this connection is that the steel crankshaft journal MUST be separated from the bearing metal when it is running or the bearing will melt. The heat generated by friction when steel moves rapidly on soft dry metal WILL melt the soft metal. Therefore in an engine we use a film of oil between the journal and the bearing. THERE MUST BE SPACE PROVIDED FOR THAT FILM. The film serves to hold the two metals apart and also circulates to carry away the heat that is generated by friction. The space is not great - it is measured in thousandths - but those thousandths are all important. Experts say that engine

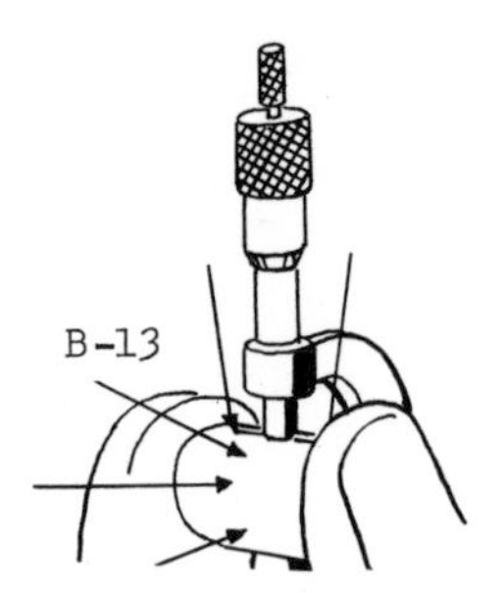

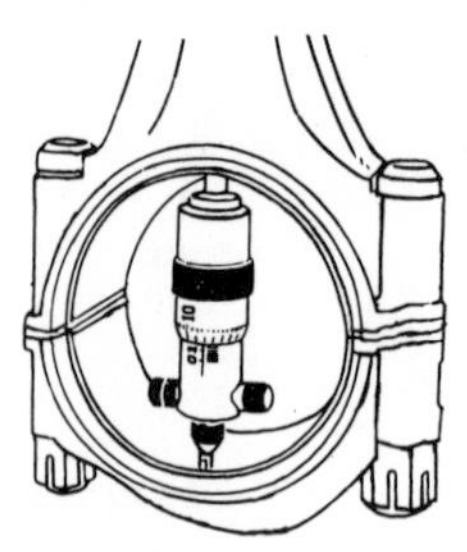

B-13. Bearing journals should be measured at several points around the diameter and also along the length of the bearing surface.

B-14. The inside bore of the bearing is measured for size and roundness with an inside micrometer or a special dial gauge.

oil can be spread out in a film a millionth of an inch thick. We do not need to go to this extreme in an engine, but we do have to measure carefully.

This film thickness will vary with the design of the engine and the type of lubrication system used. In general, a splash lubrication system is less critical of oil clearances than a pressure lubrication system. In the splash system the oil in the oil pan is churned up by the internal parts of the engine into a combination of liquid and mist which is sprayed over the entire interior of the engine.

Some of this oil is collected in pockets above the main bearings and flows through the bearing by means of grooves in the bearing surface. The connecting rods dip into the oil and obtain lubrication. These bearings can be operated when slightly out-of-round and are often made adjustable for wear.

CLEARANCE MEASUREMENT

The accepted method of measuring oil clearance is to measure the diameter of the journal with a micrometer caliper. The diameter of the shaft is measured at three or four points around the circumference to determine the size and to check for roundness. See Fig. B-13. It is also measured at each end of the bearing surface to determine the amount of taper, if any.

The inside of the bearing is then measured with the cap bolted in place using a telescoping gauge or an inside micrometer. See Fig. B-14. The difference in these two measurements represents the clearance between the journal and the bearing.

In splash lubricated bearings where the requirements for out-of-round are not so critical, the minimum clearance is often measured by means of shims. In this method the cap is removed and shims of known thickness are inserted between the journal and bearing until a slight resistance to rotation of the shaft occurs. This involves repeated removal and addition of shims and the bearing cap must be removed and replaced each time. See Fig. B-15.

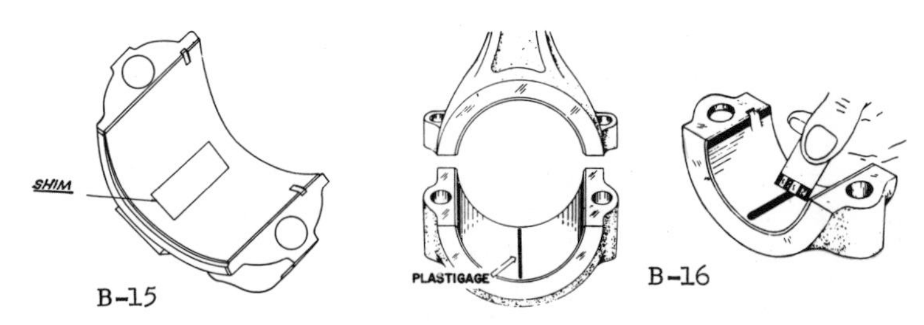

B-15. Clearance between the shaft and the bearing can be measured by the insertion of shims of different thicknesses.

B-16. Somewhat faster than the shim method of measurement is the use of a plastic material which deforms under pressure.

An alternate method is the use of a plastic material which deforms or flattens between the journal and the bearing when the cap is drawn down to the proper tightness. The amount of increase in the width of the plastic material as it flattens out is then measured with a gauge provided to determine the clearance between journal and bearing. See Fig. B-16.

With the integral type of bearing it is not necessary or possible to measure the bearing bores with the crankshaft in place. With the precision type of bearing it is desirable when possible to measure the bearing bores for roundness when replacing bearings. If the bores are out-of-round the bearing shells will be distorted when the caps are bolted on tightly. In this case - as with the journal and bearings - we are not dealing in fractions of an inch; we are working with fractions of thousandths of an inch.

The amount of diametral clearance is specified by the manufacturer. These dimensions should be followed. In the absence of specific instructions, it is customary to use a minimum of .0005 to .001 for small shafts. Any clearance in excess of .005 on either main or rod is usually regarded as reason for adjustment or the installation of new bearings.

ENDWISE CLEARANCE

Obviously the crankshaft must not move endwise to any great extent; so one of the main bearings is usually provided with cheeks or flanges that

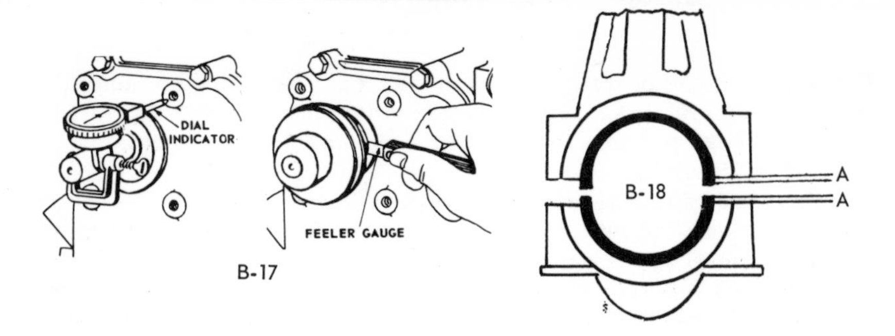

B-17. Endwise motion of the crankshaft is usually checked by means of feeler gauges, but can also be checked by means of a dial gauge suitably mounted.

B-18. The edge of the bearing shells should extend a few thousandths beyond the bearing seat in order that they will be forced into intimate contact with the seat when the cap is drawn up tight.

bear against a machined flange on the crankshaft. In other cases bronze washers are installed on one of the main bearings to absorb the end thrust. There is always some end thrust on the crankshaft.

Just as in the case of diametral clearance, there must be some clearance on the thrust faces. Otherwise expansion of the shaft and bearings from the normal heat of operation would cause metal-to-metal contact and burning of the thrust bearing. Here again the manufacturer's instructions should be followed. In general, it is customary to provide a minimum of .004 and a maximum of .008 of an inch clearance. End thrust can be measured with a feeler gauge as shown in Fig. B-17.

BEARING REPLACEMENT

In the case of poured or integral bearings, it is possible to ream or bore them straight and true to whatever dimension is wanted. This is made possible by tools of great accuracy which are now available.

Modern boring equipment has sufficient accuracy to produce almost a 100% surface contact with each bearing in precise alignment with the other bearings. The boring is done with the bearing caps and shims, if used, all in place and bolted down to the specified tightness.

REPLACEMENT OF INSERTS

Insert or shell type bearings require no fitting by hand as they are made to extremely close limits of accuracy. It is only necessary to install the proper size.

If the crankshaft journal is round and smooth and not worn to any extent a new standard size bearing shell is simply inserted in place. If the crankshaft is round and smooth, but worn slightly undersize, a shell of the proper undersize bore is used. If the crankshaft has been damaged and then reconditioned to a standard undersize dimension, a still smaller undersize bearing is used.

If the crankshaft journal has been reduced in diameter so much that a standard undersize bearing shell will not fit, shells are available with excess bearing metal that can be bored out to the size desired.

If the bearing bore and journal are round, these new inserts require no fitting or adjustment. If the journal is out-of-round more than .0015, it should be trued up or machined until it is round. The same applies to the bearing bore in which the insert seats. Any errors in the bore will distort the bearing shell when the bolts are drawn down.

The bearing seat and bearing shell MUST be round and true as there MUST be intimate contact between the inside of the bearing seat bore and the outside of the bearing shell. If true and intimate contact does not exist, the heat will not flow from the shell to the crankcase or connecting rod and the bearing will melt. It may thus be seen that no shims of any sort should be used between the shell and the seat in an effort to correct for wear or distortion.

This matter of heat dissipation is one reason for bearing "crush." Crush means that the two halves of the bearing shell extend a few thousandths beyond the bearing seat bore as shown in Fig. B-18. When the bear-

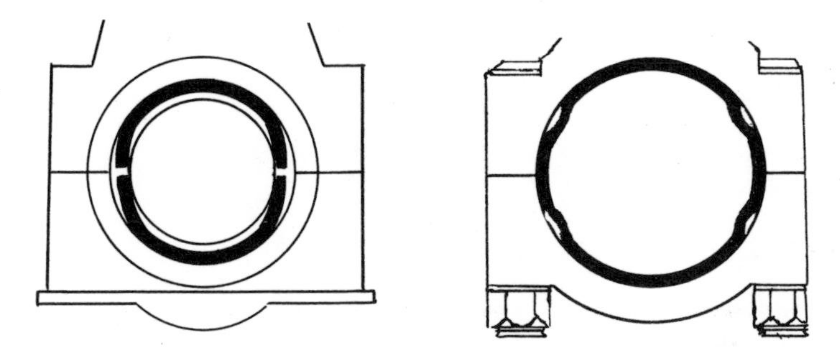

B-19. Lack of proper crush in bearing installation may permit the edges of the bearing to curl in toward the shaft.

B-20. An excessive crush will of course cause the bearing to buckle when the cap is drawn down tight.

ing cap nuts are drawn down to the specified tightness the shell is thus forced to seat solidly and intimately in the bearing seats.

Another reason for bearing crush is to make sure that the bearing remains round. If it were not tightly held on the edge it might distort as shown in Fig. B-19, enough to allow the edges to touch the journal.

Still another reason for crush is to avoid any possible movement of the shell in the seats. If the shell should become slightly loose it might oscillate in the seat and wear on the outside.

This crush must always be there and therefore the edges of the shell should not be dressed down flush with the bearing seats. Of course the amount of crush must not be excessive. If it were, the shell would be distorted when the cap is drawn down and the bearing would distort as shown in Fig. B-20.

The amount of crush is only .001 or .002 in. and is finished to dimension the same as the bore and outside diameter. These shells are extremely accurate as they come from the manufacturer and are available in undersize dimensions as required to compensate for normal journal wear. They should be purchased to the exact size desired and inserted with no alteration or fitting.

MAIN BEARING ADJUSTMENT

When main bearings of the integral type require adjustment it is accomplished at the bearing cap. The result will probably be a bearing that is out-of-round, but an engine lubricated by the splash method can operate satisfactorily with a slightly oval bearing on a round shaft. See Fig. B-21.

An adjustable bearing is usually provided with thin shims on each side. See Fig. B-22. These shims are placed between the cap and crankcase or rod when the bearing is poured so we start out with a round bearing. Each time the bearing is adjusted for wear by the removal of these shims, it becomes more oval.

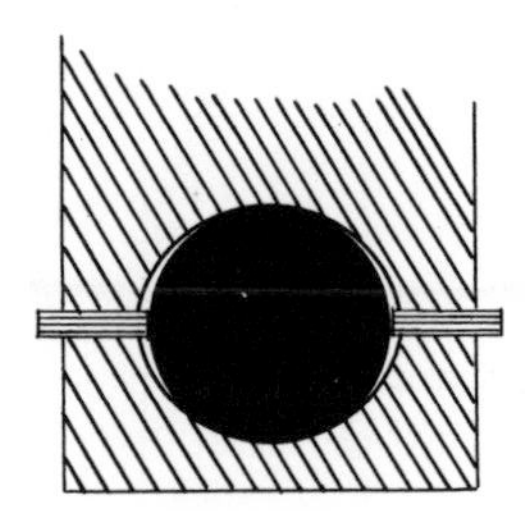

B-21. Continued removal of shims will result in an oval shaped bearing as shown in this exaggerated diagram.

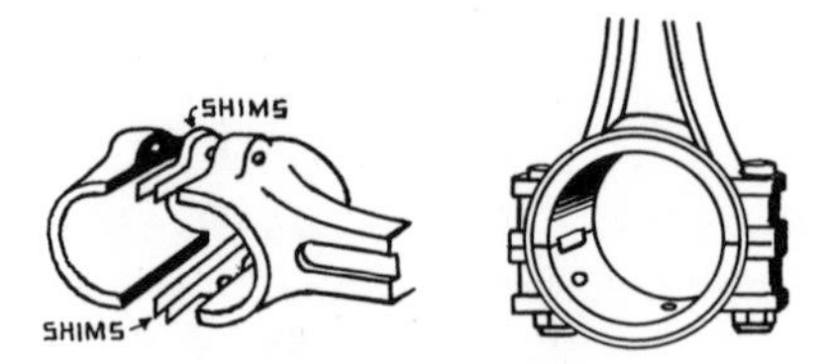

B-22. An adjustable connecting rod bearing provided with shims for adjusting clearance.

These shims are usually installed in several thicknesses; that is, .0005, .001, .002, etc. . . and the same quantity of each on both sides. Also the shims are made in laminated form; that is, a stack of shims each .0005 thick are soldered together into a block. By peeling off as many layers as desired the shim is thus reduced in thickness. See Fig. B-23.

The usual procedure is to loosen all bearing caps and adjust one bearing at a time. Shims are removed in equal numbers of the same thickness from each side until a slight resistance to rotation of the shaft is felt. Shims of proper thickness to provide the clearance desired are then reinserted and shaft rotation again checked.

If the bearing cap is warped so that the faces are not flat and level or if the bearing is not provided with shims, the cap is dressed down. This is usually done by placing a sheet of emery paper on a face plate or piece of plate glass and rubbing the cap on the abrasive. Care must be exercised to avoid lapping the cap crooked when this method is used. A skilled machinist can dress the cap down with a file, but an amateur will ruin the cap by filing it crooked.

When all bearings are adjusted properly and the caps drawn up tight, there should be little resistance toward rotation of the shaft. If there is

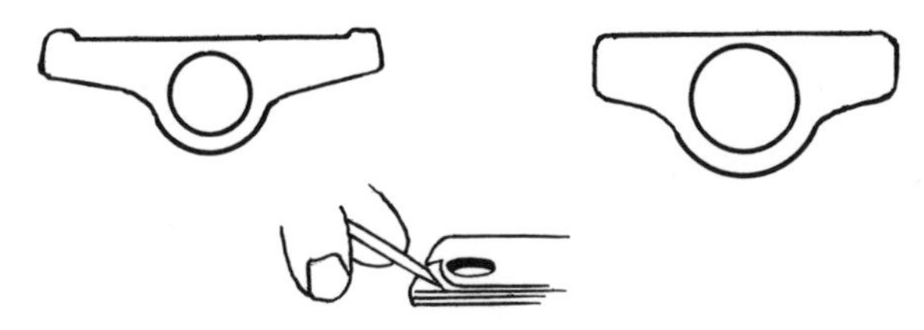

B-23. Laminated shims may be of any shape desired and if equipped with a babbitt edge, this babbitt will need to be dressed down as the laminations are peeled off.

resistance, one or more bearings are fitted too tightly, there is insufficient end clearance on the thrust bearing, the crankshaft is sprung or the bearings are not in proper alignment. If the engine is stiff after a bearing job, it should not be started until the cause of the stiffness is located and eliminated.

SIDE CLEARANCE

The connecting rod bearing must have some side clearance. If it has too much, the bearing may move endwise and knock. The clearance is measured by inserting a feeler gauge between the end of the bearing and the cheek of the crankshaft journal. While manufacturers' specifications vary somewhat, the usual clearance is .005 to .01. As there is no adjustment of the side clearance, an excess of clearance requires replacement of the bearing.

BEARING OIL GROOVES

As the function of the oil grooves in the bearings has to do with bearing lubrication, it will be dealt with in the chapter devoted to lubrication.

PISTON PIN FITTING

As the fitting of the piston pins is perhaps more closely related to pistons than to connecting rods, it will be considered fully in the chapter devoted to pistons and rings.

CONNECTING ROD ALIGNMENT

In addition to the proper fit of the connecting rod bearing on the crankshaft and the proper condition of the piston pin at the other end of the connecting rod, we must consider the alignment of the rod itself.

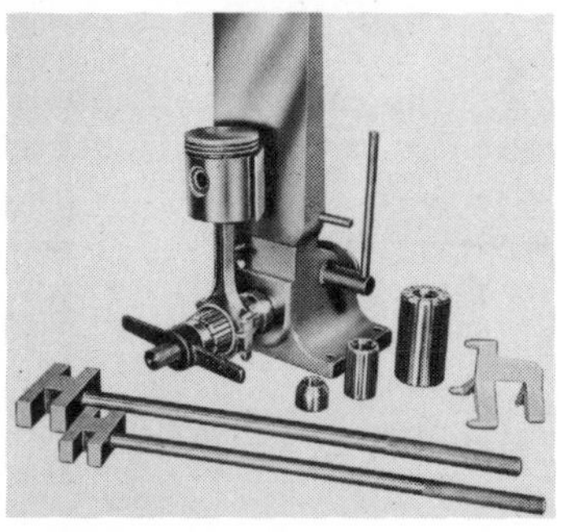

B-24. A typical connecting rod aligning outfit including checking fixture, mandrels and bending bars.

Obviously, the piston pin and crankshaft journal must be parallel - not just approximately parallel, but precisely parallel. If the piston pin is not parallel every force on the piston will cause it to try to slide endwise on the piston pin. This will of course cause the piston to "slap" in the cylinder and create a knock or noise. The connecting rod and bearing will also have a tendency to knock.

Special equipment of suitable accuracy is available for checking the connecting rods as shown in Fig. B-24. This equipment checks the rods for twist as well as bends. EVERY connecting rod should be checked for proper alignment just before it is installed in the engine. Many hard to locate noises in an engine originate in misalignment of the connecting rods.

Each rod should be again checked for location after it is installed in the engine. This for the reason that the rod might have a double bend in it which would not be noticed on the alignment tester. Such a double bend might leave the pin parallel with the crankshaft; yet the upper end of the rod might be close enough to one of the piston bosses to cause a knock. See Fig. B-25.

CAMSHAFT BEARINGS

Camshaft bearings are usually made of bronze and are bushings rather than in the form of split bearings. They are not adjustable for wear and are replaced when worn.

In order to replace the camshaft bearings, the camshaft must be removed. This involves removal of the valves and operating mechanism or else raising and holding the valve lifters up off the camshaft against the tension of the valve springs. Actually it is seldom necessary to replace a camshaft bearing or bearings until the engine is dismantled for other work.

After the camshaft is removed the bearings are pressed out of their bores with a special tool made for the purpose. Of course the bushings can be driven out with a hammer and drift, but the special tool will be needed for inserting the new bushings and might as well be used to remove the old ones.

New bushings are available in the proper outside diameter and standard as well as undersize inside diameter. If the camshaft has been undersized by regrinding worn journals, or if the proper inside diameter is not available, the bearings can be line reamed to any size desired by the use of the proper equipment.

Before the new bearings are pressed into place, they are coated lightly on the outside with white lead. The white lead facilitates insertion by acting as a lubricant and helps avoid reduction of the inside diameter of the bushing. The oil holes in the bushing are lined up with the oil holes in the crankcase before pressure is applied as the bushing cannot be turned after it starts in the bore.

It is essential to start the bushing squarely in the bore and apply pressure steadily and evenly. If the bushing cocks in the bore, it will be distorted and the inside diameter decreased. It is possible for an experienced mechanic to insert these bushings with a hammer and a pilot driver of suitable size, but if the mechanic is experienced enough to do it successfully, he is experienced enough not to try it.

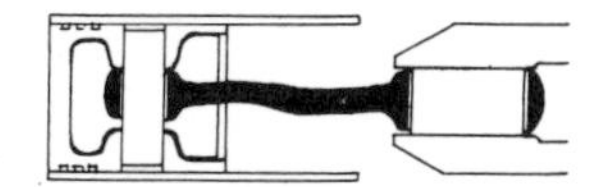

B-25. Exaggerated illustration of a connecting rod with a double kink causing the upper end of the rod to ride against the piston boss.

The bushings should be pushed fully into the bore as if one end extends, the valve lifter might strike it. It is good policy to check the installation after the valve operating parts are installed to make sure there is sufficient clearance for the lifters. Also the end-play of the camshaft should be checked and corrected if it exceeds the manufacturers' specifications which are usually about the same as for crankshafts.

Usually the camshaft is provided with a thrust plate to which shims can be added or subtracted to obtain the proper endwise clearance. In other cases there is a spring and button at the end of the shaft that holds the camshaft against a flange on one of the bearings to eliminate excessive endwise movement.

Small engines, particularly of the two cycle type, quite often use bearings of the anti-friction type on main bearings, connecting rod bearings and piston pin bearings. These bearings are often of the ''quill'' or roller type, but may be of the tapered roller or ball bearing type. Several types are illustrated later in this text.

The tapered roller bearing is readily adjustable by moving the cone endwise. The quill or roller bearing is adjusted by installing oversize rollers. The ball bearing, when worn must be replaced.

Any anti-friction bearing must be absolutely smooth in operation with no excess looseness. The inner surface of the bearing shell, the outer surface of the journal and the balls or rollers must be absolutely true and smooth. Any discernible scratches, wear or etching on any of these surfaces means replacement or surface regrinding.

Even if the bearing looks perfect but fails to turn freely and smoothly or makes any noise it should be replaced.

PISTONS, RINGS AND PINS

Engine pistons serve several purposes: they transmit the force of the explosion to the crankshaft through the connecting rod; they act as a guide for the upper end of the connecting rod; they also serve as a carrier for the piston rings used to seal the piston in the cylinder. In a two cycle engine they also serve as a valve.

Pistons operate under exceedingly difficult mechanical and thermal conditions and therefore must be made and installed with the utmost care. They must be strong enough to stand the force of the explosion and yet be as light as possible to avoid excessive inertia forces when their direction of travel is reversed twice each revolution. As they must slide freely within the cylinder, they cannot be fitted too tightly. If too loosely fitted in the cylinder, they will knock and rattle.

PISTON MATERIALS

Cast iron or semi-steel is used as a material in many cases. It is strong enough for the stresses imposed; has a melting point above the cylinder operating temperature; expands at the same rate as the cylinders and does not generate excessive friction when properly lubricated. The principal objection is that of weight.

Aluminum is also used as a material for pistons. It is lighter than cast iron, is readily cast and machined and does not generate excessive friction in the cylinder. Aluminum does expand much more rapidly than cast iron when subjected to the heat of operation and also has a much lower melting point. In material and design, the aluminum piston has been developed to a point where its advantages apparently outweigh its disadvantages, because it is now almost universally used in engines.

The lighter weight means less inertia for the reciprocating parts and thus higher speed for the engine along with better acceleration. This lessened inertia also decreases bearing loads at high speeds and reduces the side thrust on the cylinder walls. Due to the greater heat conductivity of aluminum, the piston head runs cooler and in general, it is possible to use higher compression ratios.

Early aluminum pistons were noisy because they had to be fitted in the cylinder with considerably more clearance than cast iron pistons. This resulted in piston slap and rattle when the engine was cold and until the piston expanded in the cylinder. This difficulty has been largely overcome by designing the piston skirt so that it is flexible and by alloying the material of which it is made.

Aluminum pistons possess the desirable characteristic of conducting the heat away from the combustion chamber more rapidly than cast iron, but they also melt at a much lower temperature. Aluminum pistons seldom melt entirely, but their strength decreases very rapidly as the temperature increases. In many cases of stuck or broken rings the top edge of the piston or the aluminum lands between the rings may soften and melt or be blown away by the hot gas.

Severe and continued detonation is also claimed to be responsible for broken pistons and wedged rings. The aluminum is said to become soft

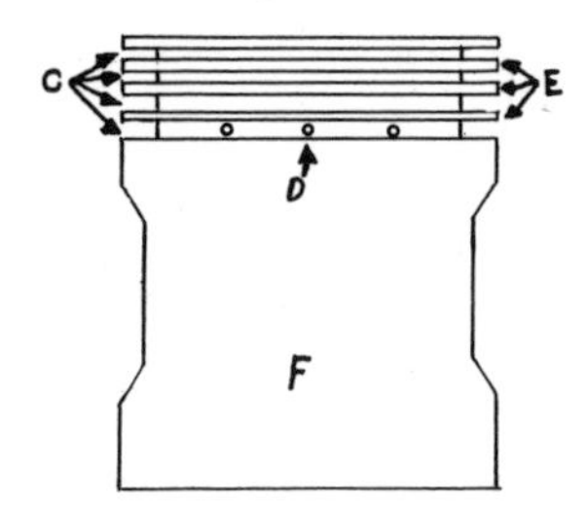

B-26. C indicates the ring grooves in the piston, D the oil drain holes in the lower groove and E the lands between the rings. The skirt of the piston F is relieved or reduced in diameter at the sides near the piston pin ends.

and plastic enough when overheated to allow the ring grooves to deform. The strength of aluminum pistons can be increased by alloying the aluminum with other metals and also by heat treatment processes. Some of the materials added to the aluminum are copper, magnesium, nickel, silicon, etc.

PISTON CONSTRUCTION

The piston head or "crown" is the top surface against which the explosion force is exerted. It may be flat, concave, convex or a great variety of shapes (as shown later herein for two cycle engines) to promote turbulence or control combustion. A groove is sometimes cut into the piston at B to serve as a "heat dam" to reduce the amount of heat reaching the top piston ring.

The piston ring "grooves" are shown at C, Fig. B-26. Sometimes another groove is located below the piston pin. The piston rings are carried in these grooves and are of two types: "compression" rings and "oil"

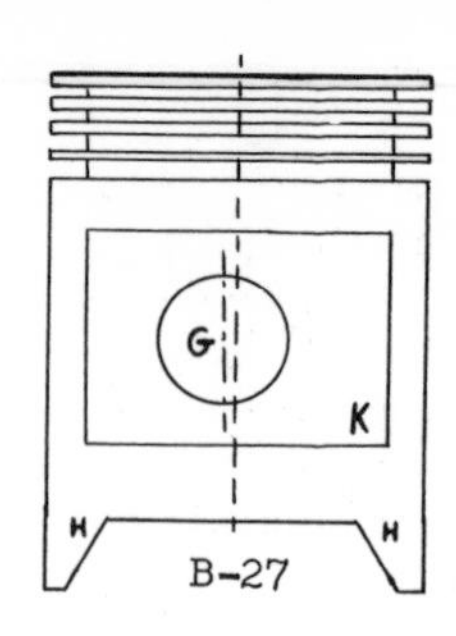

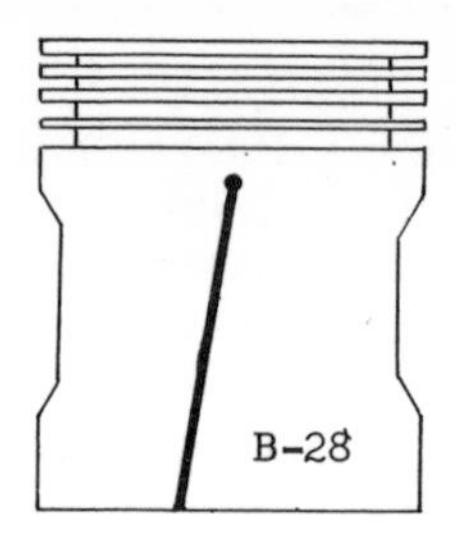

B-27. The piston pin may be off-set to one side of the piston center line as shown at G. It may or may not have a relief area as shown at K. The bottom of the skirt may be square or may be of the slipper type as shown at H.

B-28. Aluminum pistons may have a diagonal slot cut through the skirt on the minor thrust side.

rings. The upper ring or rings are to prevent compression leakage, and the lower ring or rings are to control oil. The lower groove or grooves usually have holes drilled at D to permit oil drainage from behind the ring.

The piston ring "lands" are the parts of the piston between the ring grooves as shown at E. These lands provide a seating surface for the sides of the piston rings.

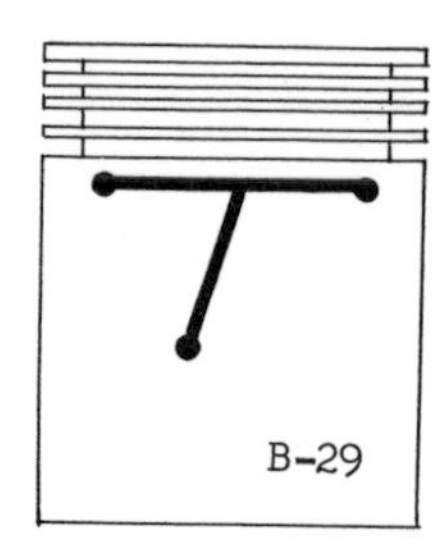

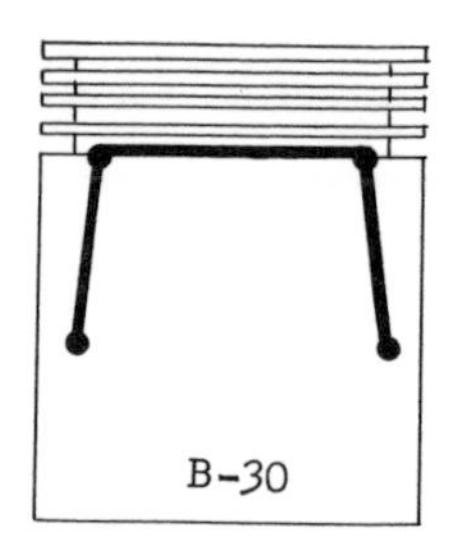

B-29. In some cases, a slot shaped something like a T is cut in the piston skirt.

B-30. Two slots may be connected by a third slot to form a U-shaped slot design.

The main section of the piston is known as the "skirt" (F in Fig. B-26) and forms a bearing area in contact with the cylinder wall which takes the thrust caused by the crankshaft as previously described. There is some thrust on both sides. The "major" thrust side is the side opposite the crank throw as it goes down on the power stroke. The "minor" thrust is of course the other side which is opposite the crank throw as it goes up on the compression stroke. Pistons are internally braced to make them as strong as possible.

The piston pin hole at G (Fig. B-27) may be a bearing also as described previously, depending upon the type of piston pin used. This hole may not be located in the exact middle of the piston. It may be placed as much as 1/16 of an inch to one side in an effort to lessen the side thrust on the cylinder wall.

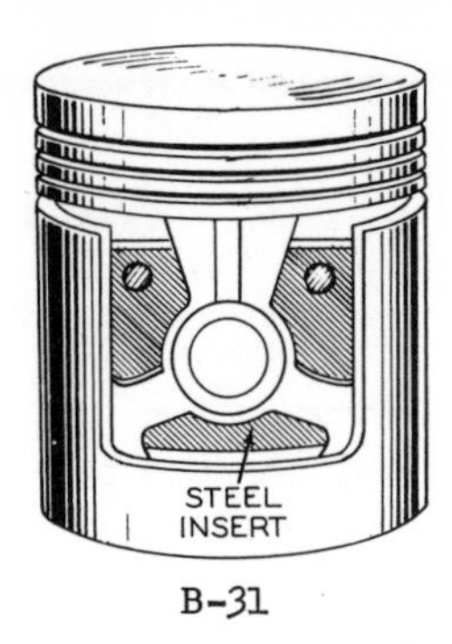

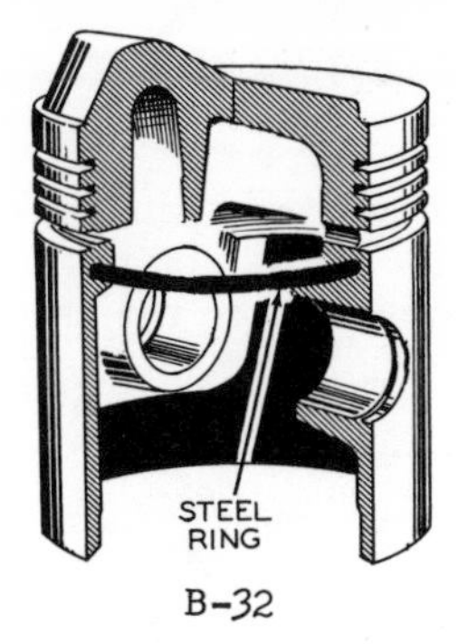

B-31. A steel insert may be cast into an aluminum piston to help control the expansion rate.

B-32. Instead of a vertical insert, a steel ring may be cast into the piston to help control the expansion.

In some cases the piston skirt is extended downward on the thrust sides as shown at H in Fig. B-27. This forms what is known as a "slipper" piston and the purpose of this design is to increase the area of the piston contact with the cylinder walls on the thrust faces.

Some pistons are also cut away, or partially cut away around the piston pin holes, K in Fig. B-27. This is known as a "relief" and is intended to provide additional clearance to avoid "seizing" if the piston should become overheated and expand excessively.

PISTON DESIGN

Cast iron pistons never have split skirts. Alloy pistons, however, have the skirts split in a number of ways. Shown in Fig. B-28 is one method of splitting the skirt. Fig. B-29 illustration a "T slot" piston. Fig. B-30 illustrates a "U slot" piston. These slots are placed on the minor thrust side of the piston and provide flexibility in the piston skirt. By this means the piston can be fitted more closely when cold and can expand when hot without damage.

Still other pistons are of the "strut" type. See Fig. B-31. In this case an alloy steel insert is cast into the aluminum piston to control the expansion of the aluminum and thus maintain more constant clearance. Such pistons are skeleton like and do not contact the cylinder walls around the piston pin holes.

Another design is known as the "steel belted" type. In this case a steel ring is cast into the aluminum piston above the piston pin holes to help control expansion. See Fig. B-32.

Many aluminum pistons are "cam-ground" - that is, they are purposely machined with the skirts oval. See Fig. B-33. The reason for this is that the skirts will be out-of-round when cold in such fashion that the thrust faces will have the greater diameter but the skirt will become more nearly round when the piston expands at operating temperature. In this case the piston contact surface is something like the pattern shown in Fig. B-34.

Pistons are also slightly tapered in many cases. The top or crown of the piston runs much hotter than the bottom or skirt so therefore the top is smaller in diameter. This is particularly true of the piston above the top ring. When the entire piston is not tapered, the top lands are at least smaller in diameter than the skirt which needs less clearance.

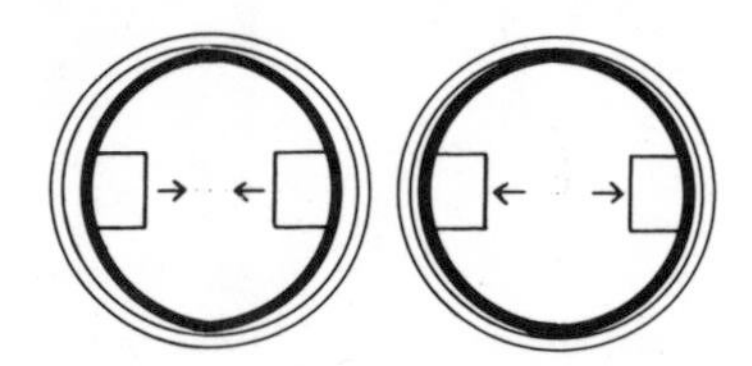

B-33. This exaggerated drawing shows a cold aluminum piston at the left which is cam ground in form. As the piston heats up, it expands as shown at the right into a more nearly round form.

PISTON CLEARANCE

There is no set rule on the amount of clearance to be provided between the piston and cylinder. Much depends upon the design of the engine cylinders and cooling system, the piston design and material and to a certain extent the service conditions under which the engine operates.

In general it is customary to fit solid skirt cast iron pistons to about .00075 to .001 in. per inch of diameter. A four inch piston would thus be .003 to .004 in. smaller than the cylinder. Some aluminum pistons can be fitted more closely but much depends upon the design of the piston and the instructions of the manufacturer should be obtained and followed.

Surface treatment will also have a bearing on the piston clearance. Some pistons are tin plated, others have an oxide coating and sometimes the surface is serrated or interrupted to retain oil. These treatments are intended to lessen the tendency of the piston to stick or score, particularly during the time it is seating to the cylinder wall.

CLEARANCE MEASUREMENT

The clearance between cylinder and piston is measured in most cases by means of a feeler gauge inserted between the piston and cylinder. The

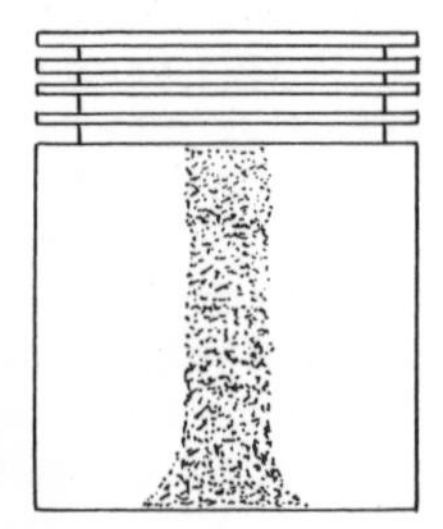

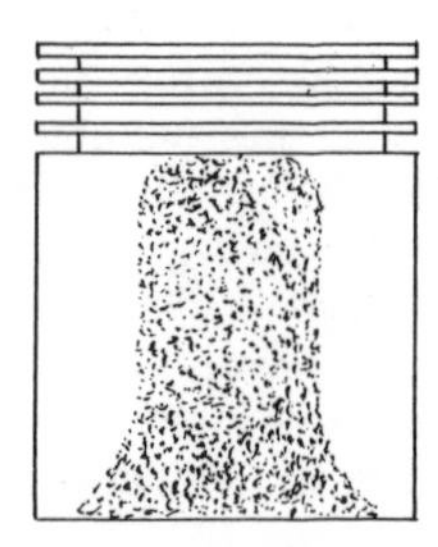

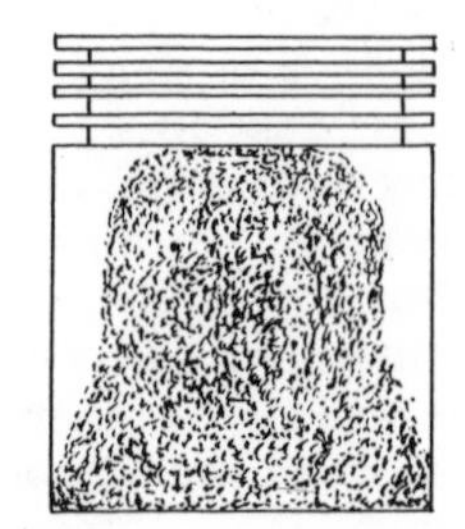

B-34. As a cam ground piston expands, the pattern of contact with the cylinder wall progresses from the cold piston at left to the warm piston at right.

strip of feeler gauge should be about 1/2 in. in width and long enough to extend the full length of the cylinder. This strip of a thickness equal to the desired clearance should be placed on the thrust side of the skirt. Four to five pounds pull as measured on a spring scale should be required to remove the feeler.

The clearance can also be measured by subtracting the maximum diameter of the piston from the minimum diameter of the cylinder as measured by inside and outside micrometers. In this case, measurement must be made at several points in the cylinder and on the piston. All piston clearance recommendations are made for use with the temperature approximately 70 deg. F.

As pistons wear, or if they become overheated, the skirt is liable to collapse or become smaller in diameter. When this happens the piston will "slap" in the cylinder and will also allow an excessive amount of oil to pass up to the rings. This of course places an undue load on the oil control rings and may result in oil pumping.

There are several ways to resize the pistons. One method consists of heating the piston and expanding it with special equipment made for the

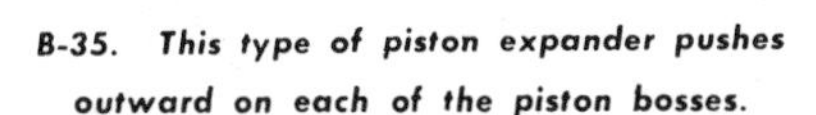
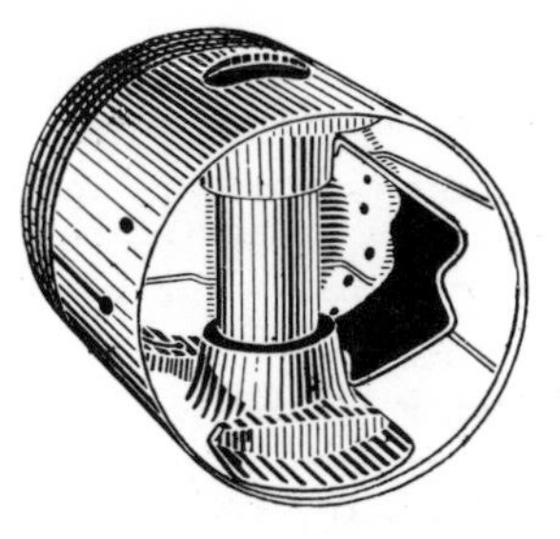

B-35. This type of piston expander pushes outward on each of the piston bosses.

purpose. Another method also requires special equipment for "peening" the inside of the piston with steel shot. This compacts the metal inside and causes it to expand on the outside. Electric and pneumatic peening hammers are made for the same purpose.

Various types of equipment and tools are available for "knurling" the piston skirt. This method raises the metal in ridges or patterns along the path of the knurling and thus increases the piston diameter. An additional claim made for this method is that it creates "pockets" on the piston surface which gather and retain a film of oil to assist in lubrication and sealing.

Another procedure is to install piston expanders inside the pistons. There are a great number of these devices on the market. They vary in design but usually consist of a spring steel strut that is compressed and installed in such manner that it exerts internal pressure on the split piston skirt. See Fig. B-35.

Such expanders are often effective for collapsed pistons, but they should not be installed in only one of the cylinders. If used, they should be installed

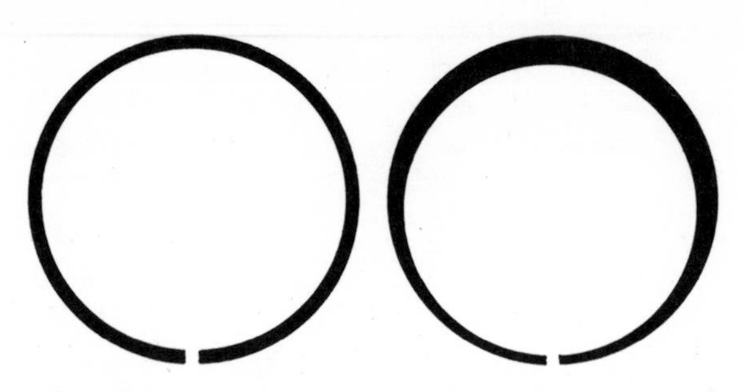

B-36. A concentric piston ring is shown at the left and the eccentric type at the right.

in all pistons of any one engine because of balance requirements. The expanders are made as light in weight as possible, but most modern engines have pistons matched in weight at the factory to a few hundredths of an ounce. Any replacement piston should also be carefully matched for weight with the other pistons as otherwise engine vibration may occur.

PISTON RINGS

Piston rings have been designed with such a multitude of variations as to be almost unbelievable. Originally they were a simple split ring made of cast iron.

The simple cast iron piston ring was either concentric or eccentric (see Fig. B-36), had a butt, miter or step joint. See Fig. B-37. It was made by casting a tube of iron to approximate size, turning down the outside in a lathe to the desired diameter, boring out the inside and slicing off at the desired width. By this method the finer grained iron was removed and the coarse core used.

As the finer grain iron was the most desired, centrifugal casting of individual rings was developed. This method provided a uniform fine-grained casting with better wearing qualities and more uniform tension around the ring. Another method of obtaining uniform tension was to peen or hammer the inside of the ring. Rings usually have enough tension to

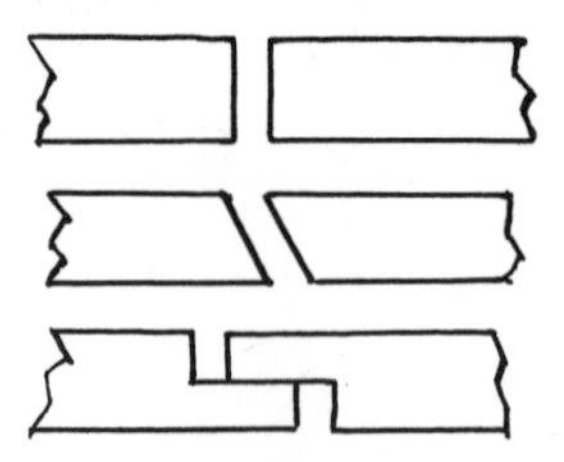

B-37. Three common types of piston ring gap design. Many designs more complicated in form have been used.

exert a pressure of 8 to 12 lbs. on the cylinder wall. As they wear, or if they become overheated, this tension is lost and the rings need to be replaced.

RING DESIGN

Modern piston rings are made of steel as well as cast iron and are often of multiple sections instead of a single piece. They are often quite complicated in design, are heat treated in various ways and plated with other metals. Furthermore, there are two distinct classifications: compression rings and oil control rings. Several representative types are shown in Fig. B-38.

Piston rings would not present much of a problem if cylinders and pistons did not expand, distort out-of-round and warp when at operating

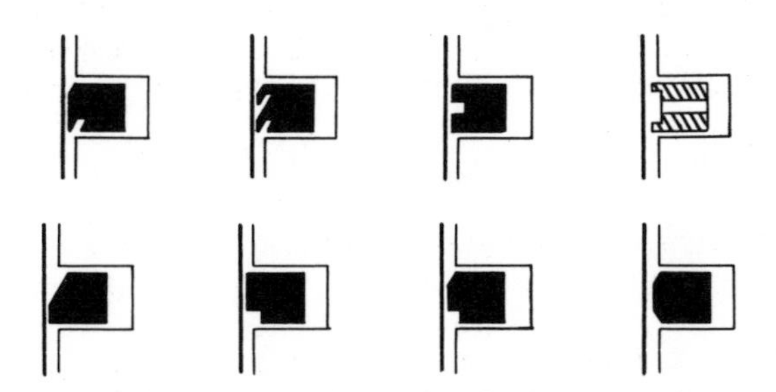

B-38. Cross-section shapes in considerable variation are available in piston rings.

temperature. But they DO expand and may also distort and warp, so the ring must be capable of conforming to these changing conditions. Furthermore, the ring itself is exposed to heat and alternating pressure and vacuum. It is expected to prevent the passage of pressure in one direction and to control the flow of oil in the other direction.

RING BLOW-BY

The compression pressure and explosion pressure can go past the ring

B-39. Oil can creep around in back of the rings to find its way into the cylinder and gases can creep down into the crankcase from the cylinder in a similar manner, but in the opposite direction.

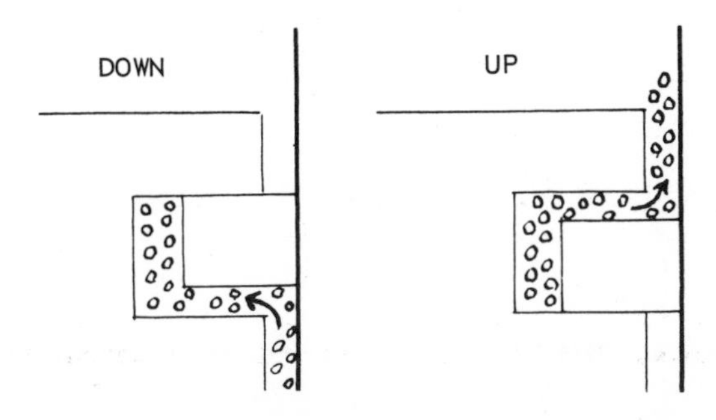

in several ways. This is known as "blow-by." The pressure can go through the gap which changes in width according to the expansion and contraction of the cylinder and ring. If it were fitted so precisely that the ring ends touched to seal the gap, it would score the cylinder when the ring expanded from the heat of operation.

Blow-by can also occur by going behind the ring as shown in Fig. B-39. If the ring were fitted tightly enough sidewise in the groove to avoid possible leakage, it would be liable to stick when the piston and rings expand.

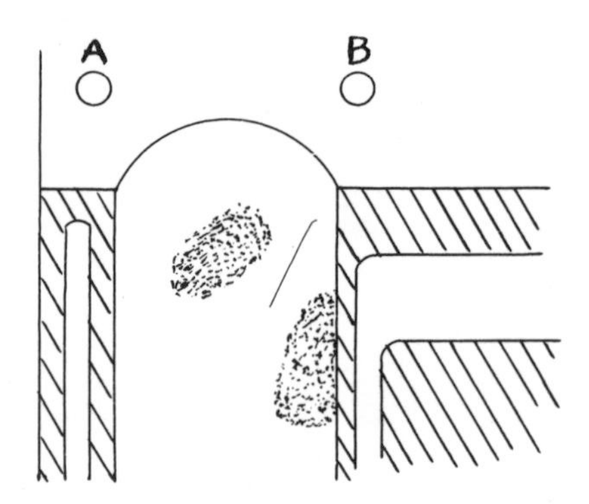

B-40. Distortion of cylinder walls can cause the cylinders to be out-of-round or to distort in spots as indicated here.

Blow-by is a serious problem when the cylinder walls distort out-of-round when at operating temperature. This can be caused by improper cylinder design, improper cooling or unequal tightening of adjacent bolts. This distortion may occur in more than one spot on the cylinder wall and the different spots are often of different size and shape. See Fig. B-40.

In the same ways that compression leaks down past the ring, oil can also pass upward into the cylinder and the result is known as "oil-pumping." This causes fouling of the spark plugs, excessive deposits of carbon in the combustion chamber and smoking at the exhaust as well as waste of oil.

In fact, it is easier for oil to pass upward in some cases than it is for compression to leak down past the rings. Therefore, we might have an engine with good compression and power which is also an oil-pumper. For example, the oil might act to seal excessive side clearance in the ring grooves and prevent leaks of compression. At the same time, the alternating vacuum and pressure in the cylinder may cause the ring to act as a pump. See Fig. B-41.

This condition is of course aggravated if the walls of the ring grooves and the sides of the rings are not flat and true. The volume of leakage past the back of the ring can be much greater than through the tiny gap at the ends of the ring.

It may be seen from the foregoing that great care is required in reconditioning cylinders to make sure that they are round and true when new

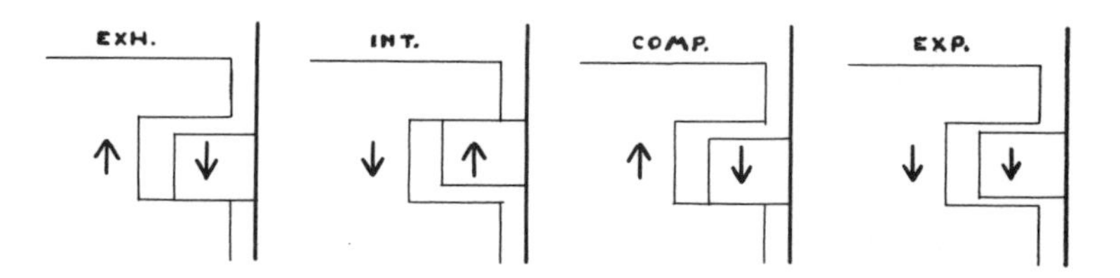

B-41. *There must be some clearance between the ring and the bottom of the groove and also on the sides of the ring. The result is that a ring can act as a pump in the manner shown. On the exhaust stroke, the exhaust gas tends to hold the rings in the bottom of the groove as the piston travels up. On the intake stroke the vacuum in the cylinder tends to hold the ring against the top of the groove while the piston goes down. On the compression stroke, the pressure in the cylinder again tends to hold the ring against the bottom of the groove. But on the explosion stroke, the expanding gases tend to push both piston and ring in the same direction thus permitting the ring to float in the groove.*

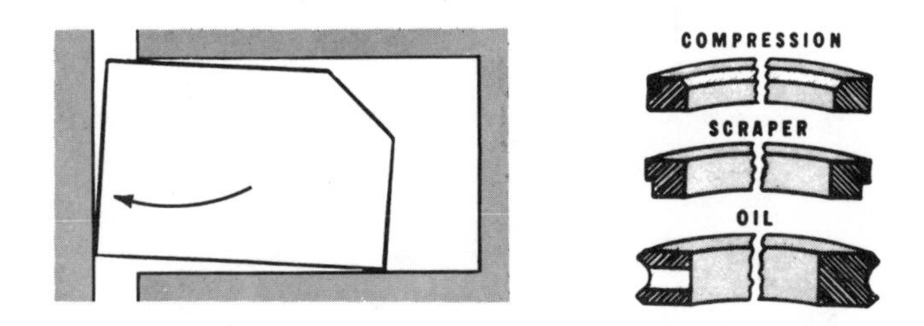

B-42. *A grooved compression ring has a tendency to tilt in the groove rather than remain flat.*

B-43. *Various combinations of grooves and tapered sections are used.*

rings are fitted. Equal care is required in selecting the new rings and fitting them to the pistons and cylinders. Many other things enter into the matter and will be considered in this text.

COMPRESSION RINGS

The top compression ring is usually a plain ring, rectangular in cross section or with a groove cut into the inner top corner. See Fig. B-42. Sometimes it is also chrome plated on the contact surface. Other designs are tapered on the face. Sometimes the tapered face is used with the inside bevel and chrome plating.

The idea of the groove on the inside upper corner of the ring is to cause the ring to twist in the groove in such manner that the outside lower edge presses on the cylinder wall more tightly than the rest of the ring face. The tapered outer face of course does the same thing. In both cases the limited area in contact with the cylinder wall offers a high pressure at that point to effect a better seal. Such rings must be installed right side up and are usually stamped "top" on the side to be installed on top.

The second ring is also usually a compression type ring, but it does help in oil control. It may be a plain ring, or it may consist of more than one piece. It may have a groove cut around either the outer or inner corner. This groove may be combined with a taper on either the inside or outside. See Fig. B-43.

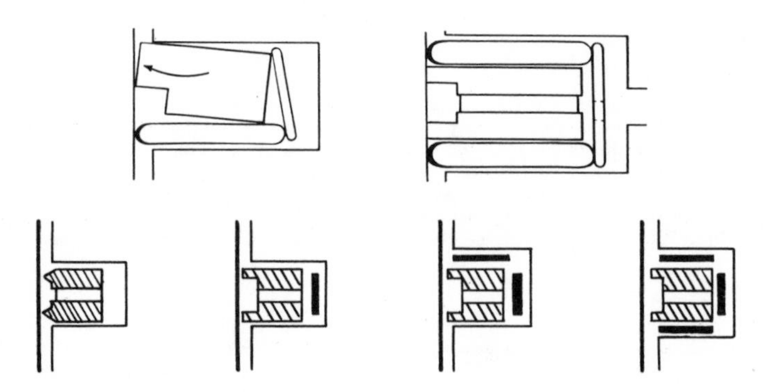

B-44. *Various types of oil control rings with and without expanders are shown here in cross-section form.*

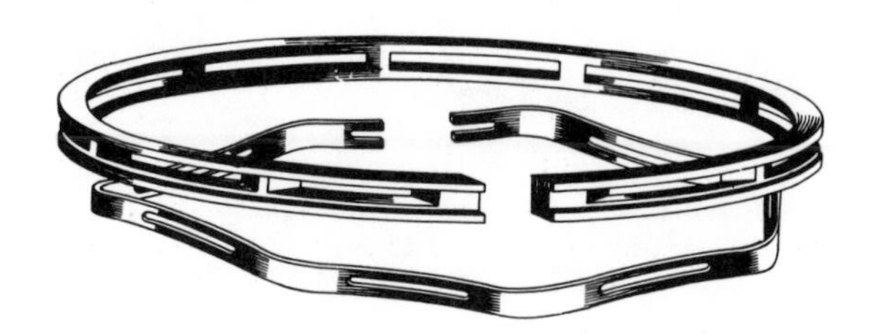

B-45. *A typical slotted steel expander as used with a slotted oil control ring.*

OIL RINGS

The third ring from the top, and the fourth if used, are of the oil control type and vary all the way from simple to extremely complicated types. Several varieties are shown in Fig. B-44. In any case it must be remembered that the oil scraped from the cylinder wall by the oil ring must have a free passage to the inside of the piston. For this reason holes or slots are cut in the lower ring groove. Also an inner ring or expander may be used. See Fig. B-45. These openings must be kept open if the oil ring is to function as intended.

A typical piston ring installation is shown in Fig. B-46. No. 1 ring has a full face contact on the cylinder wall and the ring expansive pressure is therefore distributed over a wide area. Ring No. 2 is also a compression ring but has a narrower contact surface and therefore a higher pressure on that area because the entire expansive force of the ring is concentrated on the narrow area in contact. The result is that the top ring will show less

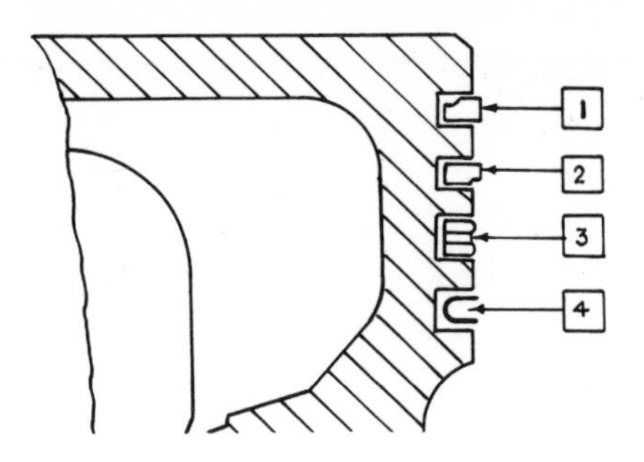

B-46. A typical piston ring installation with an extremely flexible bottom oil ring used.

tendency to wear the cylinder in the dryest and hottest part and the second ring will seat more quickly to the cylinder wall even though it has more lubrication than the top ring.

No. 3 is an oil control ring and has two narrow edges in contact with the cylinder wall. Having slots cut between the two edges, the oil will be scraped from the cylinder wall into the channel or slots of the ring. Ring No. 4 in this case is of the extremely flexible type which follows closely the contour of the cylinder walls even when they are slightly out-of-round.

In this connection, it is well to remember that the piston ring moves in the groove. Due to the constant reversing of direction of piston travel and the necessity of sidewise clearance between ring and groove, it may be seen that the rings move up and down in the ring grooves. See Fig. B-41. A film of oil cushions this movement.

Likewise it will be understood that if the cylinder is worn tapered, the rings will expand and contract as they move up and down in a bore that is larger at one end than the other. Similarly if the cylinder is out-of-round in spots, the rings will be pumping in and out of the groove as they try to follow the cylinder wall.

PISTON RING GAP

Further consideration will indicate that the top piston ring runs hotter than the lower rings and therefore the top ring will expand the most. This means that the top ring will need more gap clearance and more groove clearance than the other rings. The manufacturer specifies the clearance needed and his instructions should be followed.

Piston ring gap clearance is measured as shown in Fig. B-47. The ring is pushed into the smallest diameter of the cylinder bore, which is usually below the travel of the bottom ring. A piston without rings is used to push the ring in place as this method places the ring squarely in the bore. The rings should be purchased for correct size to avoid fitting. Minor increase in gap clearance can be made by filing the ends of the ring. This should be carefully and accurately done on equipment made for the purpose.

In case specific clearance dimensions are not available, it is customary to allow .004 in. gap clearance per inch of piston diameter for the top ring and .003 in. per inch diameter on the other rings. For example, a three inch diameter cylinder would require .012 in. gap on the top ring and .009 on the other rings. The exception to the foregoing is the "U" type oil ring that is extremely flexible. See Fig. B-48. They require no endwise clearance.

RING GROOVE CLEARANCE

The sidewise clearance of the ring in the groove is measured as shown in Fig. B-49 using a feeler or thickness gauge. In the absence of specific

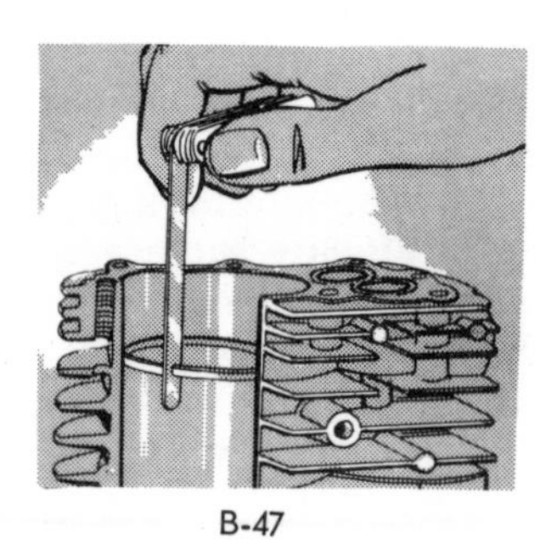

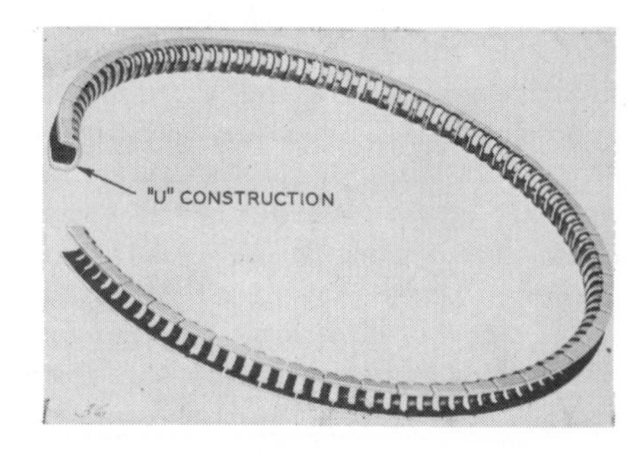

B-47. A piston without rings is used to push the ring down in the cylinder to make sure that it is square. The ring is actually measured at a point lower in the cylinder bore than indicated here.

B-48. An oil control ring of the extremely flexible type.

instructions it is customary to allow at least .0025 in. side clearance on the top ring and at least .003 in. on the other rings. More than .005 side clearance on any ring calls for new rings.

New rings can be purchased in almost any size as well as oversize and overwidth as desired. Overwidth may be used if the ring grooves are flat,

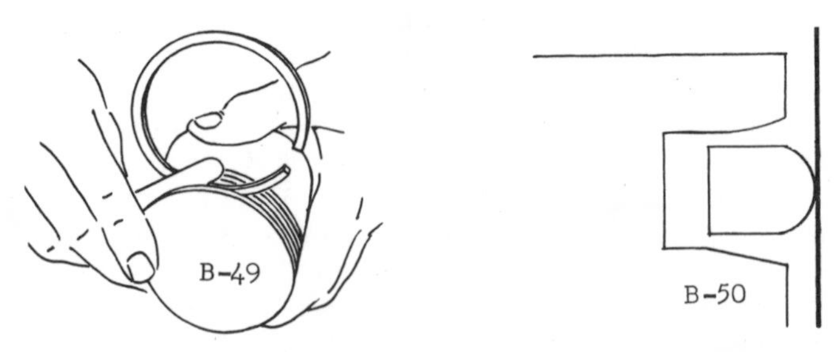

B-49. Method of measuring sidewise clearance of ring in groove.

B-50. When a groove is worn bell-mouth it can be recut wider and an overwidth ring installed.

smooth and square. If the grooves are worn bell-mouth or tapered as shown in Fig. B-50, they can be repaired in two ways. One way is to machine the grooves out wider and install wider rings. The other way is to install spacers with standard width rings after the grooves are machined true. See Fig. B-51.

The depth of the ring groove must be checked also when replacing rings. Sometimes shallow grooves are used with thin rings and a replacement of normal thickness rings will cause them to "bottom." The groove must be deep enough to allow the ring to enter the groove below the land surface as

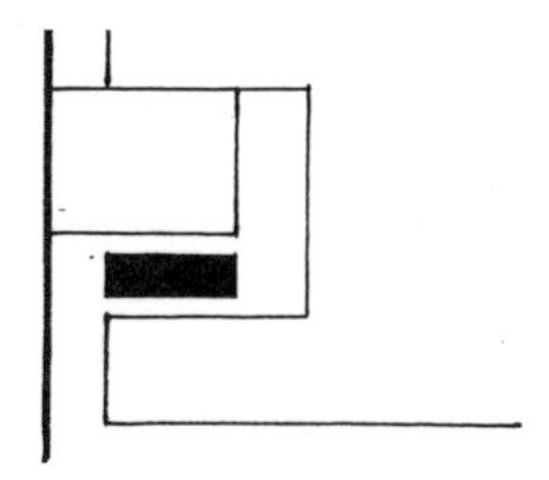

B-51. After the groove is squared up a spacer and a standard width ring may be used rather than an overwidth ring if desired.

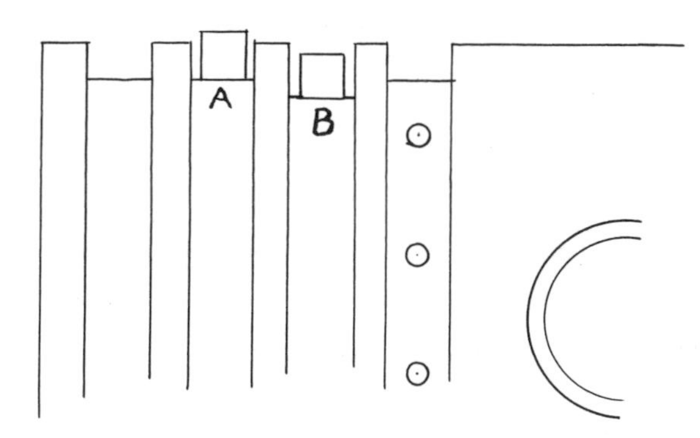

B-52. The ring should fit freely in the ring groove below the surface of the lands as shown at B.

shown in Fig. B-52. If too shallow, the grooves can be machined to proper depth.

Sometimes rings turn slightly in the grooves and sometimes they do not. When installing rings, the gaps are usually spaced around the pistons to avoid any possibility of the gaps getting in line one above the other and encouraging blow-by. Some manufacturers pin the rings in place to avoid this possibility. One method is illustrated in Fig. B-53. In this case the rings must be fitted so that the proper clearance is provided at the ends of the rings and on the pins. Otherwise the rings will ride on the pins and score the cylinders when expansion of the rings occurs.

The manufacturers' instructions should always be followed when installing new rings. They know how their own products should be fitted and they have studied the peculiarities of the different engines. For example, one type of piston has a wide slot in the bottom ring location. If an expander type of ring is placed in this groove, the expander will fall into the slot. For this reason the ring manufacturer supplies a set of "bridges" to be placed in this groove to support the expanders.

Piston rings are fragile and should be handled carefully. They should be placed in the piston ring grooves with the aid of a ring tool and not by stretching them over the piston. Even if they do not break, they may become so distorted by careless handling as to be useless.

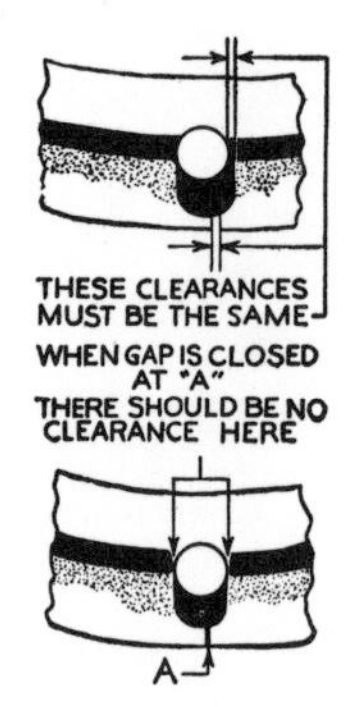

B-53. Pinned rings must be carefully fitted as to endwise clearance.

PISTON PINS

Piston pins, also known as "gudgeon" pins and "wrist" pins, are the connection between the upper end of the connecting rod and the piston. As previously described there are three types:

A - Anchored in the piston with the bushing in the upper end of the connecting rod oscillating on the pin.

B - Clamped in the rod with the pin oscillating in the piston.

C - Full floating in both connecting rod and piston with lock rings or plugs in the piston bosses to prevent endwise movement of the piston pin.

Other than the provision for holding them in place, all three types are quite similar. They are hollow steel pins, case hardened on the outside surface. They are subjected to very heavy loads and are not adjustable for wear. When worn they must be replaced. As they have an oscillating motion in the bearing surface rather than the high surface speed between the crankshaft and the connecting rod bearing the steel pin can bear directly in the aluminum piston, or in bronze bushings in either cast iron or aluminum pistons or a bronze bushing in the upper end of the rod. Also anti-friction bearings are used as previously mentioned.

One of the problems faced by the design engineer is the size of the piston pin. If he makes it large enough in diameter to have a long wearing bearing surface, the reciprocating weight will be increased and the bearing loads correspondingly increased. If he makes it as light in weight as possible to hold down on the bearing loads it will be smaller in diameter and thus have less bearing surface to carry the load.

If it is fastened in the piston with a small screw the assembly will be lighter than where a bolt is used in the connecting rod. However, if it is clamped in the rod it will have double the bearing surface as there will be a bearing in each piston boss. If it floats in both piston and rod it will have the greatest bearing surface along with the lightest weight. One problem with this construction is that if the locking ring should fail, the piston pin will score the cylinder quickly and deeply. One late development is to have the pin pressed into the rod.

All piston pin designs therefore are a compromise in some direction and none of them appears to be ideal. One ever present complication is the fact that all three metals in contact; steel, bronze and aluminum, have a different rate of heat expansion. Obviously, being attached to the piston, the piston pins will run hot. In general, heat in any bearing promotes wear and very little wear in a piston pin or bushing will cause noise.

PISTON PIN REPLACEMENT

It is customary to find wear in both pin and bearing when pins become loose. Where the bushing is in the rod only it can be pressed out and a new standard size bushing pressed in and reamed or honed to fit a new standard size pin. The old bushing should not be removed with a hammer and drift as there is danger of bending the connecting rod.

Where the pin is clamped in the rod and the bushings are in the piston bosses the same method can be used. When replacing bushings in the piston it is extremely important to avoid hammering as the piston can be easily distorted by rough treatment. The piston boss should be firmly supported in the press while the old bushings are pressed out and the new bushings pressed in.

OVERSIZE PINS

If it is decided to install oversize new pins and ream or hone the old bushings in the piston to fit the oversize pin, the connecting rod clamp hole will also need to be enlarged accordingly. This condition also arises where the pistons are not bushed and the pin bearing is directly in the piston bosses. If difficulty is experienced in reaming or honing the rod end due to the split for clamping, a shim may be placed in the slot and the clamp bolt drawn down tight. The shim will of course have to be the same thickness as the opening in the slot when the rod is clamped on the standard size pin. The inner edge of the shim should be flush with the hole so that the reamer or hone will cut both shim and rod.

In the full floating type, the installation of new oversize pins will require reaming or honing of the piston bushings or bosses and the bushing in the connecting rod. In every case where reaming or honing is done on either piston or connecting rod, it is of utmost importance to have the finished hole at precisely a right angle to the connecting rod. Also both piston boss bearings must be in exact alignment. In other words, the hole must be straight through both bosses.

The only possible variation of the foregoing would be in the case where the pin was anchored in one boss of the piston. Here it should be a tight fit in the boss where it is anchored and have a somewhat looser fit in the other boss so that the piston could expand. If the one piston boss cannot move endwise of the pin the piston cannot expand.

PISTON PIN FITTING

Fitting piston pins is one of the most delicate operations to be found in repair work. Millions of pins have been improperly fitted - and other millions are being improperly fitted now. The reason for this is that suitable equipment for properly fitting piston pins is a comparatively recent development.

In previous parts of this text we have dealt with an accuracy measurement of thousandths and tenths of thousandths of an inch. In dealing with piston pin fits we are involved with micro-inches. In fact it is useless to use the term micro-inches in most cases without specifying the temperature at which the measurement is made. This is because a few degrees rise or fall in temperature will expand or contract the metal enough to change the measurement in micro-inches very considerably.

Furthermore, as previously mentioned, we are dealing with steel, bronze and aluminum, each of which has a different rate of heat expansion. We fit the piston pins at room temperature (assumed to be 70 degs. F.) and then put them in an engine which quickly attains a temperature of at least 140 deg. F. This temperature expands the pin, the bushings, if used, and the piston. If it is a cam ground piston it also changes shape from oval when cold to round when hot.

This change in shape of the piston may also disturb the alignment of the two holes in the piston bosses. If we had a round, straight hole through the two bosses - which would stay round and straight when hot - and a round and straight pin to fit it would then be only a matter of suitable clearance for the oil film. There must be room for a film of oil around the piston pin. Otherwise metal-to-metal contact will occur and the friction thus generated will score the pin or bushing or both.

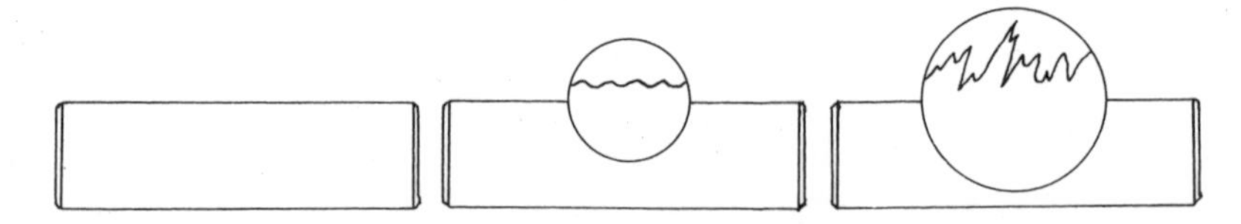

B-54. To the naked eye the surface looks dead smooth, when magnified one hundred times it begins to look a little wavy and when magnified one thousand times as at the right it looks rough indeed.

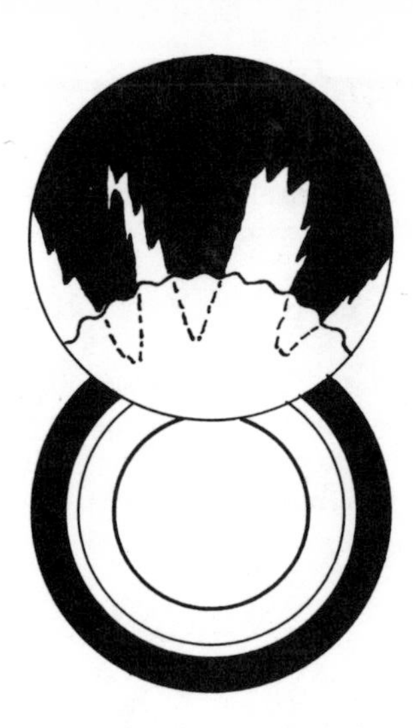

B-55. Forcing a smooth pin into a rough hole will cause the high points of the peaks to be sheared off and we will actually have metal-to-metal contact between the pin and parts of the bushing.

Standards of manufacture have improved and most piston pins are round and straight within one ten thousandth of an inch. A pin so finished looks perfect and appears to be glass smooth. When the surface is magnified 100 times it does not look so smooth and when magnified 1000 times it looks rough indeed. See Fig. B-54.

Reaming, grinding and honing equipment is now available which will produce a hole that appears to be dead smooth. It is, like the pins, accurate to one-tenth of a thousandth, but when magnified it looks much like the pins on the bearing surface. It is possible, however, with the use of good equipment to produce a hole that enables a good working fit to be made. It should be obvious that in working with such close dimensions, the clearance will be determined by the surface finish.

If the hole finish is not practically perfect, it will be seen that when the pin is forced into the hole the "peaks" will be sheared off as shown in Fig. B-55. The result of such a condition is rapid wear of the peak base and the pin and bushing are worn OUT before they wear IN to a working fit.

In this connection, it has been found that many experienced mechanics fit piston pins entirely too tight. These same mechanics wonder why many of the jobs they do develop knocks and rattles and pump oil in a short time. The reason is of course that the tight fit they insist on having results in the condition shown in Fig. B-55 with consequent rapid wear.

If the hole is properly finished to the proper size there will be room for a film of oil to prevent metal-to-metal contact and thus reduce wear. See Fig. B-56. When such a fit is obtained, the pin will enter the hole readily without force being applied and will have sufficient bearing to wear satisfactorily. Such a fit can be obtained by a skillful operator using modern equipment in accordance with the manufacturers' instructions.

In the case of anti-friction piston pin bearings, oversize rollers can be installed if the bearing surfaces are true and smooth. In small engines it is often less expensive to replace worn pins and pistons than to try to recondition them when they are worn or damaged.

ENGINE VALVES

Poppet valves as used in internal combusion engines are possibly a greater problem than any other part of the engine. This fact has led to a great amount of effort to design a valve that will be better. Various types of sleeve and rotary valves have been described previously in this text,

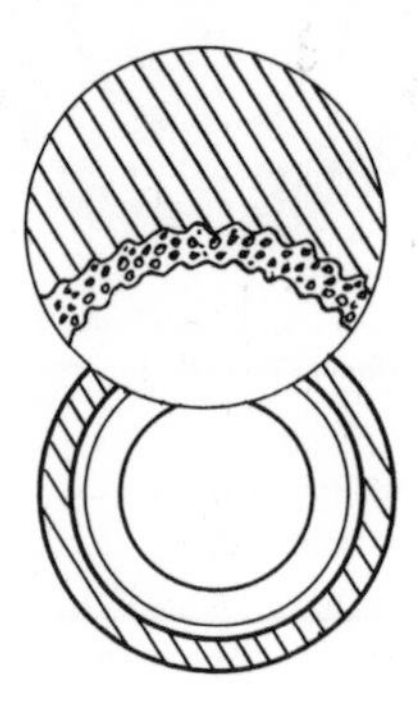

***B-56.** A proper surface on the pin and in the bushing should result in space for an oil film between the two.*

but the poppet valve seems to do a better all around job than any other type yet developed. For this reason it is almost universally used. See Fig. B-57.

It is not difficult to understand why valves are prone to cause trouble. They have an almost impossible set of tasks to perform under almost incredible conditions. First of all they are exposed to the heat of the burning gas in the cylinder. The heat of this gas may approach a temperature of 5,000 deg. F. which is far above the melting point of iron. It is not at all unusual for the exhaust valve head to operate at a red heat.

While operating at this heat, or at a termperature below zero, the valve must make a gas tight seal in the cylinder under the explosion pressure of several hundred pounds. This seal must be made and broken many times each second while the engine operates. Valves are expected to do this for many months without failure.

If the engine is running at 4,000 r.p.m., each valve will seal and unseal 2,000 times per minute. Regardless of the heat, pressure and speed at which they operate, modern valves will usually function satisfactorily for about 50 million cycles of operation without causing trouble.

VALVE COOLING

Now obviously, operating under such conditions of heat for hours at a time the valves must be cooled in some manner or they would melt. While the top of the intake valve head is exposed to the burning gas in the cylinder, the underside is cooled by the incoming cold air and gas mixture every time the valve opens. The reverse is true of the exhaust valve. Every time it opens a blast of burning gas goes between the valve head and valve seat.

It would be possible to cool the valve by circulating the engine cooling water inside it, but this would be difficult and impractical. So, therefore, we depend upon contact between the valve and the cylinder block which

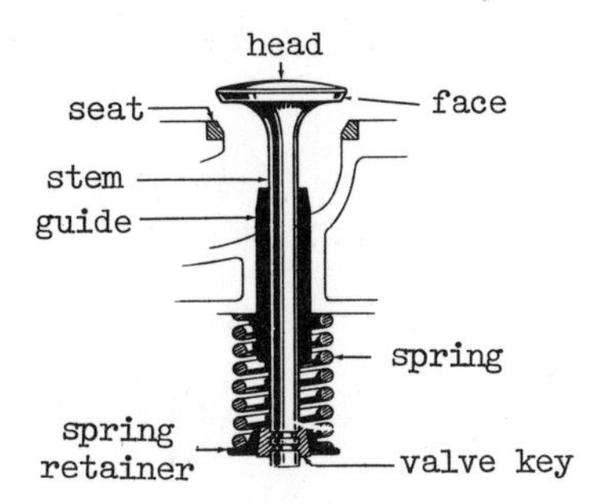

B-57. A typical poppet valve installation with an inserted valve seat.

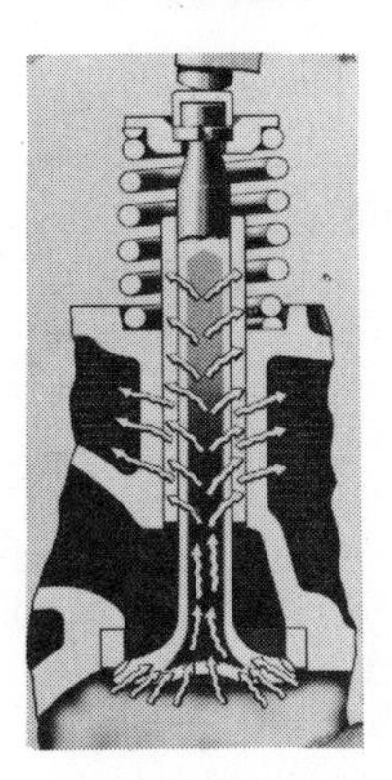

B-58. The major part of the heat from the valve head flows to the valve stem and on to the cooling water as shown here.

contains the coolant. The heat flows from the valve head to the cooling water as shown in Fig. B-58. Some heat also flows from the valve head to the valve seat during the brief time the valve is seated.

HEAT RESISTANT ALLOYS

The particular construction shown in Fig. B-58 has a special heat resistant alloy on the valve face and also bears on a heat resistant valve seat

B-59. If the valve head has a thin edge as shown at the left or if the valve head is warped as shown at the right, the thin edges thus created will become excessively hot.

insert. Furthermore, the valve is hollow and is partially filled with a metallic sodium which is an excellent conductor of heat. This sodium is normally a solid, but becomes a liquid at about the boiling point of water and thus carries some of the heat from the head to the stem for more rapid dissipation.

Heat will flow through a solid piece of metal more efficiently than from one piece of metal to another, regardless of how tightly the two pieces are held together. Therefore, an inserted alloy valve seat will run hotter than if the seat were a part of the block. However, the special alloy can also stand much higher temperature without damage and such inserts are used in many engines. Such inserts also can be replaced with new ones if they do become damaged.

VALVE TEMPERATURES

It will also be noted that the heat flows from the valve stem to the valve guide and from the guide to the block. Here again the heat transfer would be facilitated if the valve stem was in direct and intimate contact with the block. Some authorities claim that thus dispensing with the guide will lower the operating temperature of the exhaust valve as much as 100 deg. F. Of course separate valve guides can be readily replaced when worn. When no guides are used, it is necessary to ream the block or head guide holes and install oversize valves when wear occurs.

In normal operation the valve head around the seating surface will operate at a temperature of 1000 to 1200 deg. F. The central portion of the valve head will run somewhat hotter, 1200 to 1400 deg. F. and the stem adjacent the head perhaps 800 to 1000 deg. F. Under abnormal conditions such as a leaking valve, the temperature will increase.

From the foregoing, it should be realized that anything that reduces the area of contact between the valve and the cylinder block will hamper the escape of the heat from the valve. Thus if the valve seat is too narrow or the valve guide worn excessively, the area of contact will be reduced and the valve will overheat.

The area of contact could be increased by widening the valve seat, but it has been found that a wider seat also encourages carbon flakes to adhere, hold the valve open and cause burning of the seating surface. Another method of increasing the contact area would be to increase the diameter of the valve head or the valve stem or both, or increase the valve guide and valve stem length.

There are of course mechanical limitations to the amount of increase in these dimensions. Of more importance, however, would be the increase of weight in the valve. The valve is required to move endwise with such rapidity that it must be kept as light in weight as possible. Any excess

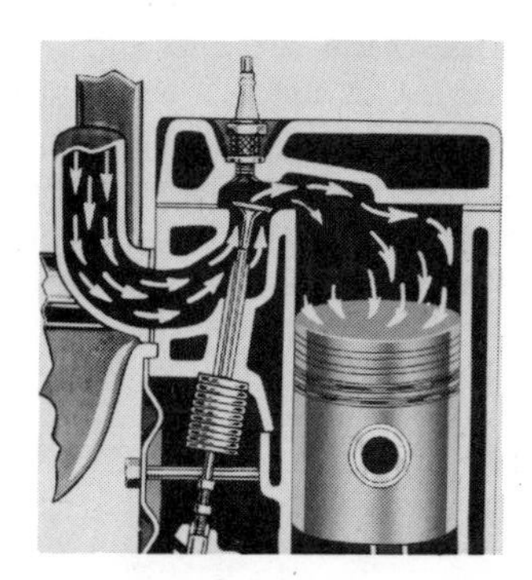

B-60. A gas in motion tends to follow a straight line and is reluctant to turn corners. As illustrated here, the velocity and volume will vary between the left and right sides of the valve. The same variation will occur when the exhaust gas tries to get out and certain parts of the valve head will be hotter than other parts.

weight would have so much inertia that the valve would slow down in movement. So here again a compromise must be made and a reasonable limitation in size imposed.

VALVE HEAT DISSIPATION

This matter of valve heat dissipation must be thoroughly understood if engines are to be properly serviced. There are several things to be considered in this connection and some of them are similar to the problems previously discussed in preceding chapters dealing with pistons and rings.

For example, the heat of operation causes distortion of the cylinder block and valve seat as well as the valve. Any hot spots in the cylinder block near the valves or any unequal tightening of the cylinder head bolts will aggravate distortion and cause valve difficulties. If the valve seat and valve were both round and true when cold and remained round and true when hot, there would be less valve trouble.

It will be readily understood that the valve head is liable to warp due to the difference in temperature at different points as previously described. This warpage will be aggravated if the rim of the valve head is thin or uneven. See Fig. B-59. Furthermore, the temperature will vary around the rim of the valve head in some cases due to the difference in velocity and the volume of hot gas going between the valve and seat at different spots. See Fig. B-60.

In addition to changes in the shape of the valve and seat, the diameter of both may change. The valve head runs hotter than the valve seat because the seat is nearer the cooling water. Therefore the valve head may expand more than the seat and as a result the valve may rise on the seat as shown in Fig. B-61. This action results in a change in the valve seat area location.

It will also be apparent that the dimension between the seat and the valve lifter will be lengthened by such expansion. Furthermore, the length of the valve itself between the seat surface and the end of the stem will be altered by lengthwise expansion of the valve and valve stem. These changes in dimension may in some cases compensate for each other to a certain extent - or they may not. Much depends on the design of the engine. The serviceman cannot change the engine design, but he must understand all of these things in order to adjust the mechanism to allow for such variations and insure satisfactory operation of the engine.

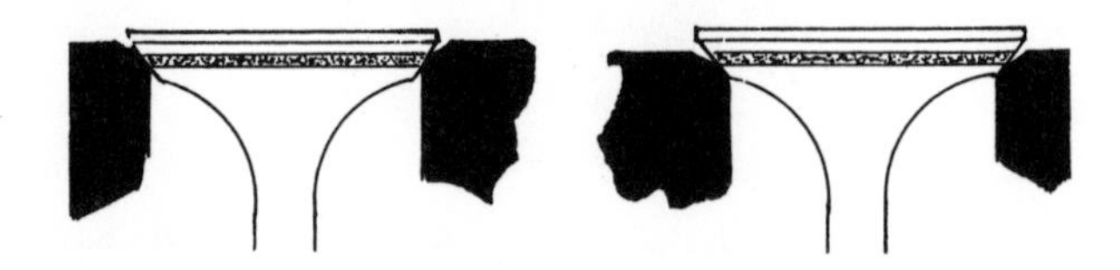

B-61. An exhaust valve may be properly seated as at the left when cold, but may expand rapidly and climb off the seat as shown at the right.

VALVE GRINDING

One of the most frequently performed jobs is to "clean carbon and grind valves." The valve service operation today is more of a precise machining operation than the hand lapping procedure of past years.

This hand lapping consisted of placing grinding compound, which was usually an abrasive paste (sometimes emery powder mixed in vaseline), on the surface of the valve face and oscillating the valve on the seat until the surfaces were mated. Light pressure was used and the compound renewed often until all the pits and signs of corrosion disappeared from the seating surface of valve and valve seat.

This procedure was assumed to provide a gas-tight valve and little attention or thought was given to valve seat width, heat dissipation, concentricity of valve with seat, strength of valve springs, wear in valve guides and all the other things that require attention.

VALVE RECONDITIONING

Modern valve grinding is a true grinding process rather than a lapping procedure. Every part of the operation is governed by careful measurement with accurate equipment. The first step is to determine whether the valve can be reconditioned or whether it must be replaced. If the stem is scored, pitted, bent or worn more than .002 in. it is usually discarded.

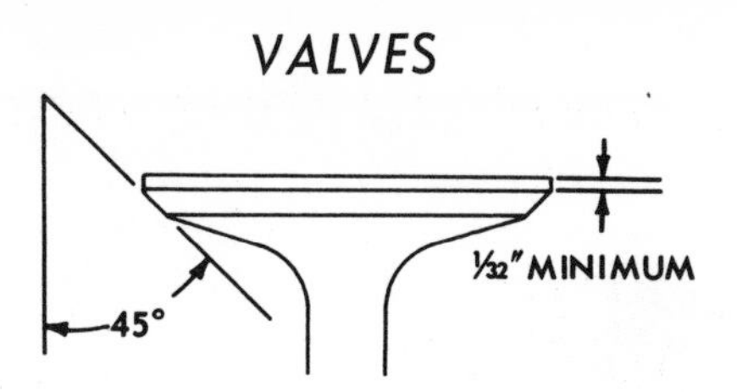

B-62. 1/32 in. is usually regarded as the minimum suitable width for the valve margin between the seat and the top surface.

If the face is burned, warped or worn to a thin margin (see Fig. B-62) it is discarded. If the valve is in good condition it is placed in a special grinding machine known as a valve refacer and a new surface ground on the face at the proper angle with and concentric with the stem. See Fig. B-63. Most valve faces are cut at an angle of 45 deg. with the stem. 30 degs. is used in some cases and 90 deg., or flat valves, have been used. When this operation is performed properly, the face surface is so accurate that very little if any lapping is required.

VALVE SEAT RECONDITIONING

The seat in the block or head is also resurfaced with the aid of special reamers or grinders. First of all it is necessary to position the tool so that it will be located to cut the seat concentric with the valve stem guide and

B-63. A typical special machine designed for grinding valves accurately.

at the proper angle. This is difficult to do if the guide is worn. Guides should be replaced if worn out-of-round, bell-mouthed or to an excessive degree at any point.

As previously mentioned valve seats that are too narrow will not dissipate enough heat and if too wide will permit carbon to adhere to them. In the absence of factory spcifications a seat 1/16 of an inch in width is usually satisfactory. If the seat is wider than this, the first operation will be to narrow the seat by cutting an acute angle under the seat and an ob-

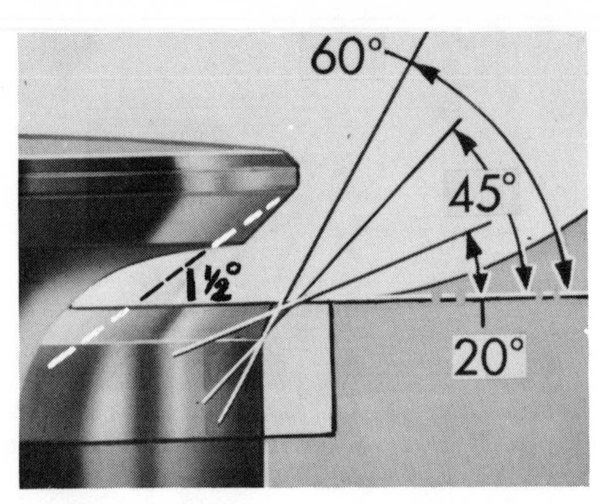

B-64. Three different angles are used to obtain the correct seat width and angle. If an interference angle is used, it should be cut from the lower edge of the valve face rather than the upper.

tuse angle above the seat. See Fig. B-64. This is done with special reamers or grinders made for the purpose.

After the seat is sufficiently narrowed, the surface is then cut or ground to the proper angle. Sometimes a slight interference angle - about 1 1/2 deg. - is cut on either the valve seat or the valve face to improve the seating ability. See Fig. B-64. This cutting or grinding must result in a smooth, true surface if the valve is to be gas-tight.

It cannot be true if the seat is not concentric with the valve stem. A method of testing with a dial gauge is shown in Fig. B-65. The seat should be concentric with the guide within .001 in.

B-65. A specially mounted dial gauge is used to check the concentricity of the valve seat with the valve guide.

VALVE SEAT INSERTS

If the seat is of the inserted type and is badly worn or burned, it may be easier to replace the valve seat. These seats are made of hard, heat

B-66. In this case the exhaust and inlet guides are identical, but are installed differently.

resisting metal and cannot be reamed like an integral seat on a cast iron block. The inserts are refaced by grinding with special grinders.

If the seat is of the screw in type, it is a simple matter to unscrew the old seat and screw in a new valve seat insert. The seating surface is of course ground after the insert is installed. The pressed in or shrunk in inserts are usually held tightly in place by rolling or peening the cast iron over the top of the insert after it is installed.

As it is sometimes difficult to clean up the peening enough to allow the insert to be pulled, the inserts are in such cases broken up for removal. Whether the old insert is pulled or broken out, it is essential that the hole for the insert be round and true. If the insert does not bottom fully in the hole or if it does not fit tightly all around the hole, there will be poor heat transfer from the insert to the cylinder block and coolant.

For this reason the inserts are often of such size as to provide an "interference fit"; that is, the insert is one or two thousandths larger in diameter than the hole into which it is to be inserted. In this case, to avoid the difficulty of pressing them into place, the inserts are often shrunk for insertion. If the inserts are placed in a deep freeze for a few hours or packed in dry ice for a few minutes, they will shrink enough to drop readily into the hole. When so frozen, the inserts must be handled carefully as they are very brittle and will crack or split easily.

After insertion, the metal around the insert is lightly peened or rolled over the top of the insert to hold it tightly in place. The final step is to grind the seat for the valve on the insert true with the valve guide.

VALVE STEM GUIDES

Most engines have separate valve guides of the press-in or slip-in type, but some engines are built with the valve stem in direct contact with a hole bored in the cylinder block or head. Heat dissipation is better where guides are not used, but the guides cannot be replaced when worn. They must be bored oversize and new valves with oversize stems fitted. In most cases the separate guides are made of cast iron, but bronze has been used in some engines because of the superior wearing characteristics and more rapid heat dissipation.

The press-in type is used most often and is made to fit tightly in the block or head. Such guides are often identical for the exhaust and inlet valves, but are sometimes installed differently. In other cases the exhaust and inlet guides are not interchangeable. In still another case the guides are identical, but the inlet guides are installed upside down from the exhaust guides. See Fig. B-66. Some exhaust guides are cut off shorter in the port opening and others are counterbored in the port end to reduce the tendency for carbon to accumulate in the guide. See Fig. B-67.

Carbon does accumulate in the guide bore and on the stem of exhaust valves and causes them to stick open or slow down in action. The tendency for carbon to accumulate increases as the valve stem and guide wear because more hot gas blows by between stem and guide. Wear on the intake valve stem and guide is equally undesirable because such wear permits air to be drawn in through the clearance and dilute the gasoline air mixture. Under such conditions it is impossible to obtain a satisfactory carburetor adjustment.

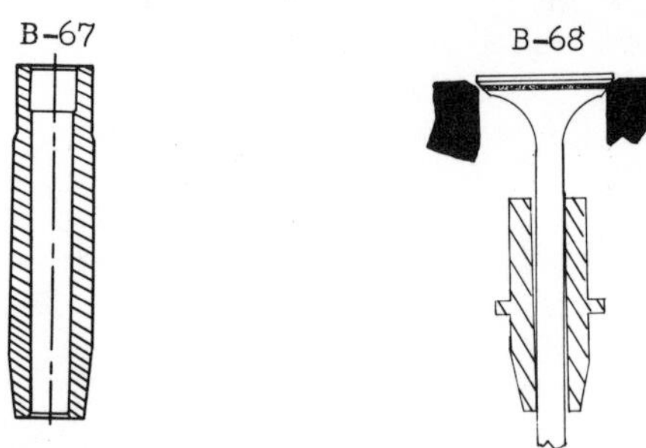

B-67. A slight counterbore is sometimes made in the port end of exhaust valve guides to lessen carbon accumulation.

B-68. Looseness in the valve guide permits the valve to wobble and cause undue wear of valve and seat.

Another undesirable result of excessive wear in valve guides is to permit the valve to wobble enough to cause it to ride to one side of the valve seat. See Fig. B-68. This of course interferes with proper seating and sealing of the valve and also promotes additional wear. It is customary to replace the valve guides or valves or both whenever more than .005 in. clearance exists between valve stem and guide. One method of measuring clearance is shown in Fig. B-69.

Before any measurement is made, the valve stem must be cleaned and polished and the valve stem guide thoroughly cleaned of carbon deposits. The measurement for clearance should be made with the valve slightly off the seat as shown in Fig. B-69. The valve spring must also be removed while measuring.

REPLACING VALVE GUIDES

In some cases where an unusual amount of trouble is experienced with exhaust valves sticking due to rapid accumulation of carbon, it has been found helpful to cut off the end of the exhaust guide. This is often done with a drill as shown in Fig. B-70. The guide is cut down even with the opening in which it is located.

After the guides are pressed in place, it is usually necessary to ream them to proper size and provide clearance for heat expansion of the valve stem. Special reamers are made for this purpose. This operation must be performed carefully so that the hole will be straight and true with a smooth inner surface or bore.

Exhaust valve stems will require more clearance in the guide than inlet valves. In the absence of specific instructions, it is customary to fit intake valves with .001 to .003 in. clearance and exhaust valves with .002 to .004 in. clearance depending upon the size of the valve stem.

VALVE SPRINGS

Valve springs do not receive the attention they deserve in most cases. They are an exceedingly important part of the engine and have much to do with the engine performance. They are seldom replaced unless broken, yet

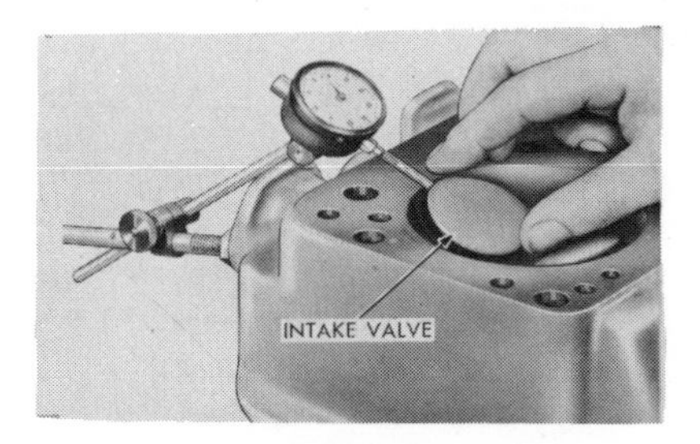

B-69. When measuring the clearance between valve and guide, the valve must be off the seat as shown here.

B-70. A specially ground drill can be used to cut the end off of the exhaust guide.

should be replaced when they are not up to specifications. They work hard, being subjected to millions of cycles of high speed operation and all of it under shock conditions.

The valves are opened with lightning-like speed by the action of the cam and the spring is expected to close the valve just as fast as it is opened.

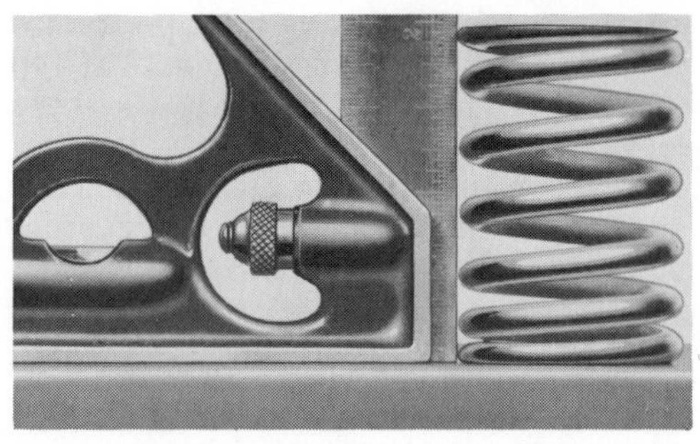

B-71. Valve springs should be square on each end and of the proper length.

The valve lifter is thus kept in contact with the cam. If the spring is weak and does not hold the lifter in contact with the cam, noise will be created and the valve, spring, lifter and cam will be subjected to hammer-like blows that cause metal fatigue. Many broken valves result from shock caused by sticking stems, weak valve springs or excessive tappet clearance.

The manufacturer provides specifications on the free length of the spring and the pressure in pounds that the spring should exert when it is compressed to a measured length. Special tools are available for measuring the length and strength of the spring. Valve springs are simple, inexpensive coil wire springs and should not be expected to last forever.

They should be square on each end as otherwise they will have a tendency to pull the valve stem to one side and cause undue wear on the valve stem and valve guide. They can be checked for squareness and free length as shown in Fig. B-71.

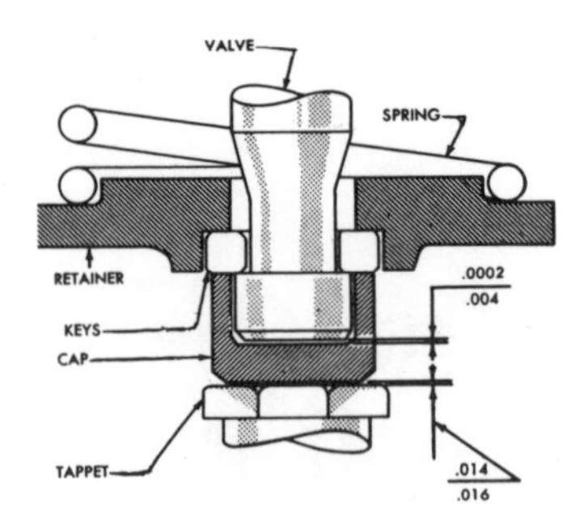

B-72. With this free valve device, it is important to maintain the clearance between the end of the valve and the cap.

Periodic replacement is also good to avoid unexpected failure. Valve springs often become "etched" when the valve chamber is subject to corrosive vapors. Some valve chambers are not well ventilated and steam or moisture containing acids formed from combustion will collect and cause flecks of rust to form on the valve springs. This etching is liable to cause the spring to break. This is similar to the corrosive action that causes pits and rust to eat into valve stems.

VALVE SPRING RETAINERS

Valve spring locks or "keepers" are usually a pair of C shaped washers that fit into a slot cut near the end of the valve stem. A cupped washer called a retainer fits over these semi-circular keys and the tension of the spring bearing on the retainer holds the locks in place. Other methods have been used. Slots cut near the end of the stem and a key or pin pushed through the slot, threads cut on the end of the stem for a nut and lock nut, etc.

Removal is accomplished by holding the valve stationary while the spring is compressed enough to allow the retainer to be raised from the locks. The locks are then removed and the valve spring released. This allows the valve to be removed and then the spring and retainer can be removed.

Some retainers are more complicated and are intended to permit or encourage the valve to rotate slightly with regard to the seat. Some of these are called "free valves" and the purpose is to provide a longer lasting seal between valve and valve seat. Rotation of the valve will discourage the formation of carbon deposits and valve warpage.

Some of these free valve devices release the valve from the valve spring tension at one point in the cycle of operation so that it is free to rotate slightly. One type is illustrated in Fig. B-72. With this type it is important to maintain the clearances between the stem and the cup and between the cup and retainer within specified limits.

Other devices are known as valve rotators and impart a positive rotational effort to the valve once during each cycle of operation. One such type is illustrated in Fig. B-73.

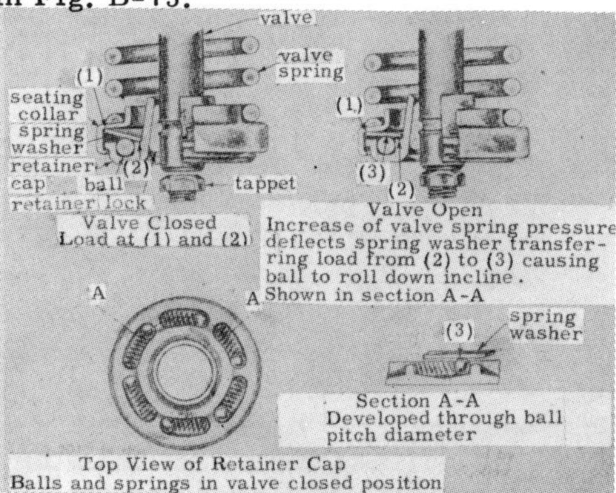

B-73. In this case, positive rotation of the valve is caused by the inclines down which the balls roll when pressure is applied.

Regardless of the type of device used to provide or permit rotation of the valves, there appears to be no question about their ability to assist in retaining a satisfactory seal between valve and seat. They are also claimed to minimize sticking and wear between guide and stem.

VALVE OPERATING MECHANISM

The camshaft is rotated by the engine crankshaft by means of gears or chains and thus is kept in definite relation or "timing" with the crankshaft. In four cycle engines the camshaft gear or sprocket is twice the size of the crankshaft gear or sprocket and therefore the camshaft operates at half the speed of the crankshaft. See Figs. B-74 and B-75.

We have already considered the accuracy with which the cam contour or shape is formed in order to provide the proper operating characteristics for the valves. Ordinarily the surface of the cam is so hard that the exact shape remains substantially unaltered. There is of course some

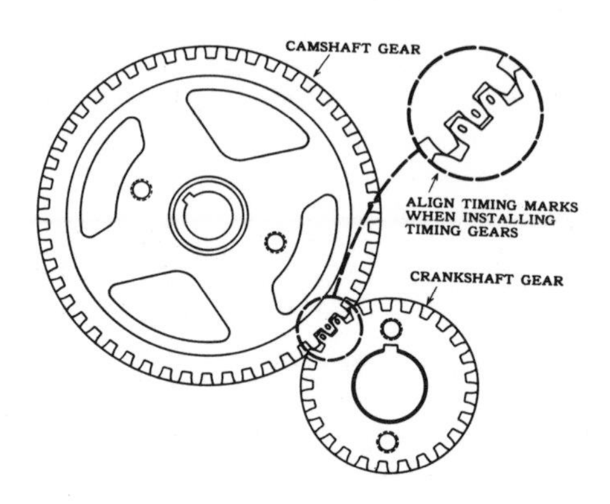

B-74. Timing gears are usually marked as shown to insure that the valves will be correctly timed.

friction between the cam and the valve lifter that rides on it and some wear is bound to occur in time. This wear is usually on the highest part of the cam and will thus decrease the height or "lift" of the valve. The result is that the valve does not open as wide as it should and the "breathing" ability of the engine suffers.

If the wear on the cam is at the sides or on the ramp the valve action will become noisy and also the valve will open late or close early, or both. Excessive wear in the valve lifters will have the same results; noise, and faulty valve timing.

Usually the wear on cams is so slow and the loss of engine performance so gradual that it goes unnoticed unless the valve lift is checked against factory specifications. In rare cases a defective camshaft has been found and the loss of engine performance so rapid as to be noticed. In some cases the entire camshaft has not been properly hardened and in other cases it has been one or more individual cams that were soft enough to wear quickly.

VALVE TIMING

Anything that occurs to change the time that the valve opens, the duration of the time it is held open, the size of the opening, or the time that it

B-75. Timing chain sprockets are usually marked so that when a line drawn through the center of both shafts bisects the timing marks, the timing is correct. Flywheels are also usually marked to facilitate checking the valve timing.

closes, will have a decided effect on the engine performance. This fact is not often fully realized. Many engines constantly run below par because mechanics in general have too little knowledge of the necessity of proper valve clearance adjustment.

A full realization of the need for accurate adjustment can come only from a study of valve action and requirements. This study starts with the relation between crankshaft and camshaft. Due to the difference in the diameter of the circles described by the crank throw and the cam nose and the difference in the comparative speed of rotation, the crank throw may travel five or six times as fast as the cam nose. Thus, while the cam nose is moving 1/4 of an inch, the crankshaft may move 1 1/2 inches. Therefore, if the cam is a few thousandths late in opening the valve, the crank throw and the piston attached to it will move a considerable distance farther than it should before the valve opens.

In this manner the motion of the piston is partially lost and the power output suffers. Obviously, therefore, a worn timing chain or worn timing gears should be replaced as soon as the wear exceeds the specifications rather than wait until they become noisy or break, which is all too often the case. It is common to find a timing chain worn so badly that it will "jump" a tooth before it is replaced. No engine can operate efficiently under such conditions.

Of course the camshaft and camshaft drive are only part of the mechanism used to operate the valve. To continue the study of valve action and timing, we must consider parts such as lifters, rods, rocker arms and other parts in various forms. Each one of these parts has something to do with valve timing. It is well to consider at this time that many minor faults may equal a major fault. In other words, a little wear at many points in the valve operating mechanism may be equal in effect to considerable wear at one point.

For example, suppose there is .005 excess wear between the gear teeth. This will allow the valves to open late and close early. Add to this another .005 excess wear in the camshaft bearings which will reduce the valve lift as well as increase the late opening and early closing of the valves. Add another .005 worn from the cam contour which also changes the valve lift or the timing or both. Now on top of all this add another .005 excess wear between the lifters and guides. This results in the lifter moving sidewise in the guide before it starts to lift the valve.

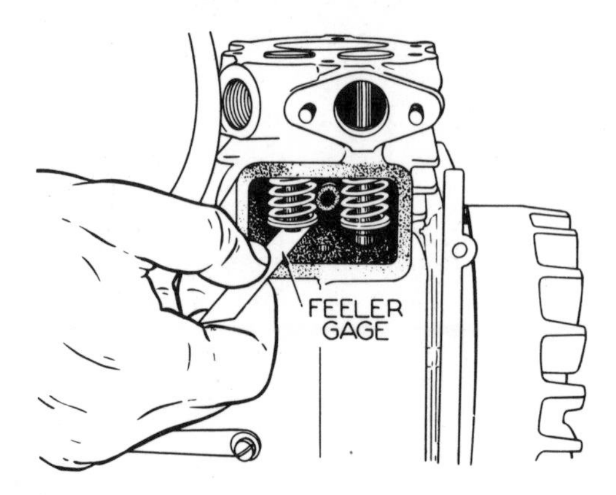

B-76. Checking valve clearance on L-head engine using flat feeler between lifter and valve stem.

Obviously all this cumulative wear will seriously interfere with the engine operation. Such conditions are often further aggravated by careless adjustment of the valve tappets. Many mechanics who do not understand valve action adjust the valves with too much clearance to make sure there is no possibility of the valve holding open. Their idea could be expressed - ''Better too loose than too tight, so who cares about a little noise.'' They do not realize that they are restricting the ability of the engine to draw in a full charge of mixture and dispose of the exhaust gas properly.

The engine manufacturer furnishes exact valve tappet clearance specifications in all cases, and these should be followed explicitly. Otherwise, the efforts of the design engineer who built efficiency into the engine are partially wasted. These specifications are so precise that they state whether the engine should be cold or at operating temperature when the adjustment is made.

It should be evident that accurate adjustment is impossible if the various contacting surfaces are worn to untrue dimensions. If such parts are not too seriously worn, they can be restored by grinding with the proper equipment. If they are worn enough to be through the case-hardened shell, they should be discarded and replaced with new parts.

Adjustment of the tappet clearance is made by means of a feeler gauge as shown in Fig. B-76.

In some engines there are no adjustment screws in the valve lifters. In such cases the proper clearance is obtained by grinding the end of the valve stem using special gauges made for the purpose and used in connection with a valve grinding and refacing machine. Thus the clearance is set at the time of a valve service operation and is not adjustable otherwise.

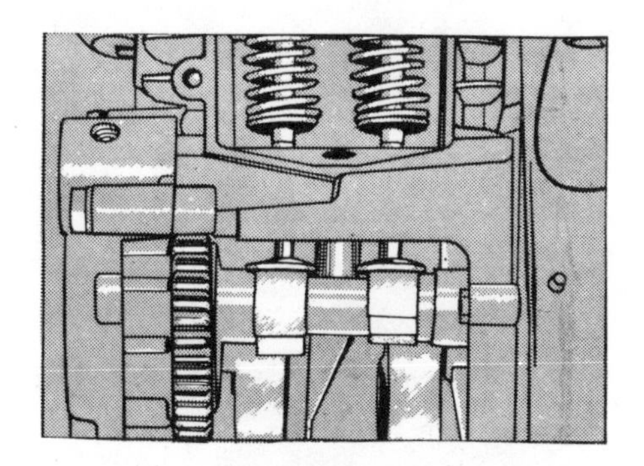

B-77. Typical camshaft and valve arrangement on single cylinder engine.

B-78. In the two cycle engine, ports in the cylinder wall and a special shape piston head are often used instead of poppet valves.

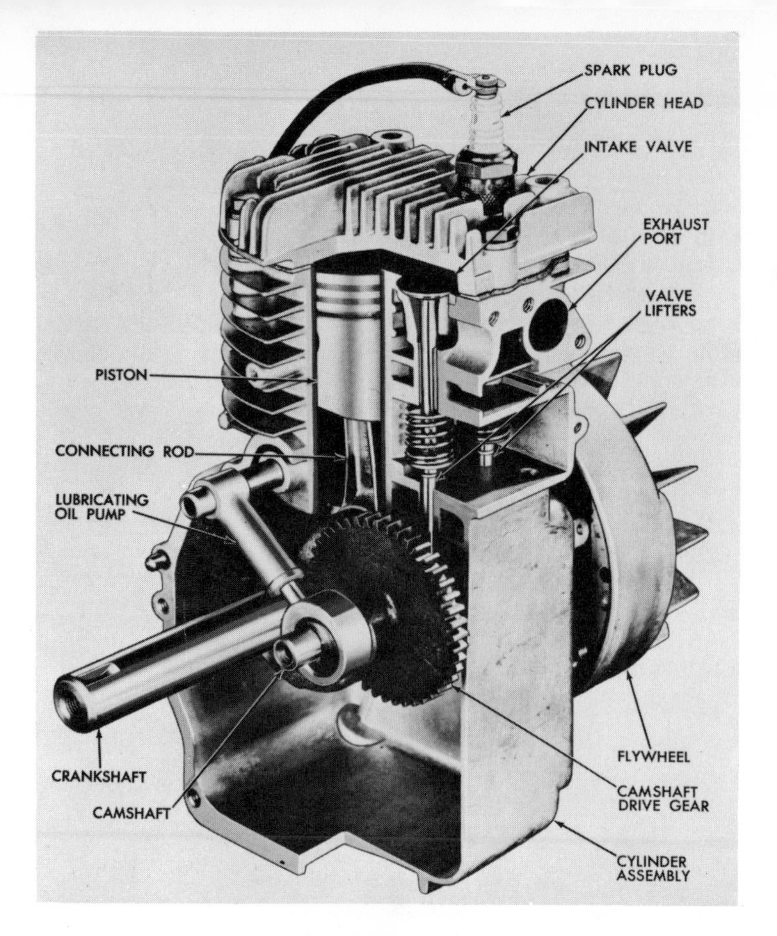

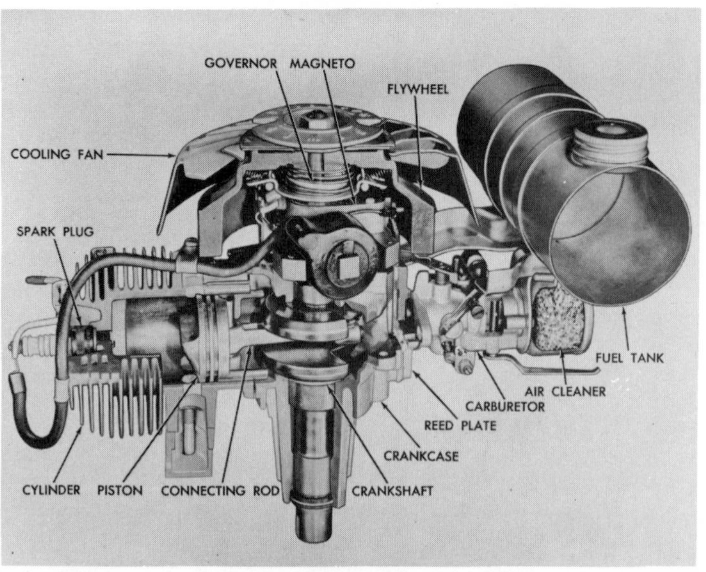

C-1. Typical single cylinder air cooled engines as built by Tecumseh. Upper, four cycle; lower, two cycle.

COOLING SYSTEMS
LUBRICATION

Some parts of an internal combustion engine would melt from the heat of the burning gas if no cooling system were provided. However, it would probably be more correct to refer to the engine cooling system as a "temperature regulation" system. We do not want the engine to run too hot, but neither do we want it to run too cool. We would like to maintain the water jacket temperature slightly under the boiling point of water, or at about 200 deg. F., at all times if that were possible.

The cylinder walls of air cooled engines operate at a temperature considerably above 200 deg. F. in many cases. This is hot to touch, but cool in comparison with the heat generated in the combustion chamber of the engine.

As the fuel is burned in the combustion chamber, about one-third of the heat energy in the fuel is converted into power. Another third goes out the exhaust pipe unused and the remaining third must be handled by the cooling system. This third to be handled by the cooling system is often underestimated and even less understood.

HEAT TRANSFER

The heat flows or transfers from the cylinder iron to the cooling water. If, however, there is a coating of lime or rust between the water and the bare metal, the flow will be retarded because lime and rust are very poor heat conductors.

COOLING SYSTEM DEFECTS

We are always liable to have some rust in a cooling system. Rust is a combination of iron, water, and oxygen and we have iron in the cylinder block, water in the water jacket, and some oxygen is in the water. Additional oxygen enters the cooling system in the air that finds its way into the cooling system.

In addition to rust, we usually have some lime in the cooling system. In most parts of the country there is some lime in the water supply, more in some locations than in others, along with other minerals. Alternate heating and cooling of the engine causes the lime to collect on the inside walls of the water jacket in the same manner that lime collects in a tea kettle.

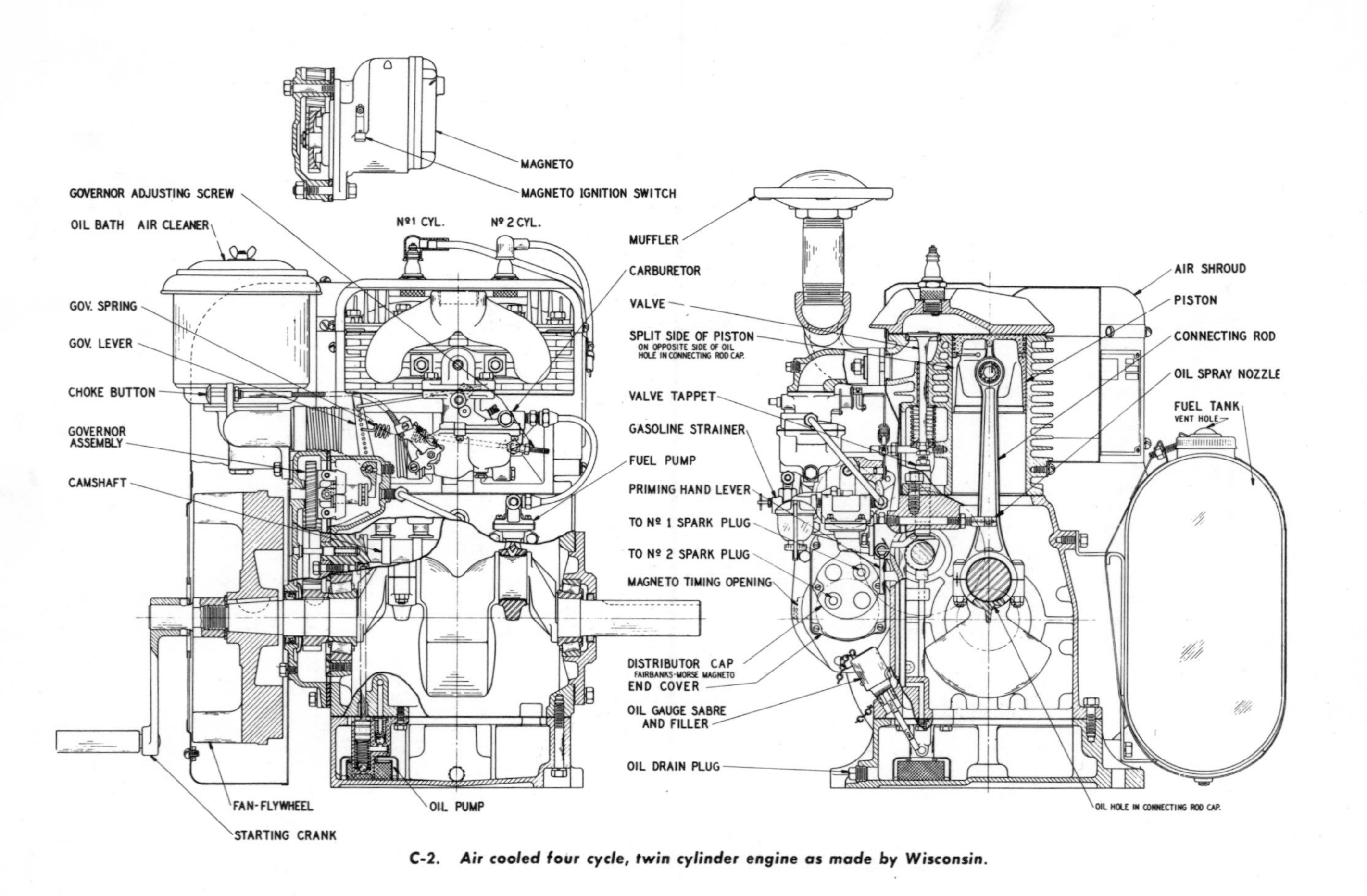

C-2. *Air cooled four cycle, twin cylinder engine as made by Wisconsin.*

The rust and lime in the cooling system combine with a small amount of grease or oil, which often acts as a binder to hold the lime and rust to the iron, and soon we have an insulating coat on the inside of the water jacket.

In addition to coating the inside of the water jacket, this scale will collect in corners or pockets of the water jacket where the circulation is sluggish. This often causes "hot spots" which in turn cause distortion of cylinders and valve seats.

SCALE REMOVAL

Minor accumulations of scale and trash can be removed from the cooling system with the aid of prepared chemicals. The chemical manufacturers' instructions should be followed closely for best results.

In case the deposits are too heavy to be removed by the foregoing method, they can often be cleared out by power purging equipment. This equipment surges powerful streams of chemicals through the system in alternate directions and is claimed to clear out the most stubborn accumulations.

If lime and scale has been allowed to accumulate over a period of years, it may be desirable to remove the water jacket cover from the cylinder block, when the block is so equipped. This permits access to the inside of the jacket for chipping and scraping the lime from the metal. In such cases the cover plates should be inspected for corrosion before replacement. New gaskets and new copper washers should be used along with a suitable sealing compound when the covers are replaced.

The water circulation passages between the cylinder block and cylinder head are made as large as possible, but some restriction of the flow cannot be avoided. For this reason the openings in the cylinder head gasket should fit the openings in the block and head rather well to avoid further restriction.

AIR COOLED ENGINES

Air cooled engines are used almost exclusively for small machinery such as wood saws, lawn mowers, gardening equipment, etc. Single or twin cylinder engines of both two and four cycle types are entirely satisfactory and operate for long periods of time with little attention and few repairs. See Fig. C-1 and C-2. Also see later chapters on air cooled engines.

Such small industrial engines are usually self-contained power units having built-in fuel and ignition arrangements like an outboard engine. The ignition is often supplied by an in-built high tension magneto which is part of, or attached to the engine flywheel. See Fig. C-3. Thus rotation of the engine generates electricity for ignition.

All gasoline or oil engines have substantially the same parts and differ

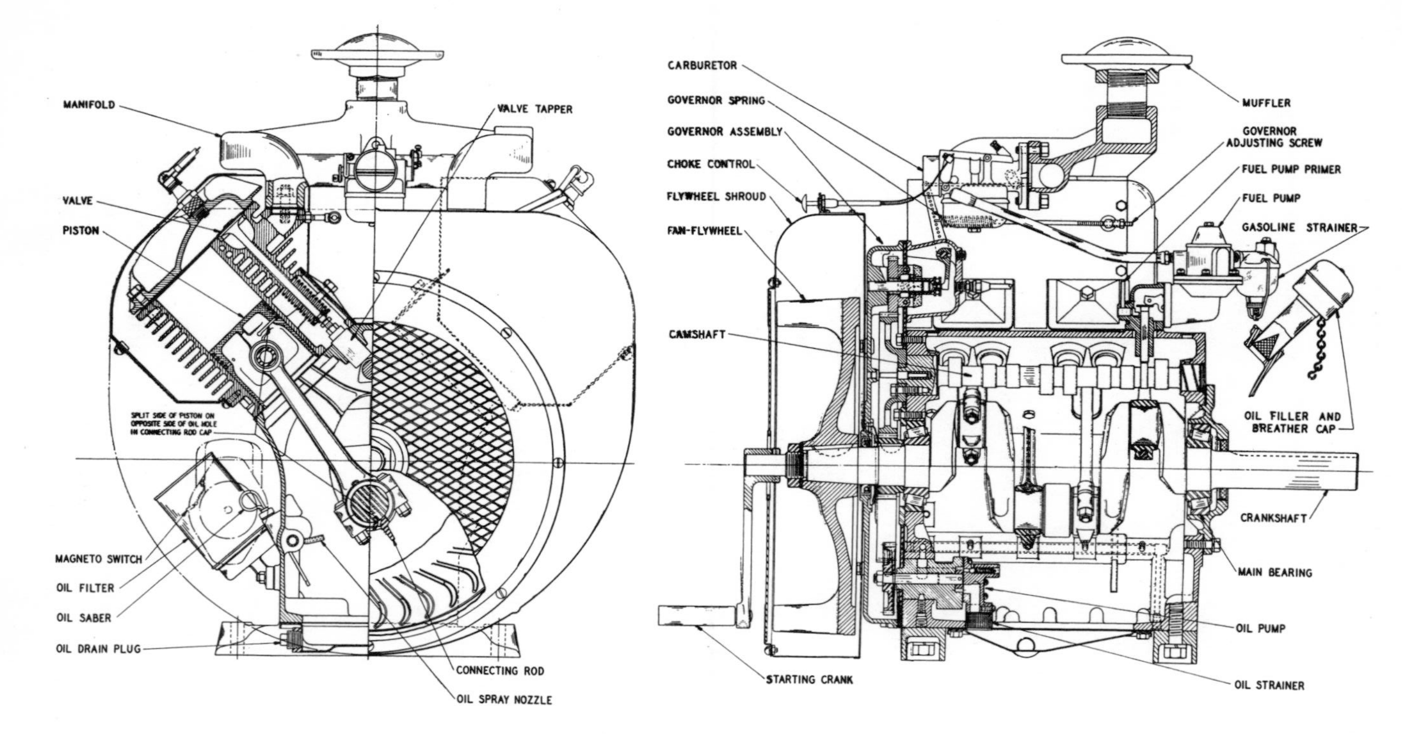

C-2A. *Air cooled four cycle, four cylinder V-type enaine.*

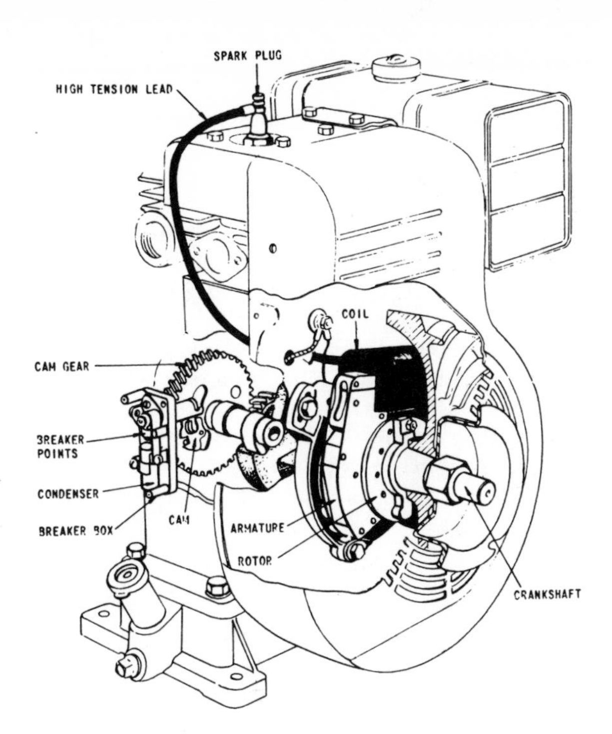

C-3. Single cylinder four cycle air cooled engine with inbuilt ignition system as used by Briggs and Stratton.

only in details of design, material and construction to adapt them to the purpose for which they are expected to be used.

If consideration is given to the operating conditions it is no great problem to service the valves, pistons, rings, cylinders, bearings or any other parts of the engine. The same requirements for accuracy of measurement, careful workmanship and understanding of fundamentals applies equally well in doing service work on any of them.

Individual types of both two and four cycle engines, both water and air cooled are given specific attention later in this text.

LUBRICATION

Excessive friction would mean rapid destruction. We cannot eliminate internal friction, but we do reduce it to a controllable degree by the use of friction reducing lubricants.

These lubricants are usually made from the same crude oil from which we obtain gasoline. The petroleum oils are compounded with animal fats, vegetable oils and other ingredients to produce satisfactory oils and greases. Lubricating oils and greases are also manufactured from silicones and other materials and have no petroleum products in them.

Lubricating oil in an engine has several tasks to perform:

1. By lubrication reduce the friction between the moving parts of the engine, thus -

A - Reduce the amount of destructive heat generated by excessive friction.

B - Conserve power that would otherwise be wasted in overcoming excessive friction.

2. By acting as a seal to prevent leakage between parts such as pistons, rings and cylinders.
3. By flowing between friction generating parts and thus carrying away much of the heat.
4. By washing away the abrasive metal worn from friction surfaces.

Furthermore the engine oil must function whether the temperature is below zero or above 100 deg. F. This is contrary to the nature of petroleum products as they tend to thicken at low temperature and thin out at high temperature. The oil therefore goes through many processes during manufacture to reduce this tendency to change viscosity with changes in temperature.

SAE OIL NUMBER

Engine oil is also manufactured in various "weights" or "thicknesses," the lighter of the oils having less tendency to "stiffen" or thicken at low temperatures. These weights are known by numbers assigned by the Society of Automotive Engineers and the lighter the weight the lower the number. Thus SAE 10 engine oil may be recommended for low temperature use and SAE 30 for use in warmer weather. THE SAE NUMBER OF AN OIL HAS NOTHING TO DO WITH THE QUALITY OF THE OIL.

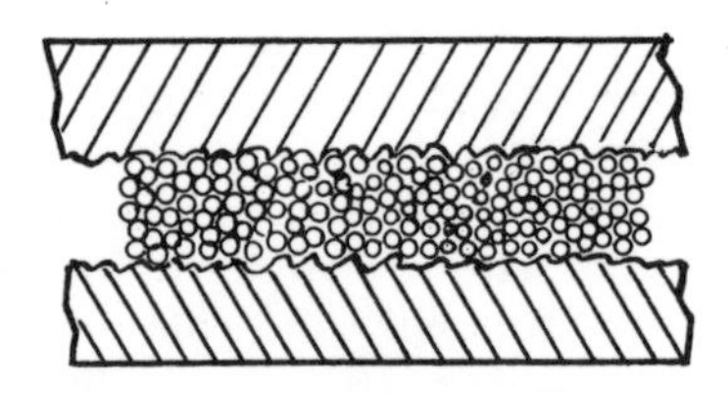

C-4. The oil molecules roll one over the other to reduce friction in a manner somewhat similar to ball bearings.

The added designation of W, such as 10-W indicates that the W oil has the added ability to remain fluid or flow at a lower temperature. Thus a number 10-W oil can be used anywhere an SAE 10 can be used, but an SAE 10 may not have the fluidity of a number 10-W at low temperatures. Many oils are branded with both numbers (SAE 10 - 10-W) and will meet both specifications.

OIL SELECTION

The manufacturer recommends the weight of oil to be used under various conditions. This recommendation is based upon the existing temperature and the clearances existing in the engine. Thus a new engine built with close fitting parts might use an SAE 20 oil in warm weather and change to a 10-W in cold weather for light service. In extreme cold a No. 5-W oil might be required for easy starting.

This same engine after considerable use and wear in the parts might require an SAE 30 oil in warm weather. In any case the manufacturer's recommendations should be followed.

In general the manufacturer recommends the lightest weight oil that he feels can be used safely under the conditions. This for the reason that a light oil facilitates cold starting and attains circulation sooner than a heavier oil. At the same time it is not desirable to use an oil so light that it cannot maintain a film of protection between the moving parts.

The moving parts in the engine are subject to speed and pressure as well as heat. The pressure has a tendency to squeeze the oil out and permit the bearing surfaces to contact each other and produce friction and wear. Even though the metal parts appear to be mirror-smooth to the naked eye, they are rough indeed when magnified. The oil is required to form a film thick enough to hold these surfaces apart. The term "thick" in this case may be a fraction of a thousandth, but the film may contain several layers of oil molecules.

These layers of oil molecules might be compared to layers of ball bearings of infinitesimal size. See Fig. C-4. One layer rolls over another with a minimum of friction and also these layers hold the two surfaces apart against the pressure tending to force them together.

LUBRICATION METHODS

The oil may be supplied to the moving parts of the engine by splashing or by pump pressure. Some engines use a combination of both types.

SPLASH SYSTEMS

In the splash system the moving parts of the engine strike the oil in the reservoir and splash it around over the other parts in the crankcase. The lubrication thus supplied is part fluid and part oil mist.

Two cycle engines have no oil reservoir and no specific oiling system. The engine oil is mixed with the fuel and as the fuel circulates in the form of vapor in the engine crankcase the oil is carried to the working parts in the form of an oily mist. It is assumed that the oil condenses or collects on the metal parts in limited quantities to provide lubrication.

OIL ADDITIVES

As previously mentioned, one of the duties of engine oil is to clean the engine operating parts. This is a washing action and of course a light oil is considered a more effective cleanser than a heavy oil. Also some oils contain natural solvents that are more active than others, and thus are more effective cleaners or "detergents." Detergents are also added to oils to give them more cleaning ability.

Many things are added to oils to give them special characteristics. These are often referred to as "additives." There are many types of additives, each serving a different purpose. For example, a "pour point depressant" may be added to cause the oil to flow freely at low temperatures. Also an "inhibitor" may be added which is intended to retard the deterioration of the oil. Another additive is known as a "dispersive." This is expected to prevent contaminants collecting in masses to form sludge. Many other chemicals are used in the refining process or are added to the oil to improve its ability to lubricate and clean under all sorts of difficult operating conditions.

CRANKCASE DILUTION

In cold weather it is necessary to use the choke on the carburetor in order to obtain an explosive mixture in the cylinders. As a result, some liquid gasoline gets into the cylinders and washes past the rings into the crankcase. It mixes with the oil and thus thins the oil out at times until the lubricating ability of the oil is seriously damaged. This lessened lubricating ability along with the oil being washed off the pistons and cylinder walls results in metal-to-metal contact and rapid wear of rings, pistons and cylinders.

It may be seen then that most of the wear in an engine often occurs in the first few minutes of operation after a cold start before the oil starts to circulate. It is also evident that racing a cold engine to "warm 'er up," will quickly ruin it because there is no lubrication of the parts.

DIESELS

Diesel engines are built in all sizes from the tiny model airplane size with a cylinder bore of less than an inch to the ocean liner size with a bore of several feet. The speed of the model airplane Diesel may exceed 5,000 r.p.m., while the ship Diesel may operate at less than 500 r.p.m. Both of them will utilize high compression ratios.

Diesel engines are very similar to gasoline engines and are built in both two cycle and four cycle designs and with any number of cylinders. In general, they are heavier in structure to withstand the higher pressures resulting from the high compression ratios used. In a full Diesel the compression ratio may be as high as 18 to 1. What is known as a "semi-Diesel" engine usually employs a somewhat lower ratio and may use spark plugs for ignition.

In previous chapters we have considered the fact that compressing a gas - such as air - generates heat. In the Diesel engine the air is compressed so much that it becomes hot enough (1000-1200 deg. F.) to ignite the fuel. The fuel in this case is a petroleum product which is lighter than crude oil, but heavier than gasoline. A gasoline-air mixture cannot be used in a Diesel because it would start to burn from the heat generated by the high compression long before the piston reached the top of the stroke.

The Diesel therefore has no carburetor. The air is compressed in the cylinder and at the proper time the fuel is sprayed into the heated air under pressure. The fuel-air mixture ignites and burns the same as in a gasoline engine to produce power. Obviously, the entry of the fuel must be "timed" the same as a spark to the spark plug in a gasoline engine. The fuel pumping device is therefore positively connected to the engine crankshaft, being driven by gear or chain.

FUEL INJECTORS

The fuel injection device is a spray nozzle located in the cylinder and the pump may be in the nozzle, or all the pumps may be in a separate unit. In either case the fuel oil must be injected at a pressure greater than the compression pressure within the cylinder which may exceed 500 p.s.i.

As there is no carburetor and therefore no throttle valve there must be some method of controlling the fuel in order to control the engine. The amount of fuel injected is what determines the speed and power of the engine as the cylinder always takes in and compresses a full charge of air.

In any case, regardless of the construction or details of the fuel system used in a Diesel the injection system must do four things:

A - Measure or meter the quantity of fuel entering each cylinder.

B - Provide enough pressure to force the fuel into the cylinder at peak compression.

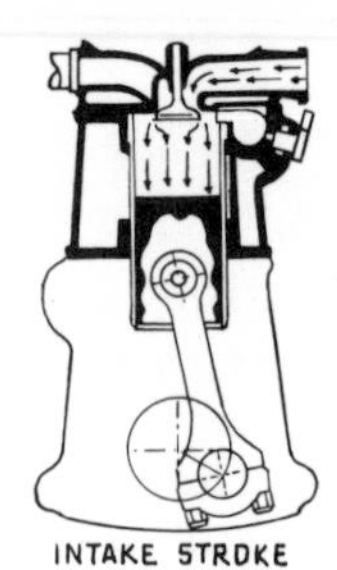

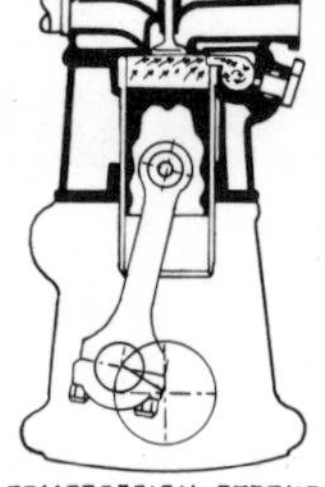

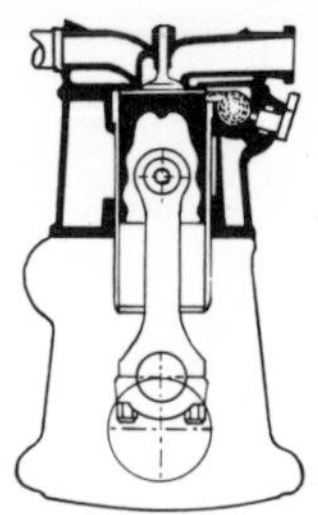

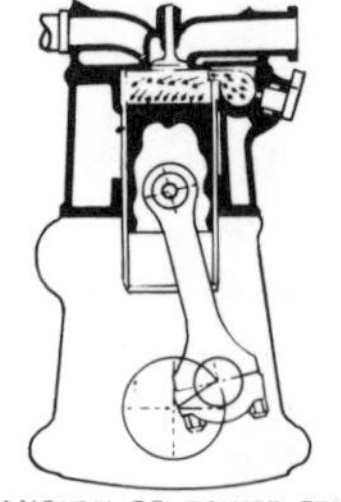

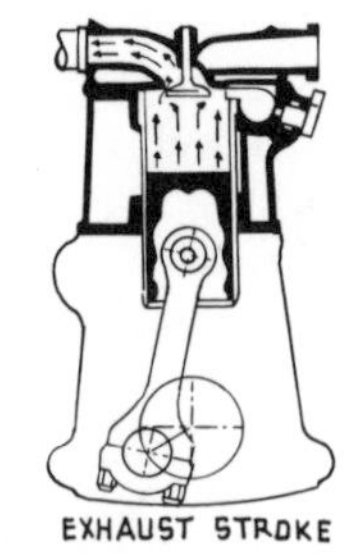

C-5. The pre-combustion chamber is located at one side of, and connected with the combustion chamber of the engine.

C - Inject the fuel at the precise time it can burn to best advantage.
D - Atomize the fuel as completely as possible at the instant of injection.

VAPORIZATION

As Diesel fuel is more on the order of oil than gasoline, it does not vaporize as readily. This means that it must be broken up into fine particles and sprayed into the cylinder in the form of mist. This is accomplished by forcing the fuel through a nozzle or series of very small holes. Thus as it enters the cylinder the fuel combines more thoroughly with the air in the cylinder to form a combustible mixture.

COMBUSTION CHAMBERS

In order to promote complete combustion of the mixture in Diesel cylinders several designs of combustion chamber have been developed. Some of these designs include what is known as a "pre-combustion chamber." One such design is shown in Fig. C-5. In this design the piston comes very nearly to the top of the cylinder and almost all of the air in the cylinder is thus compressed into the small circular chamber.

The shape of the small chamber is such, and the opening is so arranged that the air enters the small chamber at terrific speed and swirls around to create great turbulence. This action serves to mix the air and fuel very thoroughly. The fuel is injected before the piston reaches top center and therefore while the turbulence is at its maximum.

Another design that appears to be similar but operates somewhat differently is shown in Fig. C-6. This design is not designated as a pre-combustion chamber however, because all of the fuel is burned WITHIN THE CHAMBER itself and not partially burned in the cylinder. See Fig. C-7. The expansive force of the burned gas is of course applied to the piston in the customary manner.

C-6. This design appears to be similar to Fig. C-5, but the action is not the same. See text and Fig. C-7.

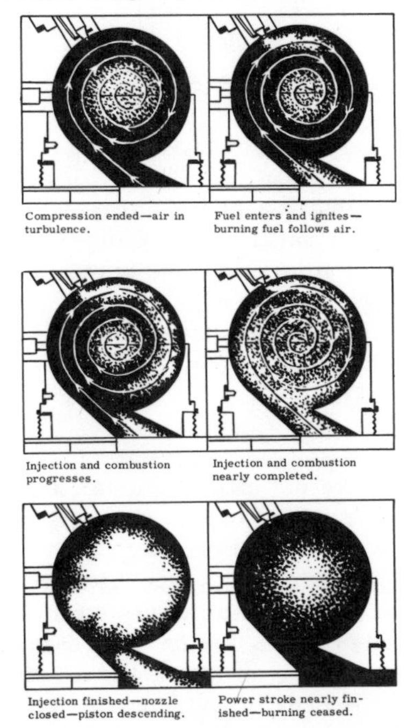

C-7. The sequence of action is detailed here.

Other Diesel designs incorporate what are known as "energy chambers" in which combustion is initiated. See Fig. C-8. In this case the injected fuel is directed by passages in the cylinder head into the energy chambers through a restricted opening or venturi. This restriction increases the velocity of the air fuel mixture and therefore the heat at the point of entry. The resultant combustion then backfires into the cylinder creating great turbulence and therefore effective combustion.

All of these variations in design have a specific purpose and that is to improve combustion of the fuel. In general, combustion will be affected by the degree to which the air is compressed, the distribution of the mixture in the cylinder, the position of the spray nozzle, the injection pressure, the degree of fuel atomization, the timing of injection, the rate of injection and the duration of injection. The compression ratio controls the compression pressure. The amount of turbulence controls the distribution of the mixture. The design of the nozzle and the injection pressure controls the atomization of the fuel.

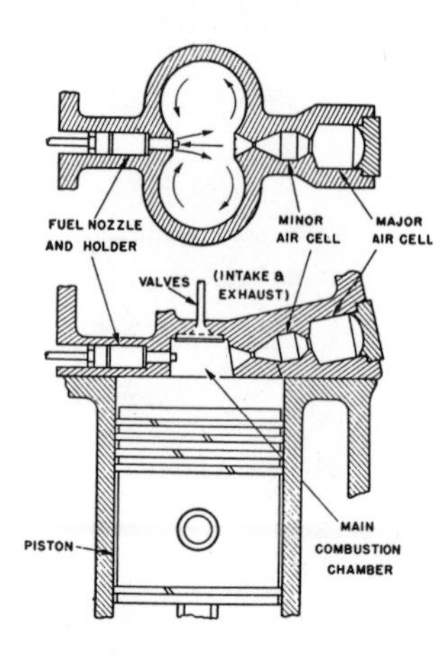

C-8. An "energy chamber" is utilized in this design to increase fuel velocity and promote combustion.

TWO CYCLE DIESELS

As two cycle engines are not efficient as an air pump, it is necessary to force air into the cylinder and to force out the burned gas. One means of doing this is to use a supercharger or "blower." The G.M. two cycle Diesel uses a positive displacement type blower as shown in Fig. C-9. There are two exhaust valves, but no inlet valve in each cylinder. The air enters the cylinder through holes in the cylinder liner as shown in Fig. C-9. The blower forces fresh air into the cylinder through these holes and at the same time forces the exhaust out through the exhaust valves during the time the holes are uncovered by the piston at the bottom of the stroke.

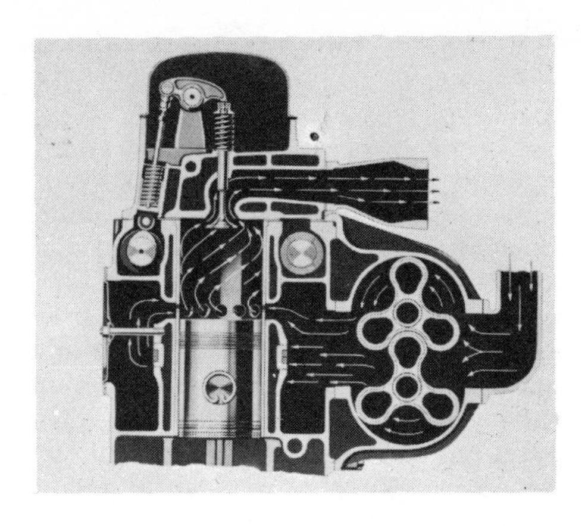

C-9. A supercharger or "blower" is used in this design to force air into the cylinders.

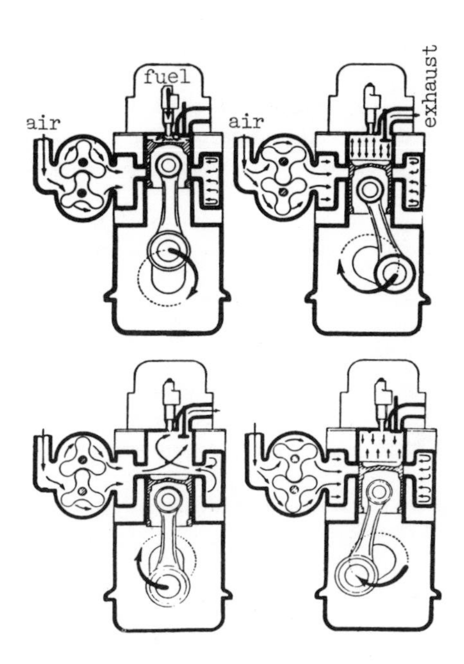

C-10. The air flow through the cylinder is indicated in these diagrams.

The operation of the engine is depicted in Fig. C-10. The fuel injection nozzle complete with pump is located between the two exhaust valves and is operated by a camshaft, push rod and rocker arm.

DIESEL OPERATION

As a Diesel engine depends upon the heat of the compressed air to ignite the fuel, the compression pressure must be maintained. Therefore leaking valves or piston rings cannot be tolerated and must be kept in good condition.

Of equal importance is the proper fuel. Diesel engines are designed to operate on a specific type and grade of fuel. Trouble will surely be experienced if an attempt is made to operate on other than the proper type.

Due to the close fitting of the parts of the fuel system which is made necessary by the pressures involved, the fuel must be clean and kept clean. Therefore a series of filters is ordinarily used to make sure that no dirt can get through to the pump plungers or injector nozzles.

MARINE ENGINES

Engines for use in boats (inboard types) are more like a truck or tractor as boat engines run at constant speed most of the time. Changes must be made in the cooling system to avoid overcooling of the engine as ordinarily there is an unlimited supply of cold water. See Fig. C-11. Unless closely regulated by suitable thermostats in the cooling system, the engine would always be operated too cold. The fan and radiator is usually discarded.

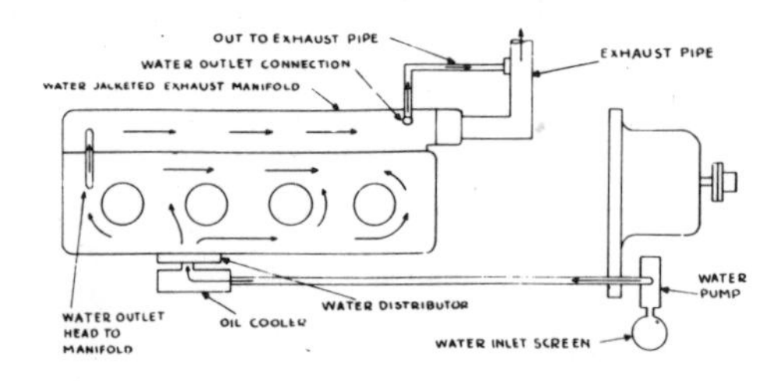

C-11. Diagram of water cooling system as used on an inboard marine engine.

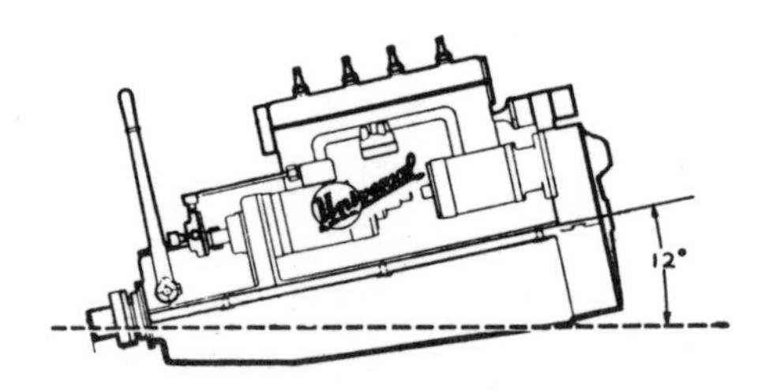

C-12. In order to reduce the angularity of the propeller shaft, inboard marine engines are often mounted at a considerable angle in the boat.

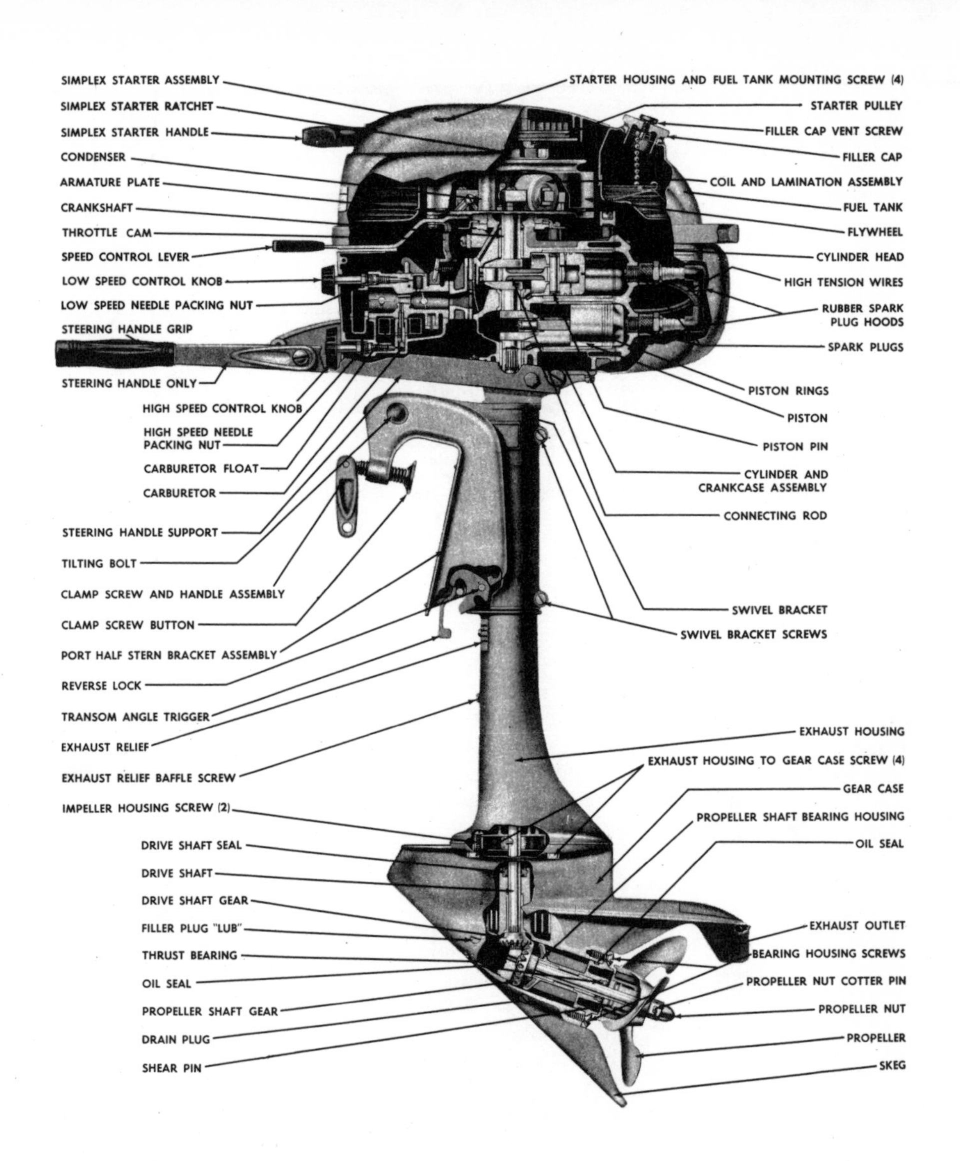

C-13. Typical twin cylinder outboard engine as made by Evinrude.

It is also necessary in many cases to use an oil pan of different shape because the engine is often installed with the rear end much lower than the front to reduce the angularity of the propeller shaft. See Fig. C-12. It is also desirable to equip the engine with a governor to prevent the engine racing itself to destruction if the propeller shears a pin or comes out of the water temporarily in rough weather.

Special marine engines of the inboard type are built quite sturdily to withstand the rigors of constant speed operation. At the other extreme out-

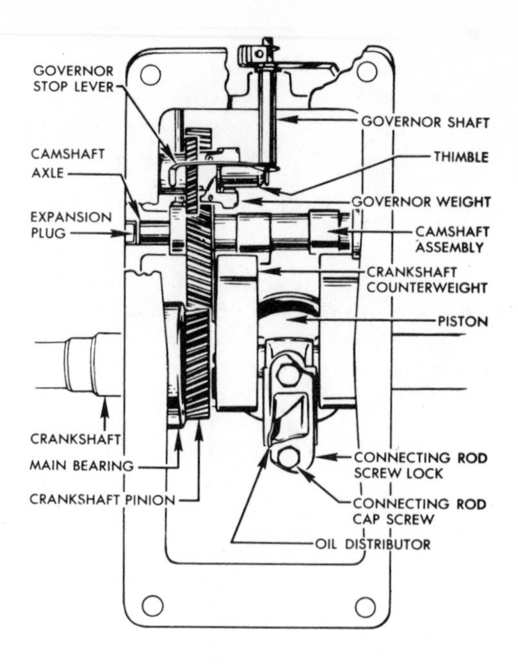

C-14. Typical mechanical governor installation.

board engines are built as light as possible as they must be portable. They are usually of the two cycle type and the oil for lubricating the engine parts is mixed with the fuel. See Fig. C-13.

C-15. Typical pneumatic governor installation.

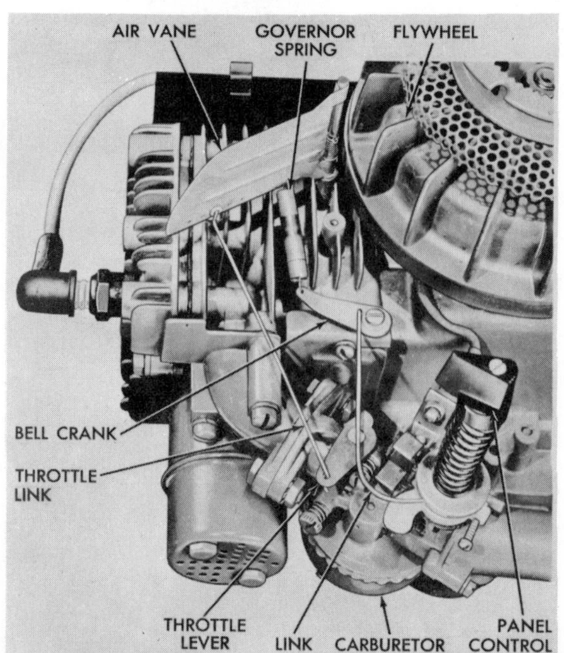

ENGINE ACCESSORIES

ENGINE SPEED GOVERNORS

Governors are used on marine and stationary engines to avoid excess speed of the engine. The engine will accelerate freely up to the maximum speed at which the governor is set. Governors can be either the mechanical or velocity type and in either case control the engine top speed, regardless of load, by regulating the throttle opening.

The mechanical type is usually operated by centrifugal force acting on rotating weights which by means of bell-cranks cause endwise movement of a rod attached to the throttle. A typical mechanical governor installation is shown in Fig. C-14. All the parts of another typical mechanical governor are shown in exploded view, Fig. C-15.

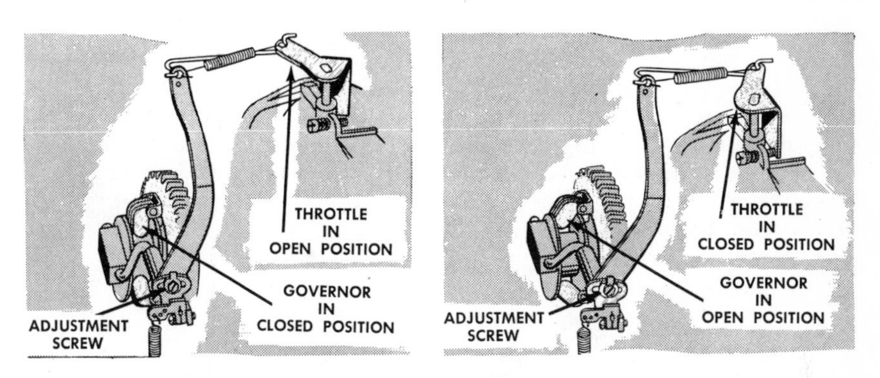

C-15A. Typical mechanical governor in operation opening and closing throttle to control engine speed.

It may be seen that, as the speed of the engine increases, the weights will tend to fly outward and shift the ball thrust plate endwise on the shaft. This causes the lever to move the rod attached to the throttle and close the throttle. As the engine speed decreases, the weights are pulled inward by the springs and the throttle opening is then increased. Thus, the speed of the engine controls the throttle opening and automatic limitation of top speed is obtained.

VELOCITY GOVERNORS

The velocity type of governor is not mechanically driven. It is inserted adjacent to the throttle and the velocity of the gas going through the manifold acts on a spring loaded floating obstruction in the shape of a ball or disk attached to the throttle. When the engine speeds up, the velocity of the gas flowing through the manifold increases and tends to carry the obstruction along with it. As this disk or ball is attached to the throttle plate, the result is to close the throttle against the spring tension and hold down on the engine speed. As the engine speed decreases the lessened velocity allows the spring to reopen the throttle again and thus control is established.

VACUUM GOVERNORS

In another type of automatic governor the intake manifold vacuum is used to regulate the engine speed. This is possible because the degree of vacuum decreases as the engine load is increased, and increases as the engine load decreases. Thus, the degree of vacuum is balanced against a spring to obtain automatic control of engine speed.

When such a governor is applied to a Diesel engine having no carburetor, a venturi is placed in the air intake pipe to supply the pressure differential or partial vacuum needed for operation.

Governors require very little attention as there are no complicated parts or functions. At times they will surge or "hunt", but this usually indicates engine difficulties that need rectifying. Other than sticking or faulty governor mechanisms such as caused by dirt or wear, the most common cause of hunting will be found to be improper carburetor adjustment. Faulty ignition is also responsible at times.

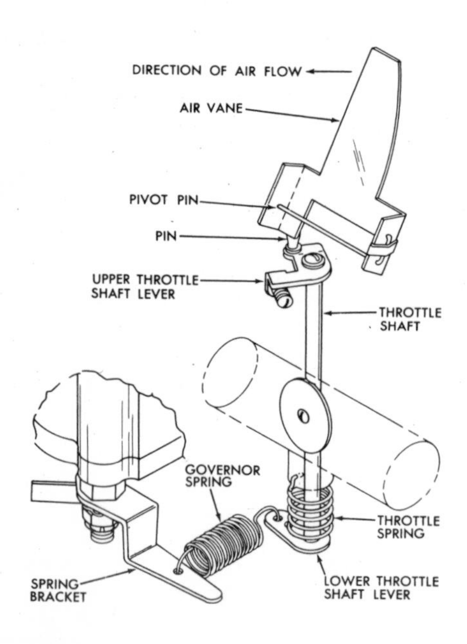

C-16. Air vane or pneumatic-type governor. Air vane extends into area between flywheel fan and flywheel. When engine speed increases, flywheel fan increases rate of flow of cooling air, moving air vane. As vane moves, lower extension moves against pin on upper throttle shaft lever, closing throttle valve partially, reacting against force of governor spring. As throttle valve closes, speed decreases, decreasing air flow so less pressure is exerted on air vane. This in turn, decreases amount of force applied to top throttle shaft lever by air vane; the governor spring becomes controlling and rotates throttle shaft to open throttle and increase speed.

TROUBLE SHOOTING, TUNEUP, RECONDITIONING

Trouble shooting in its most elementary form consists of "shorting out" a spark plug with a screwdriver in order to locate a misfiring cylinder. In its most advanced form it involves the use of elaborate testing equipment.

HIGH OIL CONSUMPTION

Quite often high oil consumption is blamed on the piston rings. The engine is disassembled, the cylinders reconditioned and the new piston rings carefully fitted. Upon reassembly the engine may use more oil than before.

While worn piston rings and cylinder walls may often cause increased oil consumption, there are a great number of other things that are at fault either singly or in combination. In most cases the oil is leaking out and being splashed or thrown up into the cylinders under the piston in such large quantities that no piston ring can control the excess. This is covered in the chapter on piston rings.

Following is a list of some causes of high oil consumption. It must be kept in mind that the fault is usually a COMBINATION OF SEVERAL DEFECTS rather than one single defect. Also oil may be leaking out as well as being burned in the cylinders.

1. Worn cylinder bores
2. Tapered cylinder bores
3. Distorted cylinder bores
4. Worn pistons
5. Collapsed pistons
6. Improperly fitted pistons
7. Stopped up piston drain holes
8. Worn piston ring grooves
9. Worn piston rings
10. Wrong size piston rings
11. Incorrectly installed piston rings
12. Rings too tight in ring grooves
13. Improperly fitted rings
14. Clogged piston ring slots
15. Worn piston pins
16. Worn piston pin bushings

17. Bent or twisted connecting rods
18. Worn connecting rod bearings
19. Loose connecting rod bearings
20. Excess side clearance in connecting rod bearings
21. Worn main bearings
22. Loose main bearings
23. Excess crankshaft end play
24. Bent crankshaft
25. Out-of-round crankshaft journals
26. Damaged crankshaft journal cheeks
27. Damaged crankshaft oil slingers
28. Worn intake valves
29. Worn intake valve guides
30. Worn camshaft bearings
31. Worn camshaft journals
32. Engine overheating
33. Clogged water jackets
34. Oil level too high
35. Excessive oil pressure
36. Clogged oil return from valve chamber
37. Clogged oil return from timing gear case
38. Clogged breather pipe
39. No baffle in breather pipe
40. Broken oil line
41. Oil leaking past front and rear main bearings
42. Cracked crankcase
43. Crankcase gasket leaks
44. Defective crankshaft seals
45. Leaking timing gear case gasket
46. Leaking valve cover gasket

ENGINE OVERHEATING

Among the reasons listed are "overheating" and "clogged water jackets." These items cause oil to be consumed in two ways. Due to the increased engine temperature, more oil is vaporized and burned up when the engine overheats. Also overheating or a clogged water jacket will result in cylinder wall distortion as previously explained. When the cylinder distorts out-of-round the rings cannot seal and the oil passes between them and the cylinder wall.

Of course there are many causes for overheating just as there are for oil consumption. And just as in the case of excess oil use these cooling difficulties are almost always a COMBINATION OF MINOR DEFECTS rather than any one major trouble. Some of the causes of overheating are:

1. Scale and rust in cylinder head
2. Scale and rust in cylinder block water passages

3. Cylinder head gasket blown
4. Incorrect cylinder head gasket
5. Cylinder block hot spots
6. Worn water pump impeller or housing
7. Sheared impeller pin or key
8. Clogged muffler
9. Valve timing late
10. Worn timing chain
11. Leaking valves
12. Ignition timing late
13. Defective ignition spark advance
14. Carburetor mixture too rich
15. Leaking piston rings
16. Overloaded engine
17. Low engine oil level
18. Stiff engine (after overhaul)
19. Obstructed air passages (or dirt on air cooling fins)
20. Bent fan blades
21. Worn fan belt
22. Loose fan belt
23. Worn drive pulleys
24. Undersupply of coolant
25. Foaming of coolant
26. Leaking cylinder head
27. Leaking cylinder head gasket
28. Leaking cylinder block
29. Leaking expansion plugs
30. Leaking water pump housing
31. Leaking water pump shaft
32. Leaking water pump gasket
33. Leaking drain cocks

It will be seen from the foregoing that many engine defects are common to both high oil consumption and overheating. There is a definite relation between the two and searching for the cause of one trouble will often disclose the need for correction in either or both the oil and water circulation systems.

Trouble-shooting is a process of reasoning supported by deduction and elimination. As an example, suppose we are trying to eliminate the cause of repeated burning of the exhaust valves in an engine.

We know that the valves are running too hot or they would not burn. Therefore the question is:

1. Are the exhaust valves being subjected to excessive amount of heat?

or

2. Are the valves - for some reason - unable to dissipate the normal amount of heat?

Among the things that will cause the generation of excess heat are:
1. Extreme high speed
2. Unusual engine overload
3. Excessively lean carburetor mixture
4. Engine "hot spots" and/or overheating
5. Late valve timing
6. Late ignition timing

Each of the foregoing are quickly and easily checked and if no defects are discovered, we may then suspect that the heat is being retained in the valves instead of being dissipated to the engine cooling water. Many things can cause or contribute to this condition. It is usually a combination of several things.

Among the defects to be found in many cases are the following:
1. Valve seat too narrow
2. Worn valve guide and/or valve stem
3. Weak valve spring
4. Sticking valve stems
5. Incorrect valve tappet clearance
6. Loose valve seat insert
7. Valve guides loose in block
8. Valve guides incorrectly positioned in block

The foregoing defects were discussed in detail in the valve section of this text.

ENGINE NOISE

One of the most difficult of all trouble-shooting jobs - and one which occurs frequently - is to locate the source of noise or "knocks" is an engine. Actually, of course every rotating or reciprocating part in the engine is a potential source of noise. In many cases however certain noises possess characteristics which help identify their origin.

These characteristics vary somewhat between different engines and experience is probably the best guide in some cases. In most cases it will be helpful to utilize an instrument of the stethoscope type to localize the noise at some definite section of the engine. These instruments magnify the intensity of the noise and the sound becomes louder as the instrument nears the origin of the noise.

LOOSE CONNECTING RODS

The conditions of operation under which the noise is heard and the "timing" of the noise are also useful in determining the source. Some noises are louder as the engine speed is increased or the engine put under load.

A rod in very bad condition will be heard at all speeds and under both idle and load conditions. One rod will make a distinct noise, and if all rods are loose the noise becomes a rattle or clatter.

In many cases slightly loose rods are confused with piston slap or loose piston pins. This is particularly true when all rods are loose and experience will be helpful in deciding which part is at fault. It is not of too much importance to definitely decide because the remedy for either fault involves removal of the rod or rods in practically all cases. Measurement and inspection of the parts will then disclose which is at fault.

LOOSE PISTON PINS

Using a stethoscope is sometimes helpful, as a piston or pin may sound loudest when the instrument prod is placed on the cylinder block. The rod knock is often loudest with the prod on the crankcase. Shorting out the spark plug on one cylinder will change the intensity of the knock but will not always eliminate it entirely.

Shorting out one or more spark plugs will thus help to locate which cylinder or rod is at fault in cases where the noise is not due to looseness in all cylinders or rods.

LOOSE MAIN BEARINGS

A main bearing knock is more of a bump than a knock and can be located by shorting out the plugs on the cylinders near it. It is loudest when the engine is "lugging", that is pulling hard at slow speed. The sound is heavier and duller than a connecting rod knock.

LOOSE FLYWHEEL

If the flywheel should be loose on the crankshaft, the noise will be similar to a main bearing knock, but will ordinarily not change when the plugs are shorted out. Furthermore, the noise may come and go rather than being constant. One sure test is to shut off the ignition and then turn it on again just as the engine is about to stop. The sudden twist thus applied to the crankshaft will produce the knock in noticeable form.

CRANKSHAFT END PLAY

Excessive end play in the crankshaft will produce an intermittent rap or knock that is sharper than a loose main bearing or flywheel knock.

WORN TIMING GEARS

Another knock that is difficult to diagnose is caused by worn timing gears. Shorting out the plugs has no effect on the noise and it is about the same intensity whether the engine is idling or pulling. A stethoscope is useful in this case to determine where the noise originates.

PISTON SLAP

There is much confusion between the noise caused by a piston with excessive clearance in the cylinder and a loose piston pin. Either defect produces a click which is very distinct. If in all cylinders it becomes a rattle. One indication of piston slap is a decrease in the noise as the engine warms up. The noise is always louder when the engine is cold. Some types of aluminum pistons (even in a new engine) are quite noisy when the engine is first started, but become quiet after the engine warms up.

A piston slap may occur in an engine when new piston pins are installed in old pistons. This is particularly true if the pins are fitted somewhat too tightly. Such noise may disappear entirely after the engine has been operated and the pins have loosened up a bit.

Loose piston pins usually, but not always, produce a double rap each revolution of the crankshaft - once at the top of the stroke and again at the bottom. On most engines the knock is loudest at idling speed and will become even louder if the spark is advanced. Quite often the knock will be louder if the plug is shorted out in cases where all pins are not loose.

PISTON RING NOISE

The installation of new piston rings will almost surely cause a knock if the ridge at the top of the cylinder is not removed before the new rings are installed. Somewhat similar is the condition where the cylinders have been rebored oversize and the cylinder head gasket extends into the combustion chamber. The piston strikes the gasket and makes a distinct knock.

Piston rings that are loose in the grooves will not ordinarily make any noise as the oil tends to cushion them. If they are excessively loose however, they may cause a clicking noise similar to a loose valve tappet. There is a difference in the timing of the click. The rings will click twice each revolution of the crankshaft, while the valve click will only be heard once every other revolution.

VALVE NOISES

Valves are a prolific source of noise for two reasons: There are two valves for each cylinder and there are several points in each unit of the valve gear that can create noise. These several points were described and illustrated in a previous chapter of this text. It is usually easy to determine which valve or valves are causing the noise by inserting a feeler gauge of suitable thickness between the end of the valve and the tappet or rocker arm with the engine running.

If the clicking is caused by wear between the valve lifter and lifter guide, pressing against the side of the lifter with one end of a hammer handle will often stop the noise. A damaged roller or mushroom on the end of the lifter next the camshaft is not so readily located. The timing of the click is helpful as well as the use of a stethoscope.

MISCELLANEOUS NOISES

At times a knock will occur in an engine when all parts have been checked for wear, or even on a rebuilt engine. Such knocks are usually due to misalignment or excessive endwise motion. Too much side clearance in a connecting rod bearing, excessive endwise motion of the crankshaft or camshaft are examples.

Improper alignment of connecting rods is a common source of hard-to-find knocks. Checking and cure of this defect has been covered previously in this text.

TUNEUP

The very first step in an engine tune-up is to make sure that EVERY ONE of the cylinders has good compression. Otherwise there is no use to proceed further. It is also important that there be no wide variation in pressure between the various cylinders. For example if the engine manufacturers' specifications call for 100 lbs. compression pressure, there should be at least 90 lbs. on the weakest cylinder. A special compression pressure gauge is used for checking.

When making the test it is essential that the engine be at operating temperature and that the engine oil is of the proper grade and not seriously diluted.

If the compression pressure varies more than 20% between the different cylinders, it is usually assumed that the cylinders, rings or valves - or all three - are defective. Of course if two weak cylinders are adjacent, it might indicate a blown cylinder head gasket. In any case the cylinder head will probably have to be removed in order to remedy the defect, but it is often wise to make a further check with a vacuum gauge before the head is removed.

When handled by an experienced operator, a vacuum gauge will provide considerable useful information about the interior condition of the engine. However, it is easy to misinterpret the readings of the instrument and reach false conclusions. In using a vacuum gauge on an engine it is much more important to note the ACTION of the gauge rather than the reading of the numbers on the dial.

When properly used and understood, a vacuum gauge will indicate several defects:

Incorrect carburetor adjustment
Ignition timing errors
Ignition defects
Improper valve action
Restricted exhaust system
Cylinder leakage
Intake system leakage

Experienced operators can break the foregoing troubles down to a finer analysis of just where the trouble lies.

With the engine warmed up to operating temperature and running slightly higher than at extremely low idling speed, the vacuum gauge is attached to the intake manifold.

NORMAL ENGINE

The needle will be steady between 17 and 21 while idling, will drop to below 5 and then bounce up to around 25 when the throttle is suddenly opened and closed. See Fig. C-17.

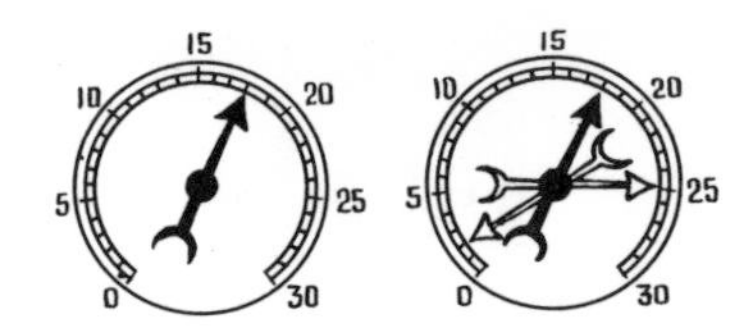

C-17. *On a normal engine the hand will remain steady between 17 and 21.*

LEAKING CYLINDER RINGS

The needle may be fairly steady but will read lower than normal, perhaps 3 or 4 points. When the throttle is suddenly opened and closed, the needle may sink to zero and then bounce back to around 22. See Fig. C-17. A compression pressure test may be necessary as a final check.

SLOW TIMING

If the compression is known to be good and the needle reads lower than it should the ignition timing may be slow. See Fig. C-18. If the reading is considerably lower than it should be, the valve timing may be slow. A check should be made to see if either or both should be advanced.

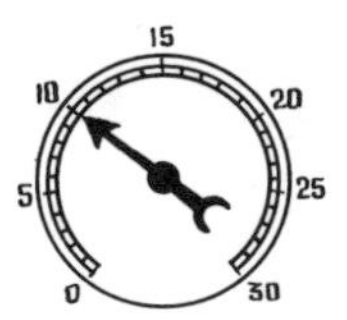

C-18. *If the needle reads low but steady and the compression is good, look for slow timing.*

C-19. *An extremely low reading indicates a leak in the intake manifold or carburetor.*

LEAKING INTAKE

If the needle is steady but extremely low, an air leak probably exists in the carburetor or intake manifold or gaskets. See Fig. C-19.

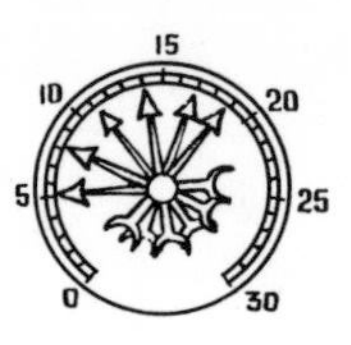

C-20. Floating regularly from a low to a high reading indicates a blown cylinder head gasket.

LEAKING CYLINDER HEAD

If the needle floats regularly between a low and a high reading, the cylinder head gasket is liable to be blown out between two adjacent cylinders. See Fig. C-20.

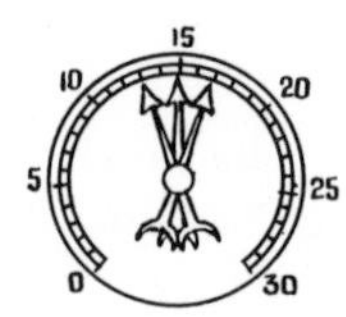

C-21. Floating slowly over a limited range indicates improper adjustment of the carburetor.

CARBURETOR OUT OF ADJUSTMENT

When the needle floats slowly over a range of 4 or 5 points, a faulty carburetor adjustment is indicated. See Fig. C-21.

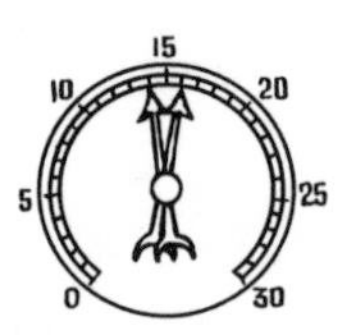

C-22. Floating over a narrow range indicates ignition trouble.

SPARK PLUG GAPS

If the needle floats slowly over a narrower range - perhaps two points - the spark plug gaps may be spaced too close. See Fig. C-22.

DEFECTIVE VALVE ACTION

Experience will help the operator to distinguish between the several

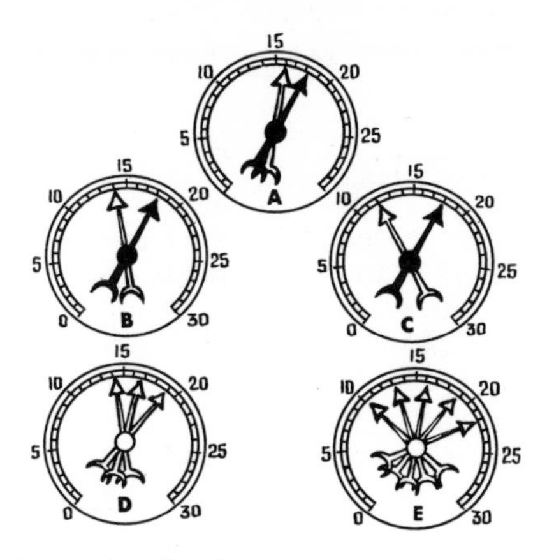

C-23. A—Leaky valve.—Steady drop.
B—Sticking valve.—Occasional drop.
C—Burned valve.—Regular drop.
D—Loose valve guides.—Fast vibration.
E—Weak valve springs.—Wide vibration as engine is accelerated.

valve troubles such as leaking, burned, sticking valves, weak valve springs and loose valve guides. The action of the needle and the range of motion are indications of which is at fault. Study of the diagram in Fig. C-23 will be helpful and as the valve will need to be removed in most cases to remedy the defect, a check will be had on the correctness of the diagnosis.

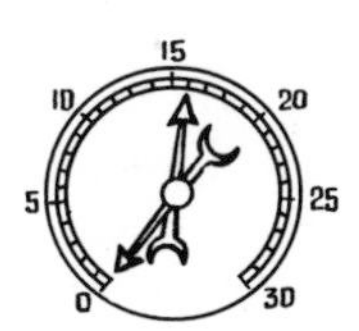

C-24. A normal reading which breaks to zero and then builds up again indicates a choked muffler or exhaust.

RESTRICTED EXHAUST

When the needle reads normally when the engine is first started, then sinks to zero followed by a slow rise to below normal the muffler may be clogged. See Fig. C-24.

If the vacuum gauge indicates loss of compression or improper valve action as described, there is no use to proceed with a tune-up until the compression is restored. If however the tests indicate timing errors, intake leaks, carburetor out of adjustment or a restricted exhaust system - the remedy for each of which is obvious - it will be in order to correct the defects as the next step.

Much of the tune-up work is concerned with the ignition system, particularly the spark plugs, timing, distributor contact points and condenser. This is a complete subject in itself and is covered thoroughly in the electrical section of this text.

COMBUSTION ANALYZERS

The last step of an engine tune-up is usually the final adjustment of the carburetor. This is often facilitated by the use of an exhaust gas analyzer which measures the mixture supplied by the carburetor. With the aid of this instrument it is possible to adjust the mixture to obtain maximum power from the gasoline.

This is important as an engine may apparently run well when the mixture is too rich or too lean. An over-rich mixture is wasteful, tends to form soot in the engine and exhaust systems and promotes crankcase dilution of the engine oil. Mixtures that are too lean cause loss of power, and tend to cause burned valves and spark plugs.

Combustion analyzers are often constructed on the fact that different gases possess a different rate of heat conductivity. That is a rich mixture conducts heat at one rate while a lean mixture conducts heat at a different rate because of the chemical difference in the two mixtures. Thus by placing a heated wire in the exhaust gas and another like wire in air a direct comparison is had and the content of the exhaust gas is an indication of how well the mixture is burning in the engine.

The subject of mixtures and combustion is covered fully in the carburetor section of this text.

HIGH SPEED TUNING

Engine tuning is carried to extremes when it is desired to obtain the maximum speed and power out of an engine. This procedure often involves mechanical alteration of the engine such as porting and relieving the cylinder block, increasing the compression ratio, enlarging the valves, altering the bore and stroke, installing camshafts having faster cams, increasing the valve lift, etc.

Intake and exhaust manifolds are increased in size and streamlined, multiple carburetors or fuel injectors installed, valve and ignition timing altered etc.

RECONDITIONING

One of the first things the old cabinet-maker told the young apprentice was: "We have LOTS of "taking-off" tools, but NO "putting-on" tools." We are more fortunate as we are working primarily with metal instead of wood and we do have several methods of changing dimensions of parts as required.

If we wish to reduce the size of a part we can cut or grind or etch the metal away or in some cases we can shrink it with heat or pressure.

If we wish to increase the size of a part, we can add metal by soldering, brazing, welding, plating or spraying. In some cases we can expand it by heat and pressure.

Thus in many cases we can compensate for wear by expanding or shrinking the metal. Or we can add metal to the worn surface to restore it to usefulness. In adding metal we have a wide choice of materials each of which possesses certain characteristics which may be desired for the particular purpose.

If we want a soft surface, we can use tin or bronze. If we want a hard surface we can add steel of any desired degree of hardness by welding. Another method is to attach a hard surface by the electro-plating process. An example of this is a chrome surface on a piston ring.

In engine repair work, we often add material to or increase the size of one part without disturbing the mating part. An example of this is to spray molten metal on a worn crankshaft journal to avoid installation of undersize bearings. Or we may expand a piston with heat or pressure or both and reinstall it in the mating cylinder. In some cases it is more economical to install new parts.

In other cases we remove metal from one part and install an oversize or undersize mating part in order to obtain the proper clearance. Examples of this are rebored cylinders and oversize pistons or a reground crankshaft and an undersize bearing.

In still other cases we may remove metal for the sole purpose of obtaining a better surface or fit of two mating parts. An example of this is the correction of a warped cylinder head by surface grinding to restore a flat surface.

For practically all of these operations special tools and equipment are available. Any of these tools or equipment will do a satisfactory job if they are properly handled. Obviously, it will be essential to measure accurately, adjust carefully and operate in accordance with the equipment manufacturers' instructions.

CYLINDER BLOCK REPAIRS

One thing that occasionally happens to a cylinder block is for a piston or pistons to seize or stick in the cylinder due to expansion of the piston caused by overheating or lack of lubrication or both. If the piston is made of aluminum, the damage may be mostly to the piston. If, however, the piston is of cast iron, the cylinder as well as the piston may be scratched.

In almost all cases the rings will be ruined and new rings cannot be used until the cylinder surface is restored. The scratches or scores will run lengthwise of the bore and if not too heavy can be honed out with a suitable cylinder hone. A hone is not intended to remove any appreciable amount of metal from the bore: It is intended only to clean up and provide the proper surface.

Thus if no stock is removed from the bore a standard size piston can be used. If a slight amount of stock is removed by the hone in an attempt to remove heavier scratches, it may be necessary to expand the pistons slightly.

When the scratches are too heavy to remove by honing, it will be necessary to regrind the cylinder bore slightly oversize and fit oversize pistons and rings.

In this connection, it is best to find out what sizes are available in oversize pistons. Otherwise the cylinders may be bored to a dimension for which stock pistons are not available. This would then involve having the pistons ground to the desired size.

Upon rare occasions a piston pin may become unlocked and slide endwise against the cylinder wall. This will usually produce a deep score in the cylinder which cannot be removed by grinding oversize.

In such cases the score may be milled out in dove-tail fashion and a strip of special repair metal or copper pressed in place. The cylinder is then reground so that the new metal will conform to the cylinder wall.

Another method is to weld or braze a strip in the groove and refinish the bore. Often it costs less to install a new cylinder than to repair the old one on a small engine.

BORING CYLINDERS OVERSIZE

Still another method is to bore the cylinder out considerably oversize and press a prepared sleeve of the proper size into the cylinder. Of course if the cylinder block is equipped with sleeves originally it is a simple matter to press out the damaged sleeve and insert a new one.

These sleeves often have thin walls and must be fitted very accurately in the block. If they fit too loose the heat transfer from sleeve to block will be poor and the sleeve will overheat and distort. If the sleeve is fitted too tightly it is liable to be distorted during installation and become out-of-round or have ridges or "wrinkles" in the bore.

After installation, sleeves should be checked with a suitable cylinder gauge to make sure of roundness, straightness and smoothness. It is sometimes necessary or desirable to hone them after installation in order to have a proper surface upon which the rings may seat or "run-in."

The proper surface for a cylinder wall is not a dead smooth or glass like surface. If new rings are installed on a dead smooth cylinder wall surface, they may never seat to the cylinder wall. In such cases they cannot control oil consumption or compression blow-by. Furthermore, a new ring in too smooth a cylinder may suffer from lack of lubrication and score the ring face and cylinder wall.

The desired finish is smooth - but not too smooth. It should have a pattern of cross-hatch scratches and no longitudinal scratches. This cross-hatch pattern consists of scratches so tiny that they can be measured only in micro-inches. As no shop has the equipment for measuring in micro-inches, the common practice is to consider the surface correct when it is possible to see - BUT NOT FEEL - the pattern.

Such a finish is obtained with a few strokes of a fine hone; pulling the hone up and down in the bore while the hone rotates. See **Fig. C-25**. When a hone is not used, abrasive cloth or paper with a fine grit is used.

This delicate interruption of the surface furnishes a mild abrasive action on the ring face to assist it to seat in. Also the exceedingly fine scratches retain a film of oil - perhaps only a millionth of an inch thick - to provide lubrication for the ring surface and prevent scoring.

DAMAGED CRANKSHAFTS

As some engine crankshafts are expensive parts, it is often desirable to repair damage rather than replace them. Before any extensive work is started however, it is well to have the shaft checked by a specialist with proper special magnetic or chemical equipment to make sure there are no visible cracks in it.

An engine crankshaft is subjected to terrific vibration and stress and may develop tiny cracks particularly at or near the ends of the connecting rod throws or at the ends of the main bearing journals. Occasionally an invisible crack may develop near the oil feed holes in the shaft.

If the crankshaft is sound and the journals are worn slightly taper or out-of-round, the shaft journals can be reground and undersize bearings fitted. Here again, as in the case of reboring cylinders it is desirable to find out the available sizes of bearings that are carried in stock so that the extra work of boring the bearings to fit the shaft will be avoided.

If the shaft is badly damaged but a new shaft high in cost, it is possible to restore the journal by spraying metal on the journal, building it up oversize and then regrind it to the desired size. This work is usually done by specialists.

If the damage to the crankshaft is minor, such as a scratch or a minor flat spot on one or two connecting rod journals, repairs can often be made with the engine in the car. Special equipment is available for doing this work and when properly used, in accordance with the manufacturers' instructions, will do a satisfactory job of regrinding the journal.

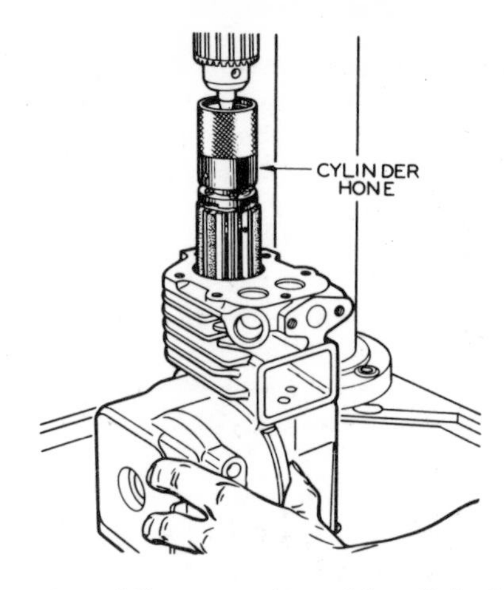

C-25. A drill press may be used for cylinder honing.

CRACKED CYLINDER BLOCKS

If the block was cracked by water freezing in the water jacket, the crack can usually be closed satisfactorily by a process known as copper-welding or brazing. It can also be welded shut with iron. In the case of welding with iron it is difficult to prevent warping of the block unless the block is preheated and the welding expertly done. See Fig. C-26.

In cases where a panel or section of the water jacket is broken out, it is sometimes possible to shape a metal plate into a patch corresponding to and slightly larger than the opening. The patch is then attached to the

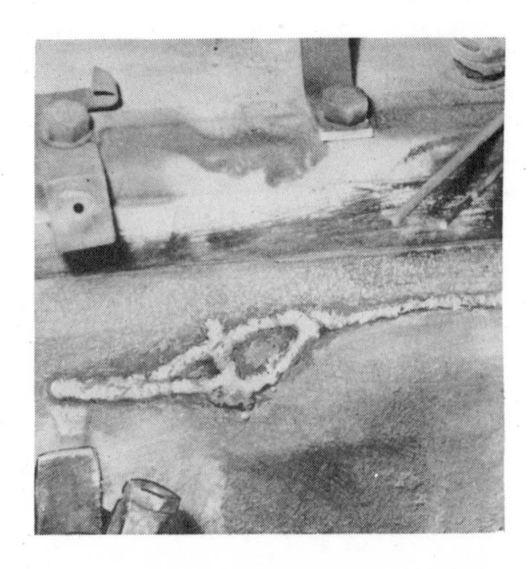

C-26. Typical repair on burst engine water jacket.

block by means of multiple screws around the edge of the patch. Holes are of course drilled and tapped in the block to receive the screws.

In the case of small cracks - depending on the location - iron cement has been used for a quick repair. If the crack is in a thin, large section of the block and is readily accessible it is even possible to tin the cast iron and solder the crack.

The choice of the method will depend upon the size of the damaged area, the location of the crack and the comparative cost of a new cylinder block.

If the crack is in the combustion chamber, such as for example between the cylinder and valve seat (see Fig. C-27) the repair will need to

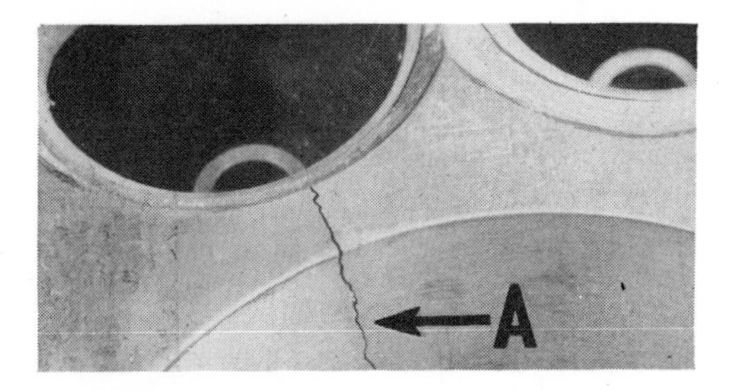

C-27. Cracks often occur through valve seat and cylinder wall as well as the water passage in the cylinder block.

be made with care. One method is of course welding. Another method is peening the metal along the crack with a power peening tool.

Still another method consists of drilling holes at the ends of the crack, threading them and inserting threaded plugs or screws. Another hole is then drilled partly in the block and partly in the plug or screw. A second plug or screw is then inserted and this process continued to the other end of the crack.

After the screws are all installed and the crack sealed the surface is then machined smooth and the cylinder bore and valve seat are resurfaced. If the valve seat is damaged, the block can be counterbored and a new valve seat inserted. Likewise if the cylinder wall is damaged the cylinder can be rebored and a sleeve inserted.

In repairs of this nature it is necessary to keep in mind that the heat and pressure in the cylinder will cause expansion, contraction and possibly warpage of the cylinder wall, valve seat and cylinder block surface as soon as the engine is operated. Therefore the work must be done as carefully and accurately as possible and no great amount of excess metal added at any point.

REVIEWING THE ENGINES SECTION

1. What is the difference between external and internal combustion engines? Name an example of each.
2. What is the purpose of the fins attached to the cylinder head of the air-cooled engine?
3. When the cylinder of an engine is laid on its side, is the design known as a vertical or horizontal design?
4. In what position are the cylinders located on an opposed type design?
5. Name the events that must occur in an internal combustion engine to make it operate, and the sequence.
6. What draws the explosive mixture from the carburetor into the cylinders?
7. In a four cycle engine how many complete revolutions does the crankshaft make to complete the cycles of induction, compression, explosion and exhaust?
8. Is there a power stroke on a two cycle engine on each revolution of the crankshaft, or every second stroke?
9. Tell how fuel gets from the carburetor, on a two cycle engine, to the combustion chamber.
10. In cylinder design there are four principal designs: T-Head, L-Head, F-Head, and I-Head. Where are the inlet and exhaust valves located on each of these designs?
11. Which type is now the predominant design?
12. Define the term "piston displacement." How may it be figured?
13. One horsepower is defined as the amount of power required to lift ______ pounds one foot in one minute.
14. Describe the Prony brake test method of determining the amount of power produced by an engine.
15. Give a definition for the term "compression pressure."
16. What is expansion pressure? Mean effective pressure?
17. What is the difference between power and torque?
18. How is torque measured?
19. A simple way of describing a supercharger is to say it is an air pump used to force air or gas into the cylinders. True or false?
20. What is compression ratio?
21. How may compression ratio be changed? Describe two methods.
22. Tell what is meant by the term "combustion chamber."
23. Does higher compression result in more or less power being developed by the explosion stroke?
24. Is there more tendency or less tendency of motor fuel to knock or "ping" as the compression is raised?
25. How does tetraethyl lead (Ethyl fluid) help eliminate fuel ping?
26. Does material from which combustion chamber is made have any bearing on compression ratio that can be used in given engine? Why?
27. What is meant by the "throws" of a crankshaft?
28. Is this statement correct? A two cylinder engine usually has the con-

necting rod throws 90 degs. apart.
29. On a four cylinder four cycle engine, how many power impulses are there for each revolution of the crankshaft?
30. How many camshafts are used in an L-Head engine; a T-Head engine?
31. The term "valve overlap" means __________.
32. Why is cast iron the predominant material used in constructing engine blocks?
33. What are cylinder sleeves? Why are they used?
34. Why do cylinders wear out-of-round?
35. The cylinder wears less on the power thrust side. True or false?
36. Does turbulence of the gas mixture in the cylinder have any effect on how the gas and air are mixed?
37. Octane rating of fuel is arrived at by ______.

ENGINE CRANKSHAFTS AND CAMSHAFTS

1. Of what material are engine crankshafts generally made?
2. What is the function of the flywheel?
3. Describe a camshaft in simple form.
4. What is the function of the camshaft?
5. What is the principal difference between cams in passenger car engines and cams in racing engines?
6. Does the location of the cams around the camshaft have any bearing on the firing order of the engine?

ENGINE BEARINGS

1. What are the two principal types of bearings used on modern engine crankshafts? Describe how each is made.
2. Discuss the importance of bearing clearances.
3. For what purpose is oil used?
4. Name two methods of measuring oil clearances.
5. Why is endwise crankshaft clearance necessary? How may it be measured?
6. What do we mean by integral bearings?
7. What are some of the advantages offered by insert or shell type bearings?
8. How are integral type bearings adjusted?
9. Are camshaft bearings usually in the form of split bearings or bushings?

PISTONS, RINGS AND PINS

1. Purposes served by pistons are ______________.
2. Of what materials are pistons usually constructed?
3. What are some advantages of aluminum pistons?
4. Name the two principal types of piston rings.
5. Piston ring "lands" provide seating surfaces for the sides of the piston rings. True or false?
6. Which section of the piston is known as the "skirt"?
7. About how much clearance should be provided between the piston and cylinder?
8. How may clearance be measured?
9. Discuss piston resizing procedure.
10. What is piston "blow-by"?
11. Is it possible to have an engine with good compression, yet is an "oil pumper"?
12. For what purpose is the top ring used? Second? Third?
13. Will the top piston ring need more or less gap and groove clearance than the other rings?
14. How is piston ring gap clearance measured? Sidewise clearance?
15. Does installing new rings always cure "oil pumpers"? Why?
16. Describe the function of the piston pin.
17. Name three types of piston pins.
18. Is it customary to find wear in both the pin and bearing where the pins become loose?
19. Describe briefly the procedure in replacing piston pins.
20. Why is proper fitting of piston pins considered of considerable importance?

ENGINE VALVES

1. What are the conditions under which engine valves operate?
2. How are valves cooled?
3. In normal operation, at about what temperature does the valve head around the seating surface operate?
4. Is it possible for an engine valve to be properly seated when cold and to climb off the seat when hot?
5. Is modern valve reconditioning done mostly by grinding or lapping? Why?
6. Under what conditions is it necessary to replace the valves, rather than recondition them?
7. At what angle are valve faces cut - 30, 45 or 90 degs.?
8. A valve seat 1/16 in. wide is usually satisfactory. True or false?
9. What happens when the seat is too narrow? Too wide?
10. Tell how to install valve seat inserts that are slightly oversize.

11. Name some advantages of the slip-in type of valve stem guide.
12. What are some undesirable results of excessive valve guide wear?
13. Do exhaust valves require more or less clearance than inlet valves?

VALVE OPERATING MECHANISM

1. How is an engine camshaft operated?
2. What effect do worn cams have on the valve lift?
3. In what way are timing chain sprockets usually marked to facilitate checking the valve timing.
4. Tappett clearance is measured by using a ________.
5. In some engines there are no adjustment screws in the valve lifters. How is the proper clearance obtained in such engines?

ENGINE COOLING SYSTEMS

1. About what percentage of the heat developed by burning of fuel in the combustion system must be handled by the cooling system?
2. Name four possible defects that should be kept in mind when overheating occurs.
3. How are inboard marine engines cooled?

LUBRICATION

1. Lubricating oil in an engine has what principle functions to perform?
2. How is the weight or thickness of oil specified?
3. Does the SAE number of an oil have anything to do with quality?
4. Is it all right to race an engine on cold mornings to warm it up? Why?

DIESEL ENGINES

1. Diesel engines are built only in four cycle designs. True or false?
2. What ignites fuel on Diesel engines?
3. In a full Diesel the compression ratio may be as high as ________.
4. Why is it impractical to use gasoline in a Diesel engine?
5. Some designs include what is known as a "pre-combustion chamber." What is a "pre-combustion chamber"?
6. Describe the difference between a "pre-combustion chamber" and an "energy-chamber."
7. How is burned gas usually removed from the cylinder of a two cycle Diesel engine?
8. Do leaking valves and piston rings cause more trouble in a Diesel than a regular automobile engine, or less trouble?

TROUBLE SHOOTING

1. List as many reasons as you can for high oil consumption.
2. Discuss the reasons for engine overheating.
3. What are the characteristics of the noise caused by:
   (a) Loose connecting rods.
   (b) Loose piston pins.
   (c) Loose main bearings.
   (d) Loose flywheel.
   (e) Crankshaft end play.
   (f) Worn timing gears.
   (g) Piston slap.
   (h) Piston ring noise.
   (i) Valve noises.

TUNE-UP

1. What do we ordinarily mean by "engine tune-up"?
2. Name four defects in the internal condition of an engine that may be indicated by a vacuum gauge.
3. To what part of the engine is a vacuum gauge attached?
4. What should the needle reading of a vacuum gauge be with a normal engine?
5. Specify what changes will be noted in the needle reading when these troubles exist:
   (a) Leaking cylinder rings.
   (b) Slow timing.
   (c) Leaking intake.
   (d) Leaking cylinder head.
   (e) Carburetor out of adjustment.
   (f) Spark plug gaps spaced too close.
   (g) Defective valve action.
   (h) Restricted exhaust.

ENGINE RECONDITIONING

1. In reconditioning an engine cylinder, is a hone used mostly for removing light scratches and light scores, or for heavy scratches?
2. How may a score in a cylinder that is too deep to be removed by grinding be repaired?
3. The proper surface for a cylinder wall is a dead smooth or glass-like surface. True or false?
4. Tell how large cracks in cylinder blocks may be repaired.
5. In cases where crankshaft journals are out-of-round, what can be done about reconditioning?

CARBURETORS

A carburetor is a device for mixing gasoline and air, in the correct proportions, so that the resulting vapor, when compressed in the engine cylinder will explode and force the piston down. The carburetor must spray or atomize the fuel and thoroughly mix these particles with air. It must also be so designed that it delivers the mixture to the engine in correct proportions under all operating conditions from idling to full load.

The original carburetors were relatively crude in design and could operate only because the gasoline available at that time was easily vaporized. Some of the earlier types of carburetors were so designed that the air drawn in by the engine would first pass over the surface of some gasoline.

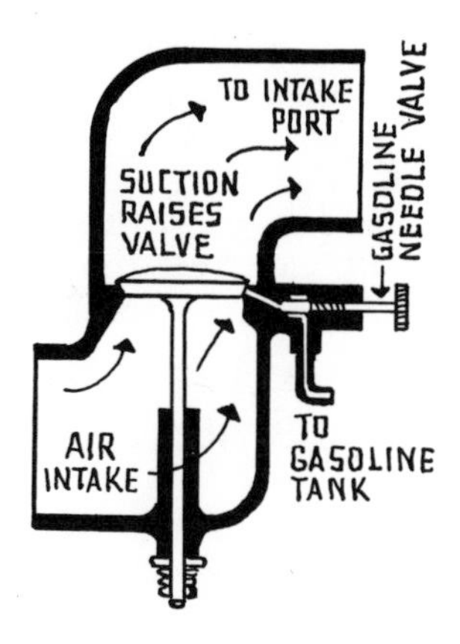

D-1. One of the early forms of carburetors, known as the mixing valve.

In that way enough gasoline vapor was carried on to the engine as a combustible mixture. Another type used a wick, the lower end of which was submerged in gasoline, while air passed over the exposed end and then into the engine cylinder. A third type was known as a mixing valve, Fig. D-1.

In the mixing valve air is drawn in through the valve which is opened by the suction of the engine. The air passing the opening to the gasoline supply draws fuel with it and the mixture of air and fuel is drawn into the cylinder. The amount of fuel is controlled by a needle valve.

However, the operation of such carburetors was erratic. The proportion of fuel to air was seriously affected by the height of the fuel supply level above the mixing valve, the quality of the fuel and the speed of the engine. For example, the rate of air flow through the carburetor, between idling speed and full load changes in a ratio of more than 100 to 1.

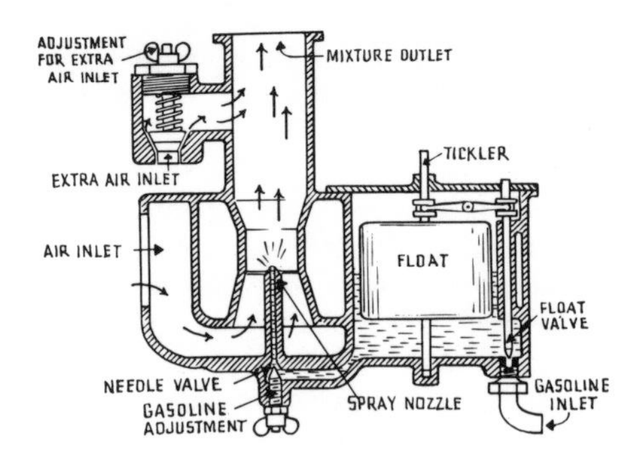

D-2. Early form of carburetor with float mechanism and main air inlet.

To overcome the difficulty in the variation of fuel flow due to the change in height of the fuel supply level above the mixing valve, Maybach designed a carburetor which utilized a float which maintained the level of the fuel within the carburetor at substantially the same level. In this design, Fig. D-2, fuel is supplied to a float chamber which is part of the carburetor. The float rises with the level of the fuel and when it reaches the desired height, a needle valve, mounted on the float shuts off the fuel supply. Then as fuel is used or consumed, the float drops and the needle valve opens permitting fuel to flow into the chamber until the desired level is again established.

REQUIREMENTS OF CARBURETION

As previously pointed out the purpose of a carburetor is to prepare and supply a mixture of fuel vapor and air, in proper proportions for efficient combustion. There are many factors which make this difficult. First of all, when an internal combustion engine is started it is cold, and a fuel mixture containing a larger portion of fuel is required. When the engine reaches operating temperatures, such a mixture is too "rich" and is not efficient. In addition the engine will not operate satisfactorily particularly at idling speeds.

Another difficulty that must be overcome by a carburetor is that when the engine is idling or operating at slow speeds, a richer mixture is required than when operating at medium speeds and power. When maximum power is required the amount of fuel in relation to air is again increased. Similarly during periods of acceleration a richer mixture is needed.

Variations in types and characteristics of fuel also are complications to be overcome in efficient carburetion. Gasoline is not uniformly volatile as it is a blend of various parts or fractions of crude petroleum. As a result some of these fractions contained in present day commercial gasoline will boil (vaporize) at 100 deg. F. and others at temperatures ranging up to 400 deg. F. Obviously when the engine and manifold are cold the problem is still more difficult.

PROPORTIONS OF GASOLINE AND AIR

For normal operating conditions the best economy is obtained by a mixture of one part by weight of gasoline to between 16 to 17 parts of air. For quick acceleration and maximum power a somewhat richer mixture is needed, having about one part of gasoline to 12 to 13 parts of air. Also for idling a somewhat richer mixture is required than for normal operation. Similarly when starting a cold engine an extremely rich mixture is needed.

PRINCIPLES OF OPERATION

Both air and gasoline are drawn through the carburetor and into the engine cylinder by the suction created by the piston moving downward in the engine cylinder. In other words, as the piston moves down in the cylinder, a partial vacuum is created in the cylinder and combustion chamber. It is the difference between the pressure within the cylinder and the atmospheric pressure which causes both air and fuel to flow into the cylinder from the carburetor.

The principle or method whereby the moving air draws the fuel from the jet or fuel supply is important and of interest. When atmospheric air flows through a pipe into a chamber, the under pressure or vacuum in-

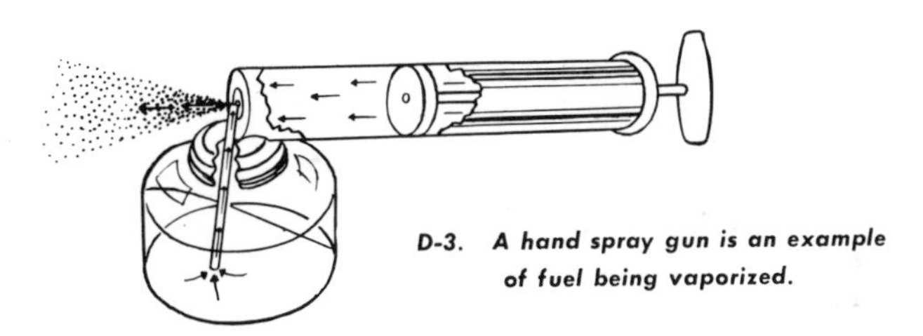

D-3. A hand spray gun is an example of fuel being vaporized.

creases from zero at the entrance and reaches a maximum at the entrance to the chamber. So, if a small tube connected with a supply of fuel is brought through the wall of the air tube, the open end of the gasoline will be subjected to under-pressure or partial vacuum and gasoline will be forced from the gasoline tube. The rate at which gasoline is discharged depends on the pressure difference between the partial vacuum and the atmospheric pressure. The area of the outlet of the gasoline tube is, of course, also a factor. An example of the method, whereby moving air draws fuel from a reservoir is found in the familiar hand spray guns, Fig. D-3.

A high suction can readily be produced by reducing the area at one point in the air tube. Such a restriction is known as a venturi and the gasoline tube or jet is placed at that point. Basically a venturi tube consists of two tapering tubes with their small ends joined. When a fluid, (in this case air) is passed through a venturi tube its static pressure is greatly reduced at the narrowest portion of the venturi and then increases again after passing the restricted area. This characteristic of a venturi is shown in Fig. D-4.

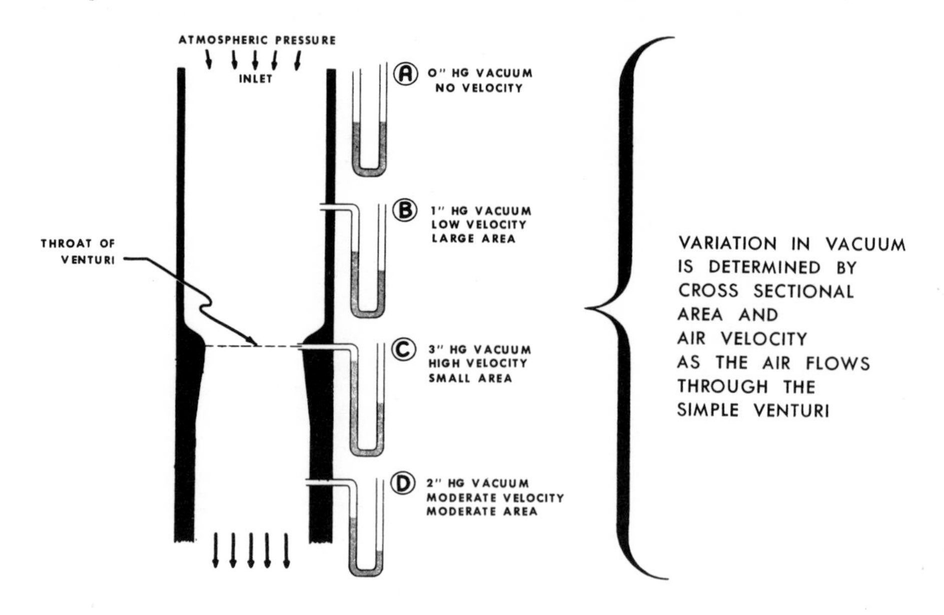

D-4. Illustrating the principle of a venturi and showing how the vacuum varies.

A vacuum gauge is used to measure the suction at different points in the tube and it will be noted that at the point where air enters the tube or carburetor that the vacuum is zero and reaches a maximum at the narrowest point.

In some carburetors, double or triple venturis are used in order to get maximum suction on the fluid tube or jet.

CARBURETOR FLOATS

The level of the fluid in the chamber which supplies fuel to the carburetor jet must remain substantially constant and in general slightly below the top or outlet of the jet. Obviously, if the level is too high, fuel will flow constantly from the jet and if the level is too low the velocity of the air stream would have to be increased in order to draw a given amount of fuel. Should the height of the fluid in the chamber vary then the operation of the carburetor would be erratic.

The level of the fuel in the float chamber is therefore maintained by means of a float operated valve, Fig. D-5. The valve is known as the float needle valve. In early designs it was mounted on top of the float with a conical seat directly above, Fig. D-6. As the level of the fuel in the chamber rises, the float also rises and when the level of the fuel reaches the

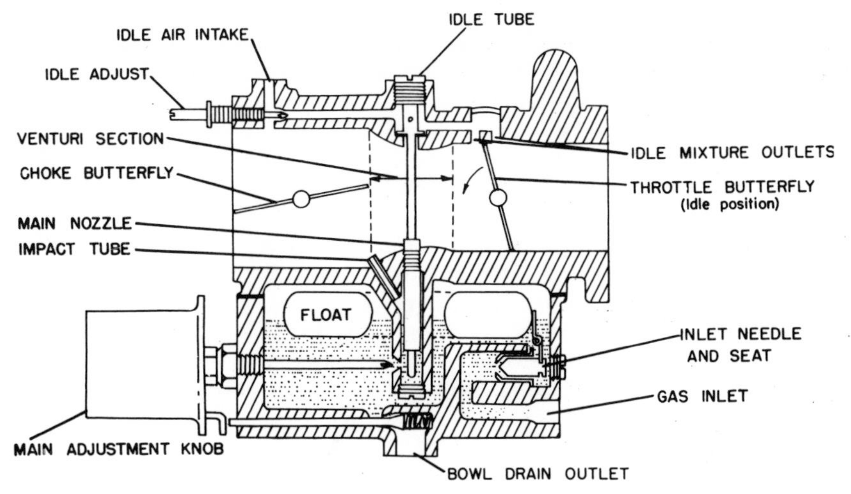

D-5. Details of float and needle valve.

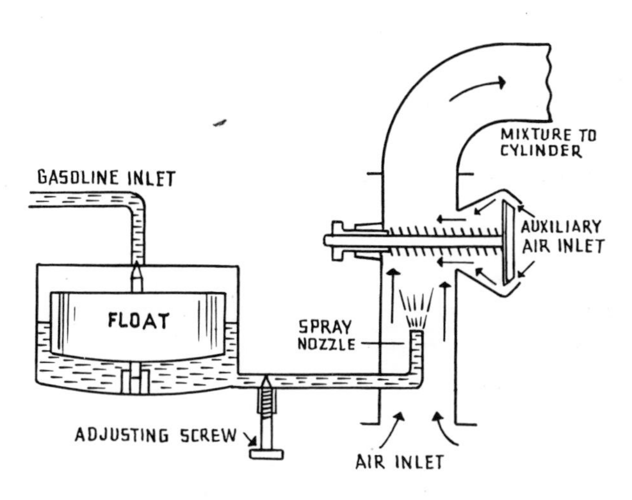

D-6. Early type of float and needle valve to control level of fuel in float bowl.

desired height, the valve closes and shuts off the supply of fuel. Recent designs, while the same in principle, usually have the float needle valve at one side of the float chamber and operated through a tab or lever on the edge of the float as in Fig. D-5.

FUEL AND AIR MIXTURE

Because the density of fuel does not change materially with changes in pressure, while that of air does, the rate of air and fuel delivery vary in different proportions with a change in pressure. For example, the velocity at which gasoline issues from a nozzle or jet varies as the square root of the difference between the air pressure in the float chamber and at the outlet of the jet. The velocity of the air passing the throat of the carburetor also variès as the square root of the pressure difference. However, the rates of delivery of the fuel and air differ because the density of the fuel does not change while that of air does. As a result, as the rate of flow of the air through the carburetor increases, the rate of flow of the fuel also increases but at a much faster rate. So in a simple carburetor the mixture will be much too rich under full throttle conditions. With such a carburetor, therefore, a correct mixture of fuel and air will be provided at one rate of delivery. That is for a single throttle opening and engine speed. For idling conditions, a simple carburetor will provide a mixture that is too lean, while at faster rates of delivery it will be too rich.

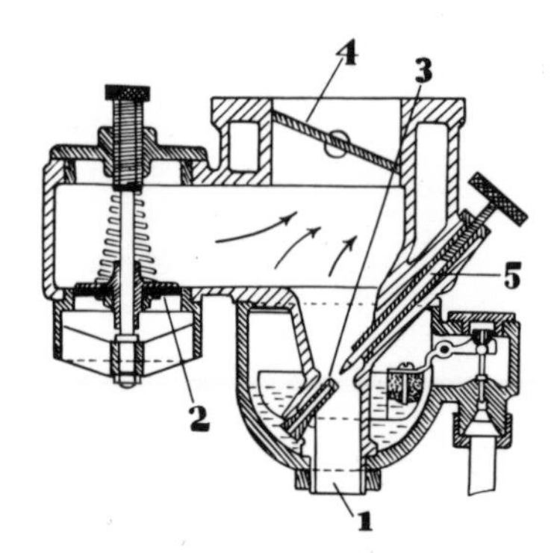

D-7. An auxiliary air valve was used on some early model carburetors to compensate for unequal increase of air delivery with changes in throttle opening. Main air intake (1). Auxiliary air valve (2). Jet (3). Throttle valve (4). Jet adjustment (5).

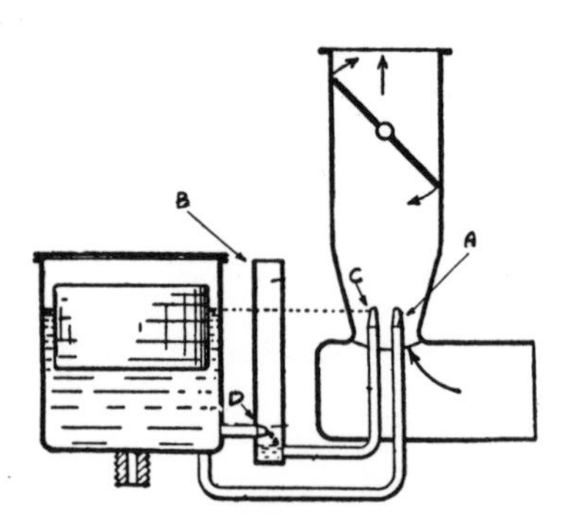

D-8. The main nozzle (A) secures its fuel directly from the float chamber and the compensating nozzle (C) receives its fuel from the standpipe (B). The fuel supplied by nozzle (C) depends on the size of the metering orifice (D) which delivers fuel to the standpipe (B).

Means must therefore be provided to give the correct mixture for all throttle openings and engine speeds. At idling speeds, when the throttle is almost closed, the suction in the throat of the carburetor is so small, that no fuel will issue from the nozzle located at that point. For that reason carburetors are provided with a special idling or low speed jet. This discharges into the mixing tube close to the edge of the throttle, when the throttle is in the closed position. At that point the vacuum is quite high when the throttle is closed.

As soon as the throttle is opened wide the suction above the throttle (updraft carburetor) decreases, while the suction below the throttle increases. Fuel will then not be drawn through the idling system but will pass through the main nozzle.

It is therefore necessary to compensate for the unequal increase in delivery rates of air and fuel with changes in throttle opening. Many different methods have been developed to attain that condition. One of the early designs used an auxiliary air valve and is shown in Fig. D-7. In this design the main air inlet is at the bottom of the carburetor, and provided sufficient air for idling and low speeds. As the throttle was opened further, engine speed increased which consequently increased the suction. This suction was sufficient to open the spring loaded auxiliary air valve permitting more air to mix with the increased flow of gasoline. In that way a better air to gasoline ratio was maintained.

DOUBLE NOZZLE PRINCIPLE

Another method of controlling the mixture of fuel and air uses is that in addition to the main nozzle there is another nozzle with a constant rate of discharge. In combination the two nozzles give a substantially constant mixture.

In Fig. D-8 the main nozzle is supplied with fuel directly from the float chamber. The compensating nozzle is supplied from what is known as a stand pipe which receives its fuel from the float chamber. The upper end of the stand pipe is open to the atmosphere. The supply of fuel to the stand pipe is through a metered opening and as the fuel in the float chamber is at a constant level the flow to the stand pipe will be constant. The rate at which fuel can be drawn from the compensating nozzle will therefore also be constant. At high engine speeds, the compensating nozzle delivers less fuel than at low engine speeds. In that way it compensates for the natural tendency of the main nozzle to deliver a mixture that is too rich at high speeds.

Also at high engine speeds, and when the compensating nozzle is delivering smaller amounts of fuel (due to reduced vacuum) the level of fuel in the stand pipe will rise until its level is equal to that in the float chamber. Then, as the suction on the compensating nozzle is such that fuel will be drawn from it, the fuel level in the stand pipe will be lowered. If the throttle is maintained at the same opening for a sufficient length of time, all the fuel will be drawn from the stand pipe, and the compensating nozzle will be supplied only from the compensating jet or submerged metering orifice.

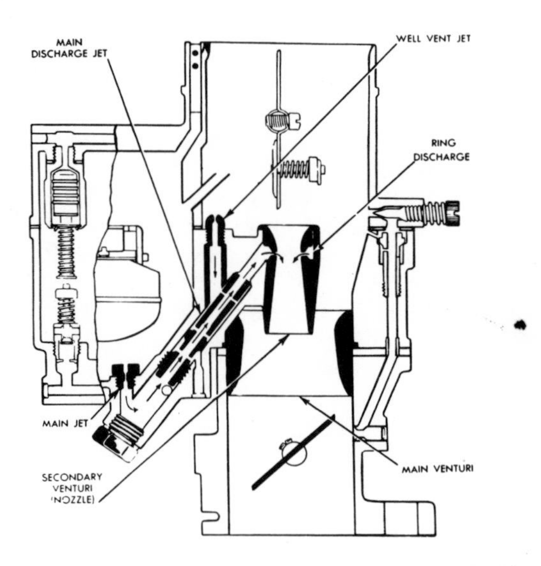

D-9. Illustrating the air bleed principle as used on the Model 228 Zenith carburetor

AIR BLEED PRINCIPLE

Another method of compensating for the increased richness of the mixture due to the effect of the plain nozzle with the increase in air velocity through the throat is by means of air bleeds. Fig. D-9 shows the air bleed systems as used on a Zenith Carburetor. Here the high speed system of the carburetor consists of a primary venturi, a secondary venturi, a main jet, a well jet and a discharge jet. The main jet controls the fuel mixture during the range from about one-quarter to about three-quarter throttle opening. The mixture is controlled by a small amount of air which is admitted through the well vent or high speed bleeder. Air bleed holes are located in the upper section of the discharge jet at a point below the level of fuel in the jet. The introduction of air into the discharge jet, below the level of the fuel, reduces the surface tension of the fuel and helps fuel flow at low suction. This bleed also restricts fuel flow through the main jet under high suction. These two factors in combination control the air-fuel ratio and offset the tendency for increasing the richness of the mixture in a plain nozzle with increasing air velocity.

In the Zenith construction, Fig. D-9, the main discharge jet is designed with a ring land, just above the lower bleeder holes. The ring land contacts the surface of the discharge jet passage and separates the idle supply from the high speed system. When the throttle is open to a point just above the idle position, enough air passes through the carburetor to lower the pressure at the discharge nozzle. The float chamber is open to the atmosphere and consequently the greater pressure in the float chamber will cause the fuel to flow through the main jet into the main discharge jet. Air admitted through the bleed holes in the discharge jet, in an amount controlled by the well vent is mixed with the fuel. This mixture of fuel from the main discharge jet passes through the discharge nozzle in the upper section of the secondary venturi and is added to the air stream in the secondary venturi.

UPDRAFT, DOWNDRAFT AND SIDE CARBURETORS

The first type of carburetor to come into general use was the updraft carburetor. In this construction air entered at the bottom or side of the carburetor, mixed with the fuel and passed out the top of the unit and then into the manifold and engine. Details of a Zenith design are shown in Fig. D-10.

A disadvantage of the updraft carburetor is that it must lift the fuel by air friction. To do this it must have a small diameter mixing tube so that

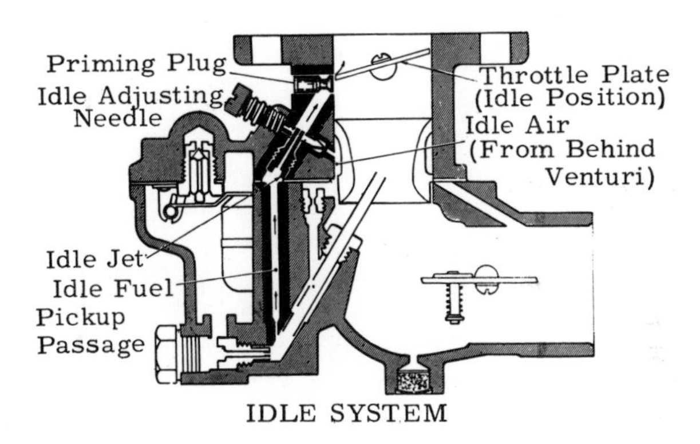

D-10. This Zenith carburetor is of the updraft type. Note that air enters at the lower right and the top of the carburetor is bolted to the manifold.

air velocities, even at idling speeds will be sufficient to lift and carry the fuel globules. However, at high engine speeds the small mixing tubes will restrict the amount of mixture supplied to the engine and it will be impossible to develop full power.

To overcome the limitations of the updraft carburetor the downdraft unit was developed. A Zenith downdraft model is illustrated in Fig. D-9. In this design the carburetor is placed above the engine, air entering at the top, passes downward, mixes with the fuel and then on to the manifold and engine. Here the fuel is not dependent on air friction to reach the engine and consequently the mixing tubes can be of relatively large diameter. In that way higher engine speeds and increased power are possible.

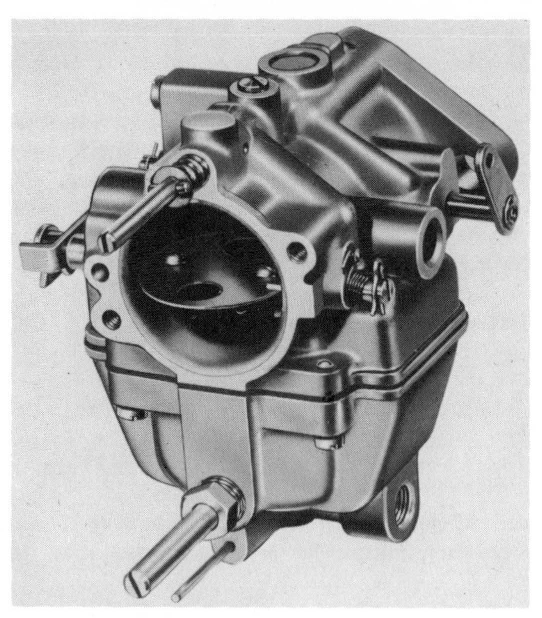

D-11. Horizontal carburetor as used on small industrial or outboard engines.

A third type of carburetor is known as the crossdraft, horizontal or side outlet carburetor. This type of unit is widely used on European cars and on stationary power plants. Such engines usually have the intake manifold built into the engine block and are partly water-jacketed. The horizontal carburetor, as its name implies, consists of a horizontal mixing tube. See Fig. D-11. An advantage of this type of construction is that it eliminates one right angle turn in the manifolding. Additional details of specific carburetors are given later herein under two and four cycle engine constructions.

ADJUSTING CARBURETORS

Formerly carburetors were provided with several adjustments so that the amount of fuel could be controled throughout the complete range of engine speeds and conditions. Obviously such carburetors required considerable time and skill to adjust and only a fair degree of accuracy could be attained.

Before adjusting any carburetor it is important that the ignition system be in good condition and that the compression is equal in all the cylinders. It is also important that there be no leaks in the intake manifold and that the engine is at operating temperature. The carburetor must be clean internally, in good mechanical condition and the float level must be correctly set.

Today many carburetors have an idle mixture adjustment only. The adjustment is easily and quickly made by turning the adjustment to the position which gives maximum idling speed. Obviously the idle speed or throttle position must not be altered until after the idle mixture has been correctly set. The usual method of making the idle adjustment is to first set it approximately one half turn open. Then with the engine running and at operating temperature gradually open adjustment until engine falters. Then turn the adjustment in until the engine operates smoothly.

A more accurate method is to attach a vacuum gauge to the intake manifold and then adjust the idle mixture so as to obtain the maximum reading on the vacuum gauge.

Many factors, in addition to the condition of the engine, will affect the reading of the vacuum gauge. Compression ratio, carburetor and valve restrictions, and the speed at which the test is made, will all influence the reading. Vacuum readings for tune-up purposes are always made at idling speed.

VAPOR LOCK

Just as water turns to steam when it is heated, gasoline turns to vapor when sufficient heat is applied. When complete or partial interruption of fuel flow results from vaporization of the fuel, the carburetor system is said to be vapor locked. This condition may occur anywhere in the fuel line, the fuel pump, or in the carburetor itself.

Whether or not vapor is likely to form and cause vapor lock depends on the vapor pressure of the fuel; in other words, the ease at which it will vaporize. The standardized method of measuring or determining vapor pressure in the laboratory is known as the Reid method. U. S. Government specifications for motor gasoline require that the Reid vapor pressure at 100 degs. F. should not exceed 12 lbs. per sq. in.

As the vapor of motor fuel occupies a greater volume than in liquid form, the amount of fuel flow will therefore be reduced. Under vapor lock conditions, loss in power and missing will occur and under extreme conditions, the engine will stop. After the fuel and carburetor system has cooled, the engine can be started without difficulty.

Carburetors are now designed with vents to overcome or reduce any tendency toward vapor lock. Engine manufacturers frequently place an asbestos gasket approximately 1/2 in. thick between the carburetor and manifold. This reduces the transmission of heat to the carburetor so that there is less tendency toward vapor lock in the carburetor. In addition, fuel pumps are placed so that they will be cooled by air blasts and shielded from heat of the exhaust manifold. Also to reduce the possibility of vapor lock, fuel lines are placed as far as possible from the muffler and exhaust line.

In addition to design of carburetor, pump, and lines, vapor lock is also controlled by gasoline refineries. This is done by changing the vapor pressure. During winter months a fuel that is easily vaporized is supplied so as to facilitate starting. During summer months when temperatures are high, engines are more easily started and a fuel that is not so easily vaporized is provided. However, during unseasonably warm weather in the spring and before refiners have supplied their summer grade fuel, it is not unusual to encounter difficulties from vapor lock.

CARBURETOR ICING

The formation of ice in carburetors has become a serious problem which will occur under certain weather conditions. It is most likely to occur when the atmospheric temperature is between 28 and 55 degs. F., with the relative humidity between 65 and 100 per cent. It usually occurs after the engine is started and before it has reached operating temperature, and the result is that the engine will stop or stall when operated at idling speed. Each time the engine stops it can be easily restarted, but when the engine speed is reduced to idling it will stop again.

The ice is formed at the edge of the throttle plate, Fig. D-12 and will restrict the flow of the air-fuel mixture when the throttle plate is at or near the idle position, causing the engine to stop. The engine will start again without difficulty as it is necessary to open the throttle, which will permit the air-fuel mixture to flow to the engine.

The formation of ice results from rapid vaporization of the fuel which may lower the temperature, or the temperature may be reduced as much as 25 degs. F. This lowered temperature causes the moisture in the air to freeze, causing ice to form on the edge of the throttle plate, where the air speed is greatest.

As soon as the engine reaches operating temperature, the carburetor will be sufficiently warm so that it will be impossible for ice to form.

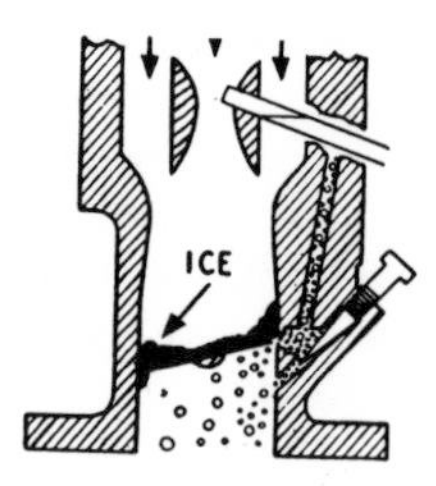

D-12. Ice and frost will collect on throttle plate, restricting the flow of fuel from idling jets, when air temperature ranges from 28 to 55 degs. F. and the relative humidity ranges from 65 to 100 per cent.

Fuel refiners and carburetor designers have difficulty in overcoming this situation. A faster than normal idling speed is of help in minimizing the difficulty and adjustment of the fast idle linkage on the carburetor should be made with care.

CARBURETOR TROUBLE SHOOTING

Complete failure of the engine to operate seldom originates in the carburetor. Therefore, when the engine does not start or operate efficiently, it is advisable to first check ignition, compression and supply of fuel to the carburetor, before examining the carburetor.

If the ignition and compression prove to be in good operating condition, the first step is to examine the choke to make sure that, with the engine cold, that the choke is closed and, if the engine is hot, that the choke is open.

If the operation of the choke proves to be satisfactory, the next step is to check for fuel to make sure that it is reaching the carburetor. To check this condition, disconnect the fuel line at the carburetor.

Clogged fuel lines or lines with leaks will prevent fuel from reaching the carburetor, provided of course, that there is fuel in the fuel supply tank.

It is also important to make sure that the nuts holding the carburetor to the manifold are tight, and that the nuts holding the manifold to the cylinder block are secure. If the carburetor or manifold are loose, air leaks will result and carburetion will be affected as air will be drawn in, diluting the air-fuel mixture.

Troubles with the carburetor itself may be caused by worn linkage, dirt, incorrect fuel level, worn parts, or maladjustment.

Carburetors are usually cleaned by first disassembling and washing the individual parts in special carburetor cleaning solutions. This gives the opportunity of inspecting and replacing any worn parts and also resetting the fuel level.

Carburetor cleaning solutions are designed to not only dissolve the grease and dirt that accumulate on the outside of the carburetor, but also the gum which is of varnish like consistency found on both the inside and outside of carburetors. Such gum is formed by heat acting on the fuel.

While the basic causes of carburetor trouble will vary somewhat with different makes and designs of carburetors, the usual conditions or difficulties and their respective causes are outlined as follows:

Possible causes of poor performance generally result from too lean a mixture. If the carburetor is correctly adjusted a lean mixture and poor performance may result from the following:

a. Air leaks at carburetor or manifold
b. Clogged fuel lines
c. Defective fuel pump
d. Incorrect fuel level
e. Clogged fuel screen
f. Dirt in carburetor jets and passages
g. Damaged or wrong size main metering jet
h. Worn idle needle valve and seat
i. Loose jets in carburetor

j. Defective gaskets in carburetor
k. Worn throttle shaft
l. Leaking vacuum lines to accessory equipment

POOR IDLING

Poor idling is usually caused by defective ignition system, leaking engine valves, or uneven engine compression. In the carburetor, the following should be checked:

a. Incorrect adjustment of idle needle valve
b. Incorrect float level
c. Sticking float needle valve
d. Defective gaskets between carburetor and manifold
e. Defective gaskets in carburetor
f. Loose carburetor to manifold nuts
g. Loose manifold to block nuts
h. Idle discharge holes partly clogged
i. Loose jets in carburetor
j. Leaking vacuum lines to accessory equipment

CARBURETOR FLOODS

The usual causes of carburetor flooding are as follows:

a. Fuel level too high
b. Stuck float needle valve
c. Defective gaskets in carburetor
d. Cracked carburetor body
e. Excessive fuel pump pressure

REVIEWING THE CARBURETOR SECTION

1. What is the purpose of a carburetor on an engine?
2. Name some difficulties that must be overcome to obtain efficient carburetion.
3. For normal operating conditions the best economy is obtained by a mixture of one part by weight of gasoline to ______ parts of air.
4. Quick acceleration necessitates using a lean mixture. True or false?
5. What causes air and fuel to flow from the carburetor into the cylinder?
6. What is a venturi?
7. Describe the purpose of a carburetor float.
8. Does the density of fuel change materially with changes in pressure?
9. Does the density of air change with changes in pressure?
10. What means are provided on present-day carburetors to give the correct mixtures at various engine speeds?
11. Describe the double nozzle principle of controlling the mixture of fuel and air; the air bleed principle.
12. In an updraft carburetor, where does air enter?
13. Is a downdraft carburetor usually placed above an engine or low on the side?

ADJUSTING CARBURETORS

1. The two principal adjustments on modern carburetors are for _______.
2. Describe two procedures for making idle adjustments.

TROUBLE SHOOTING ON CARBURETORS

1. Describe the procedure for checking the choke.
2. Checking to see if fuel is reaching the carburetor may be done by____.
3. What are some causes of poor idling? Name five.
4. Four causes of carburetor flooding are __________.

VAPOR LOCK

1. What causes vapor lock?
2. Name some things that automobile manufacturers have done to prevent this trouble.

STARTING, LIGHTING, IGNITION

FUNDAMENTALS OF ELECTRICITY AND MAGNETISM

A knowledge of the fundamentals of electricity and magnetism is imperative in order to understand the operation and servicing of engines.

Many different theories have been advanced as to the nature of electricity, but the theory that is now generally accepted by scientists is known as the electron theory.

It has been generally established that all matter is made up of tiny particles known as molecules. These molecules in turn consist of two or more atoms. Atoms in turn are still further divided into electrons, neutrons and protons. These particles are the same in all matter, regardless of whether it is a fluid or a solid, whether it is soft or hard, fragile or tough. The difference lies only in the arrangement or relative position of the electrons, neutrons and protons.

The proton is a small positive charge of electricity, while the neutron is a dead or neutral atom tied to the proton. The proton and neutron are the center or core of the atom. The electron is a small negative charge of electricity which rotates about the center or core of the atom. The positive proton neutralizes the negative electron.

Any one basic material is composed of only one kind of atom. Gold, silver, copper, sulphur, oxygen, zinc are elements, and at present there are known 98 different elements. Forty years ago scientists had discovered only 83, and additional ones will probably be discovered as the result of further research. In the list of atoms, each atom differs from its neighbor by one additional proton and one electron.

Differences in the construction of the atoms of different materials have important affects on their electrical properties, particularly in their ability to act as conductors of electricity or as insulators.

In some atoms the electrons never leave the protons and neutrons. Such electrons are known as planetary or bound electrons and that is the condition which exists in insulating materials, such as glass which is a poor conductor of electricity.

In materials in which the electrons rotate at relatively great distances from the central protons and neutrons and with the possibility of their paths intersecting the paths of electrons from adjacent atoms, the material's electrical resistance is low. Such materials are known as conductors.

When positive and negative charges in an atom are equal, they neutralize each other and the atom is uncharged. When that condition exists the continuous electron movement is concentrated about each individual atom.

An excess of electrons in any part of a circuit will cause a drift of electrons from one atom to another and this drift is known as an electric current.

COMPARISON OF WATER AND ELECTRICAL CIRCUITS

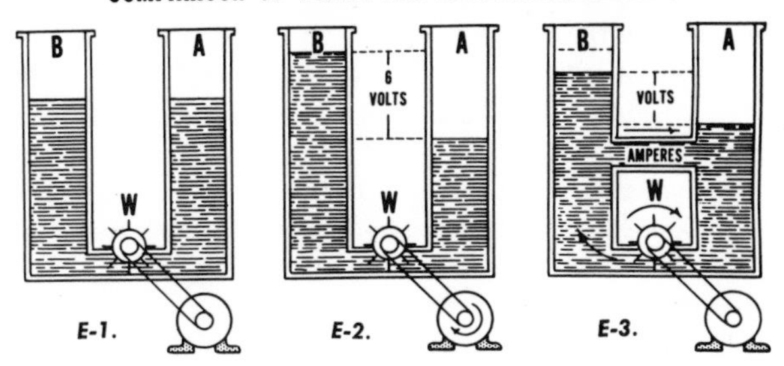

E-1. The water is at the same level in both sides of the tube and there is no current flowing.

E-2. The difference in level of the water in the two sides of the tube corresponds to the voltage.

E-3. The water passing through the connecting tube corresponds to the current (amperes) in an electric circuit. This flow is caused by the difference in height of water (voltage) in the tubes.

An object with more than its normal number of electrons is described as being negatively charged and an object with more than its normal number of protons is positively charged. When such a condition occurs in a conductor, there is a potential difference and there will be a drift or flow of free electrons along the conducting path. Such a difference is known as a potential, an electromotive force (e.m.f.) or more commonly, voltage.

The direct result of voltage or e.m.f. is an electric current. This current will continue as long as an e.m.f. exists across the ends of the conductor. The rate at which electrons pass a given section is measured in amperes. An ampere may be defined as 6,280,000,000,000,000,000 electron charges passing a given point in one second.

When an electric current flows through a conductor, the drift of electrons is relatively slow due to the fact that the free electrons which form the current are constantly colliding with protons, atoms and molecules. This opposition to the flow of current is known as resistance and is measured in ohms. An ohm is that amount of resistance which will limit the flow of current to one ampere when the pressure difference is one volt.

It is important to remember that no current will flow unless there is a complete circuit, and no current is complete until the conducting circuit returns to the original starting point where the difference of potential or voltage occurs.

As previously indicated there are three basic units of electrical measurement, the volt, ampere, and ohm, and it is important that these be thoroughly understood. By comparing the flow of electricity to the flow of water, a clearer conception of volts, amperes and ohms can be obtained. For example, a U shaped container partly filled with water is shown in Fig. E-1. It will be noted that the level of water is the same in both sides of the U. This corresponds to an electric circuit with voltage but with no current flowing. When the water wheel at the bottom of the U is started, water will be pumped from A to B, until the back pressure due to the higher level of water is equal to pressure produced by the water wheel, Fig. E-2. In the case of water, the difference in pressure would be measured in pounds per square inch and this difference in pressure corresponds to voltage in an electric circuit. In a conventional (3 cell) battery the difference in pressure or difference in potential is 6 volts.

By adding a cross tube as shown in Fig. E-3, the difference in level (and pressure) of the water, will cause water to flow through the cross tube. The water level (or voltage) will drop a little in B and rise a little in A. This reduces the pressure on the water wheel and water will flow around the circuit. The amount of water flowing corresponds to amperage in an electric circuit. In the case of water it is measured in gallons per minute and in the case of electricity it is measured in amperes.

If the tube connecting the two sides of the U is increased in size, more water will flow as it offers less resistance to the flow of water. If it is decreased in size, less water will flow. Similarly in an electric circuit, large conductors offer less resistance than conductors of smaller cross section. In electric circuits the resistance is measured in ohms.

OHMS LAW

There is a definite relation between the voltage, current (amperes) and resistance (ohms) existing in a circuit. This relationship is known as Ohms Law. It states that the electrical current in amperes passing through a conductor equals the pressure, in volts divided by the resistance in ohms.

$$\text{amperes} = \frac{\text{volts}}{\text{ohms}}$$

When writing electrical formulae the current in amperes is normally given as I, the voltage as V, the resistance in ohms as R. Using those symbols Ohms Law may be written as follows:

$$I = \frac{V}{R}$$

$$V = I \times R$$

$$R = \frac{V}{I}$$

Ohms Law is of great importance as it is used to calculate the current flow, voltage or resistance in a circuit when any two are known. The law can be applied to a complete electric circuit or any part of it.

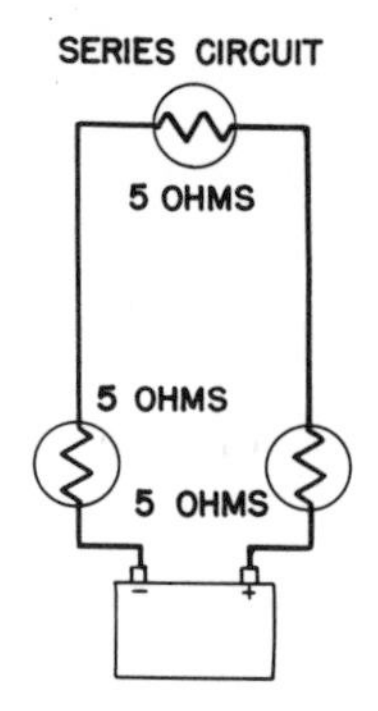

E-4. A series circuit.

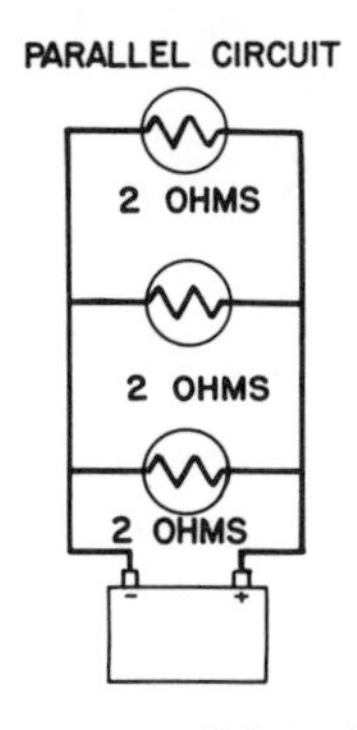

E-5. A parallel circuit.

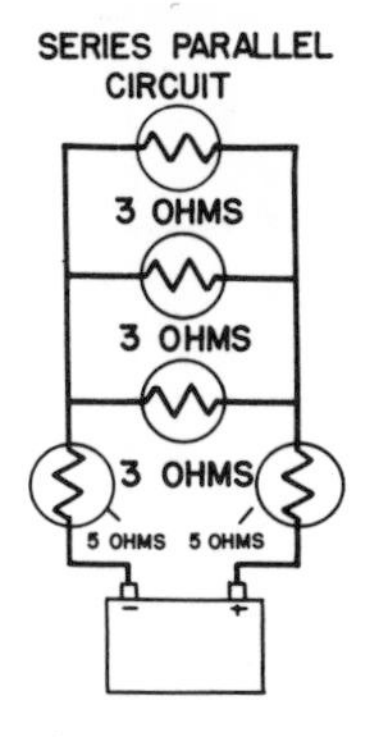

E-6. A series-parallel circuit.

In a complete circuit, the current equals the voltage across the entire circuit, divided by the resistance of an entire circuit. As an example to find the current in a lighting circuit when the voltage of the battery is 6 volts and the combined resistance of all the lights is .15 ohms. The answer is 40 amperes which is obtained by dividing 6 volts, by the resistance .15 ohms.

Similarly the current in a certain section of a circuit equals the voltage across that part divided by the resistance of that part. For example to determine the current passing through a single lamp when the voltage is 6 and resistance of the light is .4 ohm; divide 6 by .4 and the answer is 15 amperes.

TYPES OF CIRCUITS

There are, in general, three types of circuits, series, parallel, and series parallel. A series circuit, Fig. E-4, is one in which there is only one path for the current to flow. Any break or opening in the circuit will prevent the current from flowing.

A parallel electric circuit, Fig. E-5, is one which has more than one path in which the electric current can flow. In such a circuit, the current divides to pass through each of the devices forming the circuit. Then after having passed through the devices, the current returns to the point where the difference in voltage exists.

A series parallel circuit, Fig. E-6, is a combination of series circuits and parallel circuits. In other words, some devices in the circuit are connected in series, while others are in parallel.

In a series circuit, the current flowing will be the same at all points throughout that circuit and the total resistance in a series circuit will be the sum of the resistances of each individual part. The voltage across a resistance or piece of equipment is known as the voltage drop and is found by the use of Ohms Law. When a number of resistances are connected to a source of electricity, the sum of the voltage drops across the individual resistances is equal to the total voltage applied to the circuit. For example

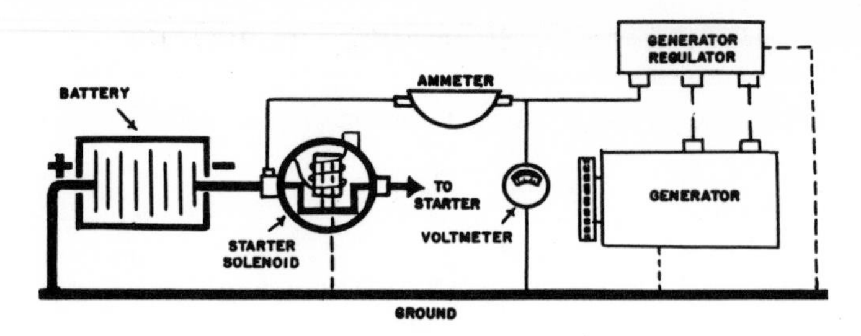

E-7. Circuit showing method of connecting a voltmeter and an ammeter.

in the series circuit, Fig. E-4, each piece of equipment has a resistance of 5 ohms, making a total of 15 ohms. There is 6 amperes flowing in the circuit. The voltage drop across each piece of equipment will be 5 x 6 or 30 volts, and the voltage applied to the complete circuit will be 3 x 30 or 90 volts.

In a parallel circuit, the resistance of the entire circuit is equal to the reciprocal of the sum of the reciprocals of the individual resistances. In other words, in Fig. E-5 there are three resistances of 2 ohms each which are connected in parallel. The total resistance of the circuit would then be

Total resistance equals $\frac{1}{\frac{1}{2}+\frac{1}{2}+\frac{1}{2}}$ or .66 ohm.

Ammeters are used to measure the current flowing in the circuit and are always connected in series, Fig. E-7, in the circuit. Voltmeters are used to measure the voltage or a circuit and are always connected across or in parallel, Fig. E-7, with the circuit.

ELECTRICAL WORK AND POWER

The electrical unit for measuring work is known as the joule, and one joule is equal to one ampere flowing for one second under the pressure of one volt.

To clarify this it is necessary to understand, that work is done when energy is expended and is calculated as the product of a force and the distance through which it acts in overcoming resistance. Power is the rate of doing work.

An electrical force may exist without work being done and is the condition which exists between the terminals of a battery when no equipment is connected to the battery. When some electrical equipment is connected to the terminals of the battery, a current will flow and work will be done.

Power is the rate at which work is done, or:

$$\text{Power} = \frac{\text{Work}}{\text{time}}$$

$$\text{Electrical Power} = \frac{\text{Electrical work}}{\text{Time}}$$

The watt is the electrical unit of power and is equal to one joule of electrical work per second. Then:

$$\text{Watt} = \frac{\text{Joules}}{\text{Seconds}} = \frac{\text{Volts x Amperes x Seconds}}{\text{Seconds}}$$

THEREFORE: Watts = Volts x Amperes.

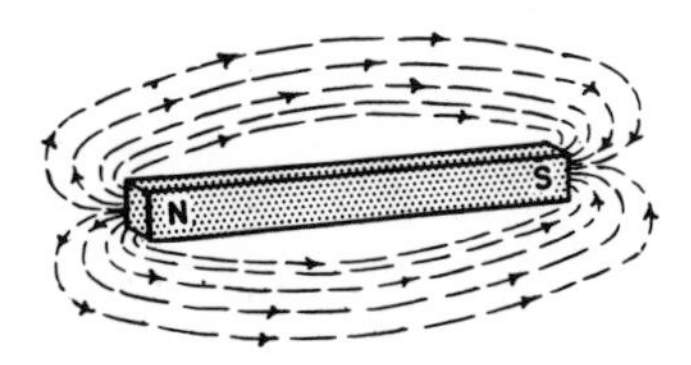

E-8. Simple bar magnet showing the lines of magnetic force.

For example, if in a lighting circuit the current is 30 amperes and the voltage is 6, the number of watts is 30 x 6 = 180 watts.

The unit for measuring mechanical power is the horsepower, and experimentally it has been found that one horsepower equals 746 watts.

MAGNETISM

Magnetism, like electricity is known better by its effects rather than what it is. We know, among other things that a magnet will attract pieces of steel and iron, but just what magnetism is, we do not know. However, without magnetism, there would be no electric generators nor motors.

The first effects of magnetism were discovered when pieces of iron ore were found to attract and adhere to other pieces of iron ore. It was also found that, when suspended in air that pieces of the iron ore would always point to the North Star. As a result of that discovery, the end of the piece of ore pointing toward the star became known as the north pole and the other end the south pole.

The area surrounding a magnet and in which its effect can be noted is known as its magnetic field, Fig. E-8. Naturally, it is strongest close to the magnet and becomes progressively weaker as the distance is increased from the magnet.

When illustrating a magnet and its magnetic field it is common practice to use lines showing the direction of the magnetic force, and these lines are known as the magnetic lines of force. The extent or area of these lines of force can be determined by means of a compass and it is assumed that the lines of force have direction, Fig. E-8, leaving the north pole of the magnet and traveling in a loop, and re-entering at the south pole.

Magnets can be made by rubbing a piece of steel with another magnet. A long bar of iron if placed so that it is parallel to the lines of force in a magnetic field will also become a magnet. In fact it has been found that steel railroad rails, laid in a north-south direction eventually are found to have magnetic properties.

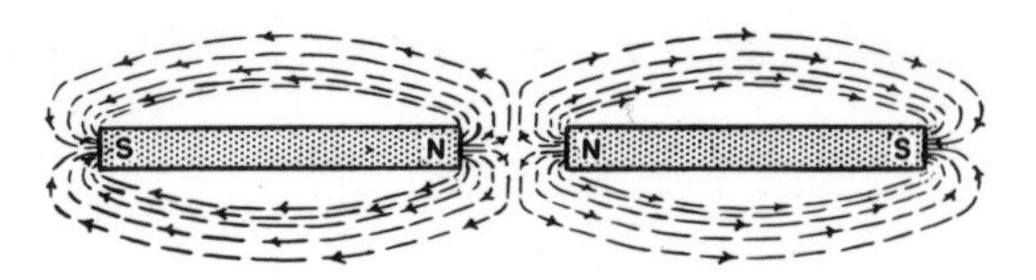

E-9. Similar poles of a magnet repel each other.

An extremely important effect of magnets is that when similar poles of two magnets are placed close together they are found to repel each other, Fig. E-9. Similarly when dissimilar poles, i.e., a north and a south pole are placed close together, Fig. E-10, they are attracted to each other.

The reason that two north poles repel each other is caused by the fact that the lines of force are in opposite directions, and the same condition results when two south poles of a magnet are brought together.

When north and south poles of magnets are brought together their lines of force are in the same direction, Fig. E-10, and consequently the magnets are mutually attracted to each other.

One of the fundamental laws of magnetism is, therefore, like magnetic poles repel each other and unlike poles attract each other.

As a result of this attraction and repulsion, magnetic lines of force do not cross each other, but when dissimilar magnetic poles are brought together the lines of force will be deflected and distorted from their normal direction.

When a non-magnetic substance is placed in a magnetic field, the lines of force will not be disturbed or affected. The magnetic lines of force will penetrate and pass through all non-magnetic materials and substances.

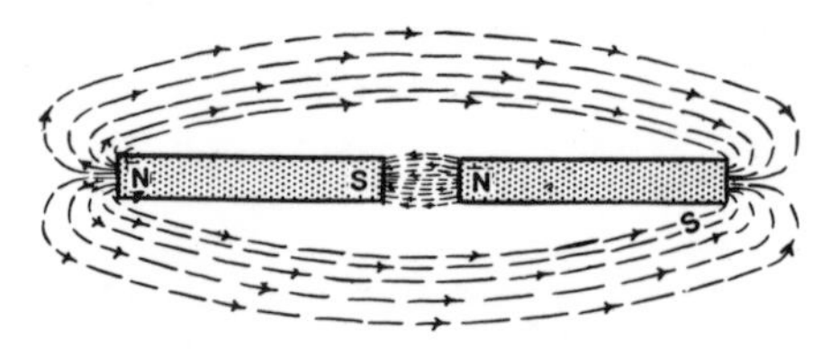

E-10. Unlike poles of a magnet attract each other.

ELECTRO MAGNETISM

Magnetic fields, having similar characteristics to the fields produced by permanent magnets of steel or hard iron, can also be produced by passing an electric current through a conductor. Electric motors, generators and equipment designed to measure electric currents are all based on the effects of electro magnetism produced by current passing through a conductor.

When a current is passed through a conductor the magnetic lines of force are concentric circles surrounding the length of the wire, Fig. E-11. However, there are no poles in the conductor at which the lines of force enter or leave. The strength of the magnetic field and the area affected is proportional to the strength of the current. That is, the stronger the current the stronger the magnetic field.

The direction of the magnetic lines of force surrounding a conductor is dependent on the direction of the current, Fig. E-11. An ordinary compass can be used for determining the direction of the lines of force or what is known as the right hand rule may be used. By placing the right hand on the conductor, with the extended thumb pointing in the direction of the current, the fingers curling around the conductor will then indicate the direction of the magnetic lines of force.

When an electric current is passed through a conductor that has been formed into a loop, Fig. E-12, the lines of force on the outside of the loop

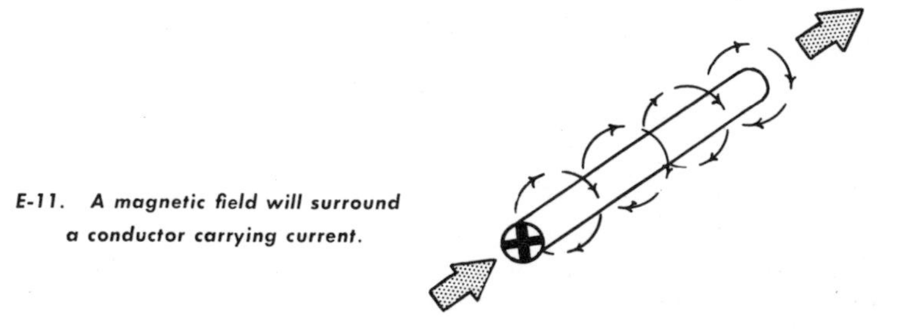

E-11. A magnetic field will surround a conductor carrying current.

will spread out into space. However, the lines of force on the inside of the loop must pass through its center and the number of lines of force per square inch is increased. In this way the strength of the magnetic field is increased and is much greater than would be obtained for the same current passed through a straight conductor. Checking the field with a compass will show that there are opposite magnetic poles on the two sides of the loop.

THEORY OF PERMANENT MAGNETS

While the effects, direction and extent of magnetic fields are easily demonstrated, a complete answer is not available as to why certain materials can be magnetized while others cannot. However, the electron

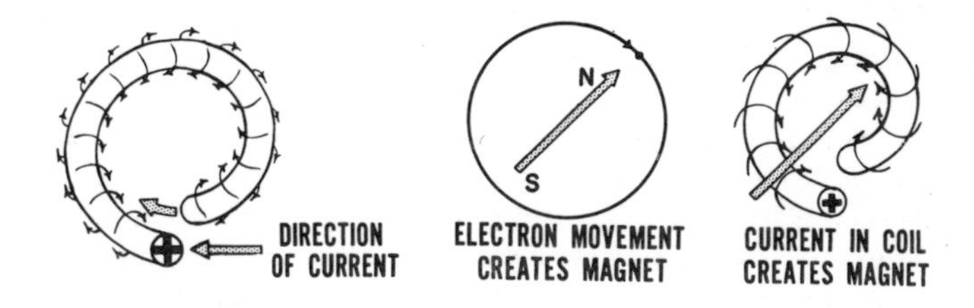

E-12. The number of lines of magnetic force within a loop are intensified.

E-13. An electron moving in a fixed circular orbit creates a magnetic field.

theory gives the best explanation for the phenomena. As explained previously, an electron carries a charge of electricity and is constantly moving in an orbit. It is, therefore, assumed that a known charge of electricity moving in an orbit is the same as the current of electricity flowing through a conductor. Thus an electron moving in a fixed circular orbit creates a magnetic field, Fig. E-13, which has a north pole on one side of the orbit and a south pole on the other. And it is believed that most substances do not show magnetic properties because the orbits of the various electrons are so arranged that magnetic fields cancel each other.

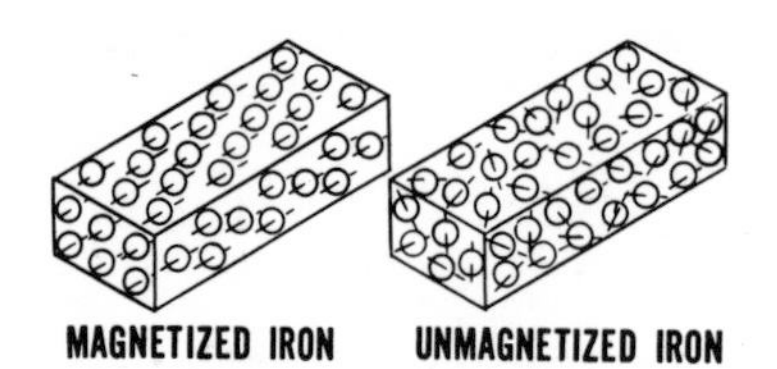

E-14. Alignment of electron orbits in magnetized and non-magnetized iron.

In iron, cobalt, and nickel, which are magnetic substances, the electron orbits align themselves in parallel planes and in the same direction when placed in a magnetic field, Fig. E-14. This arrangement of the electron created magnets produces a strong magnetic effect.

There is no explanation as to the reason why non-magnetic materials do not behave in a similar manner.

Soft iron will lose virtually all of its magnetic effect as soon as it is removed from the magnetic field. Hard steel will retain the magnetic effect for a long time. The magnetism which is retained is known as residual magnetism.

COMBINED MAGNETIC FIELDS

As previously pointed out a magnetic field will surround a conductor in which there is a flow of electrons. If two such conductors are placed parallel to each other, Fig. E-15, the magnetic field between the conductors will be strengthened if the current is flowing in opposite directions in the two conductors and the two conductors will be forced apart.

If the current in the two conductors is flowing in the same direction, Fig. E-16, the magnetic field between the two conductors will be weakened and the two conductors will be drawn together.

By the "Right Hand Rule," the direction of the lines of force can be determined. In the condition of the parallel conductors with current flowing in opposite directions, Fig. E-15, the direction of the magnetic field around one conductor is clockwise and around the other counter-clockwise. By bringing the two conductors close together, the lines of force between the two conductors will be in the same direction. The field of force between the conductors is, therefore, intensified, Fig. E-15, while the space beyond the conductors is free to spread out. Furthermore, the field beyond

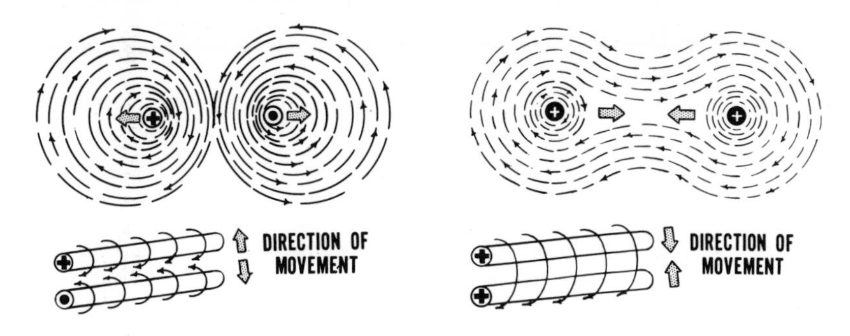

E-15. The magnetic effect produced by current flowing in the opposite direction in two parallel conductors will tend to force them apart.

E-16. The magnetic effect produced by current flowing in the same direction in two parallel conductors will tend to pull them together.

or outside of the conductors is in opposite directions, resulting in a weaker field. The lines of force between the conductors are crowded together, tending to force the conductors apart.

This phenomena of conductors being forced apart, when carrying current flowing in opposite direction is used in the operation of many electrically operated units.

OPPOSING MAGNETIC FIELDS

When current is flowing in the same direction in two parallel conductors, Fig. E-16, the right hand rule of current flow will show that the lines of force between the two conductors are in opposite directions. As the current in both conductors is the same the magnet fields will be equal. But being in the opposite direction, they will cancel each other. As the lines of force are complete loops, they never cross each other and will, therefore, take the long way around and encircle the two conductors. With zero magnetic field between the conductors and strong fields beyond the conductor, the conductors will tend to move toward each other.

When several current carrying conductors are placed side by side as in the case of generator field coils, the effect is the same. The lines of force join and surround all the coils and the individual wires are more closely drawn together.

Current carrying conductors will always move away from a strong magnetic field into a weaker field.

ELECTROMAGNETS

When wire is wound in a coil (helix) and carries current, the magnetic field of each turn affects the magnetic field of the adjacent turn. The magnetic field between adjacent turns will be neutralized as shown in the preceding paragraphs on "Opposing Magnetic Fields," but the lines of force passing through the center of the coil of wire, and those surrounding the coil will make a continuous loop. One end of the loop will be a north pole,

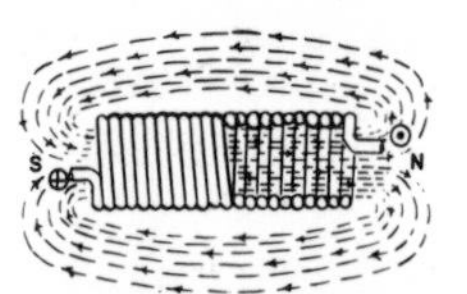

THE FIELD OF FORCE SURROUNDING A CURRENT CARRYING COIL. ALL FORCE LINES ARE COMPLETE LOOPS.

E-17. A coil of wire, with current passing through it will have a north pole at one end and a south pole at the other.

Fig. E-17, while the other will be a south pole, the same as will be found on a permanent magnet.

Another right hand rule can also be used to determine polarity of such a coil of wire. By grasping the coil of wire with the right hand so that the fingers extend in the direction of current flow, the extended thumb will then point toward the north pole of the coil.

The strength of the magnetic field is increased by each turn of wire and also by the amount of current flowing. Therefore, the more turns of wire and the greater the current flow, the stronger will be the magnetic field. In other words, the magnetic field is directly proportional to the number

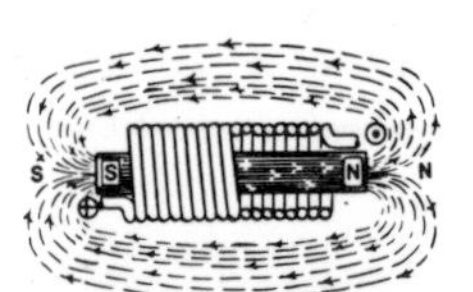

THE FIELD OF FORCE WHEN A SOFT IRON CORE IS PLACED IN THE WINDING. NOTE CONCENTRATION OF LINES IN IRON CORE.

E-18. Placing a movable soft iron core within a current carrying coil forms a solenoid.

of turns of wire and the strength of the current. This may be expressed as the number of ampere turns which is obtained by multiplying the number of turns of wire by the current in amperes.

All non-magnetic materials, including air are poor conductors for magnetic lines of force. However, air is used as the standard of magnetic conduction or permeability and is considered as having a permeability of one. Certain metals are good conductors of magnetic lines of force. That is they have high permeability. For instance soft iron has a permeability of 300 and when a soft iron core is placed in a coil of wire the lines of force (magnetic flux) will be increased 300 times. A coil of wire with a soft iron core is known as an electro-magnet.

SOLENOIDS

A coil of wire with an iron core which is free to move back and forth with the coil is known as a solenoid, Fig. E-18. When current flows through the coil, the movable core is magnetically attracted to the center of the coil. Springs are used to return the core to its original position as soon as the current is turned off.

In a solenoid, Fig. E-19, the movable core will have a south pole adjacent to the north pole of the coil. The polarity of the movable iron core results from the lines of force from the coil. This magnetic effect is explained by the direction of the lines of force created by the electromagnet. The north pole is always the point at which the lines of force leave the solenoid. Since iron is a better conductor of lines of force than air, the lines of force will enter the movable core and return through air to the pole at the opposite end of the coil. As all lines of force tend to shorten and because the adjacent poles of the coil and the core are opposite, there is an attraction which draws the movable core to the center of the coil.

When a magnet is cut, the ends adjacent to the cut will have poles opposite to the poles at the other ends of the magnet. They will, therefore, also be opposed to each other.

E-19. In a solenoid, the movable core will have a south pole next to the north pole of the coil.

E-20. Reversing the direction of current flow will have no effect on the action of a solenoid.

When the current flow in a solenoid is reversed, Fig. E-20, the direction of the lines of force is also reversed, and the induced polarity of the movable iron core is also reversed. As a result the core will again be drawn to the center of the core. The operation of the solenoid is, therefore, not affected by the direction of current flow.

When a current-carrying conductor is located in a magnetic field, Fig. E-21, there will be a distortion of the field. The reaction of the lines of force between two current-carrying conductors was explained in previous

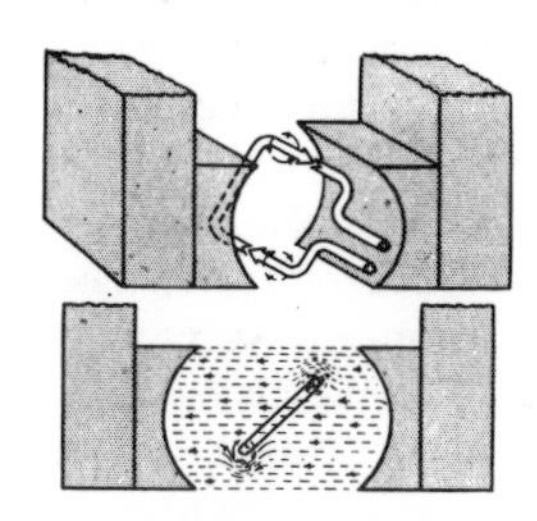

E-21. When a conductor carrying current is placed in a magnetic field, there will be a distortion of that field.

paragraphs and the result is the same in this case. Lines of force in the same direction join to make a stronger field and lines of force in opposite directions tend to cancel each other and produce a weaker field. The result is that the conductor will be caused to move toward the weaker field.

Since the direction of current flow through a conductor determines the direction of the lines of force around the conductor, a movement in the opposite direction is obtained when the direction of the current is reversed. When a conductor is formed as shown in Fig. E-21, and current flows as

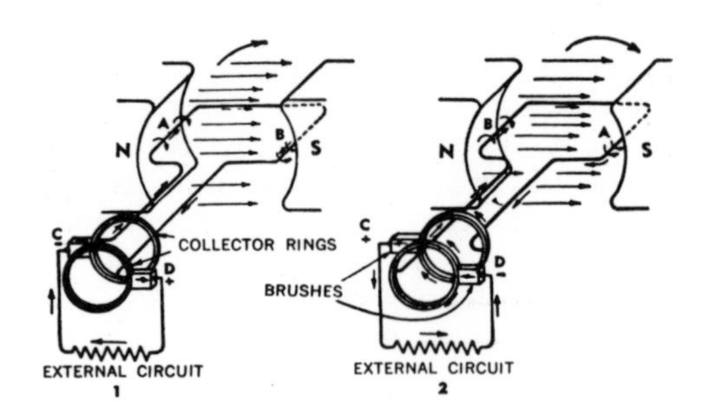

E-22. A basic generator.

indicated, there will be a tendency for the conductor to rotate in a clockwise direction. This results from the interaction of the magnetic field set up by the current in the conductor and the magnetic field in which the conductor was placed.

This is the basic principle of the electric motor and many other pieces of electrical equipment.

ELECTRIC GENERATORS

PRINCIPLES OF OPERATION

The generator operates on the principle that any conductor connected to a complete circuit, will have a flow of current induced in it when it is moved through a magnetic field. Basically the electric generator consists of two parts, the field coils, which supply the magnetic field and the armature winding, which rotates in the magnetic field produced by the field coils.

The armature consists of a number of insulated copper wires placed in insulated slots around a soft iron core. These conductors and core are assembled on a shaft so that they can be rotated.

In Fig. E-22, is shown a coil of wire in a magnetic field. The ends of the coil are each connected to a copper collector ring with a brush contacting each ring. The brushes are then connected to a light or other power consuming device. As the coil of wire is rotated, it will cut through the magnetic lines of force and current will be caused to flow through the

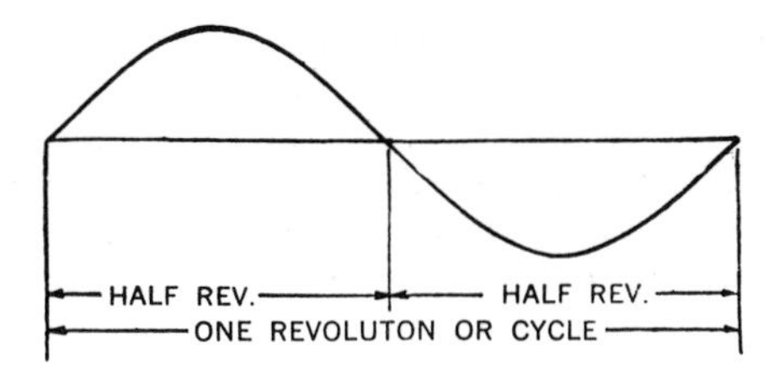

E-23. *Diagram of an alternating current, showing how it reverses in polarity.*

coil to the collector rings. It then passes through the light or other external load to the other collector ring to complete the circuit.

In the position shown, the coil will be cutting magnetic lines of force and voltage will be generated. But as the coil turns in the direction indicated, the voltage will decrease until the coil reaches the vertical position, when for an instant it will not cut any lines of force. At that point the voltage will drop to zero. As the coil continues to revolve, the voltage will again start to increase, however, the potential is now reversed as the conductor which formerly was passing up through the field is now passing down, and the conductor which was passing down is now moving up. This causes the current to reverse and it is therefore known as an alternating current, which is shown graphically in Fig. E-23.

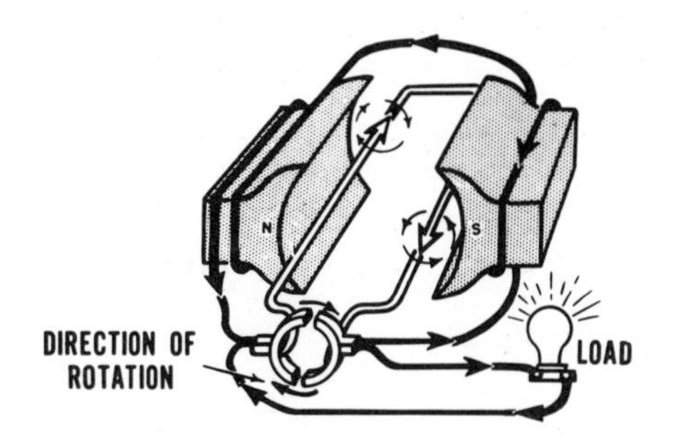

E-24. *By using commutator bars instead of the collector rings, direct current will be generated.*

However, as batteries can only be charged by direct current, it is necessary to generate direct current. The conversion is accomplished by eliminating the collector rings and substituting a commutator as shown in Fig. E-24. It will be noted that this is a two segment ring. Each segment insulated from the other and an end of the coil connected to each segment.

The operation is the same as with the alternator previously described, but as the coil rotates, and the current reverses in direction, one end of the coil is connected, (through the commutator) to first one brush and then the other. This automatically causes the polarity of the brushes to remain

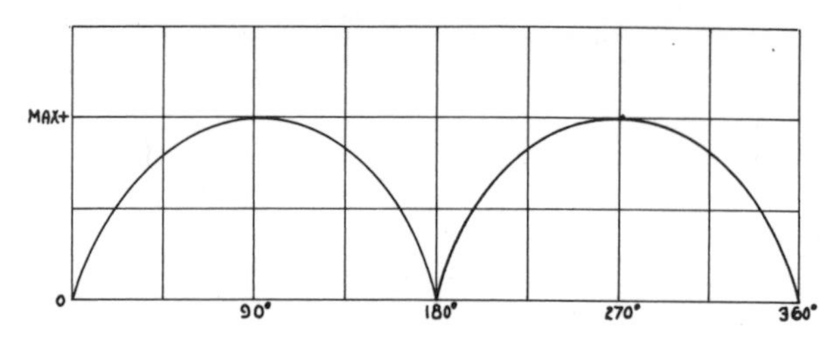

E-25. Diagram of the current produced by the generator shown in Fig. E-24. Note that the current is always in the same direction.

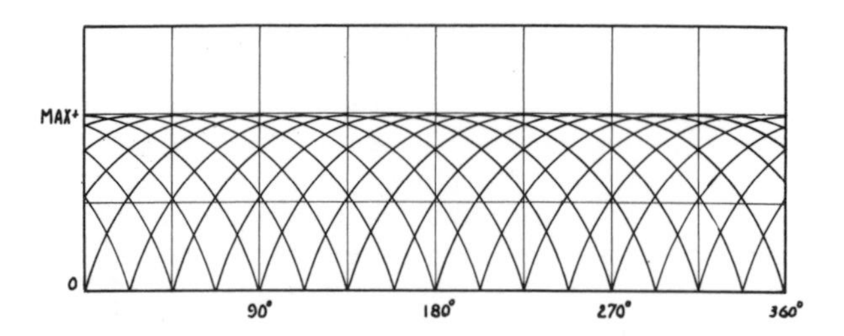

E-26. Diagram of direct current when many armature coils are used.

the same and the current flowing through the external circuit to be in the same direction.

However, the current will be of a pulsating character in the external circuit as the voltage will be at maximum when the armature coil passes through the magnetic field of maximum density and drop to zero when it is in vertical position where the magnetic field is at zero density. The current in the external circuit is shown graphically in Fig. E-25.

Instead of a single armature coil connected at each end to a commutator bar, generator armatures are wound with many coils, each connected to a commutator bar. Therefore, instead of having two peaks of current per revolution, as is obtained with the single coil shown in Fig. E-24, the number of peaks will be multiplied by the number of coils. In that way a relatively smooth direct current is produced as shown in Fig. E-26.

The armatures, Fig. E-27, used in generators are made of coils consisting of a number of turns of insulated copper wire. In some generators the coils are wound in slots, either by hand or by machine. Other armatures have form wound coils which are wound on separate forms and then bent in the proper shape to fit into the armature slots.

In the preceding description and illustration the magnetic field was assumed to be produced by a permanent magnet. However, such a field is of limited strength. In actual generators, the magnetic field is produced by electro-magnets which are supplied by current developed in the armature. These field coils may be connected in series, series parallel, or in parallel with the armature. Different types of generator windings are shown in

Fig. E-28. Current practice in generators is to connect the field coils in parallel with the armature and such generators are known as shunt wound generators.

As previously pointed out, the voltage produced by a generator is dependent on the number of magnetic lines of force that are cut by the armature coils per second. Increasing the speed of rotation of the armature or the strength of the magnetic field will therefore increase the voltage that is generated. As the speed of a generator varies from approximately 200-300 r.p.m. at engine idling speed to a maximum of 4000 to 5000 r.p.m. at full engine speed, the problem of maintaining a constant voltage is difficult of solution.

In a series wound generator, Fig. E-28, all the current in the circuit also passes through the field and armature. Therefore any change in the

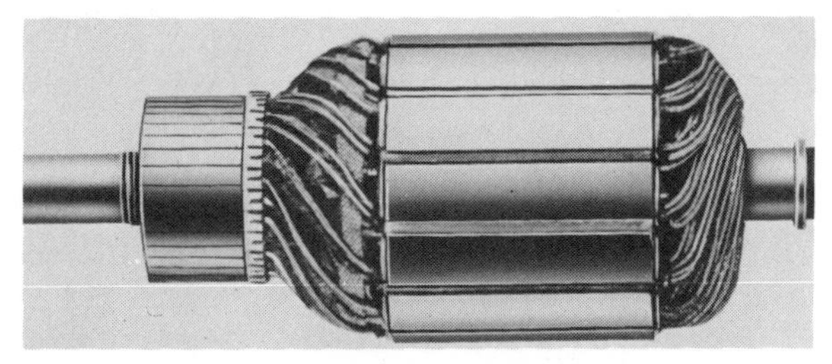

E-27. *Typical generator armature.*

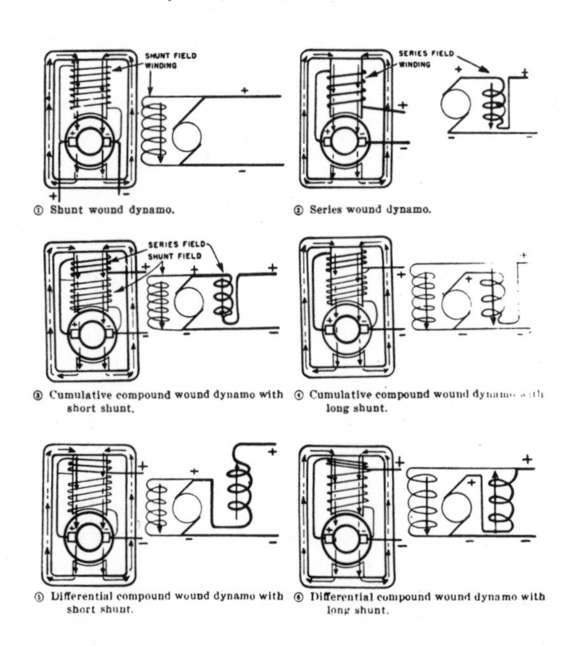

① Shunt wound dynamo.
② Series wound dynamo.
③ Cumulative compound wound dynamo with short shunt.
④ Cumulative compound wound dynamo with long shunt.
⑤ Differential compound wound dynamo with short shunt.
⑥ Differential compound wound dynamo with long shunt.

E-28. *Different types of generator windings.*

current such as would be produced by turning on lights will increase the current flowing and also the strength of the magnetic field. Extreme variations in voltage would therefore result, with still further variations due to changes in speed or rotation.

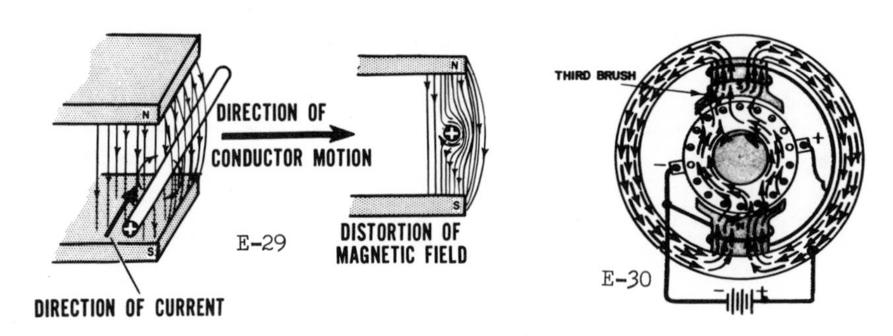

E-29. Distortion of magnetic field in a generator.

E-30. Distortion of magnetic field in a third brush generator.

In the parallel or shunt generator, Fig. E-28, the current in the armature divides, part flowing through the field coils. The current through the shunt field depends on its resistance and on the difference of potential at the brushes. Hence the current is constant, and the strength of the field is constant as long as the difference of potential of the brushes is unchanged. The voltage of such a generator, therefore, is more nearly constant than a series wound generator.

A combination of a series and parallel field winding is known as a compound winding, Fig. E-28. By selecting different size windings for the shunt and series coils, and by varying the connections, different generating characteristics can be produced. If the field from the series winding opposes that of the shunt field, the current will be reduced as the speed increases.

ARMATURE REACTION

As previously explained, conductors carrying current will be surrounded by a magnetic field. Armature and field coils in generators are no exception. The effect of the magnetic field created by the current-carrying conductors of the armature upon the magnetic field created by the field coils is known as armature reaction. This is an important factor in the operation of third brush generators.

The magnetic field set up by the armature influences and distorts the field set up by the field coils, Fig. E-29. Instead of having a magnetic field of uniform density between the field pole pieces, the reaction of the armature field on the main field causes the magnetic lines of force between the poles to shift in the direction of armature rotation. This results in intensifying the lines of force at the tips of the field poles from which the

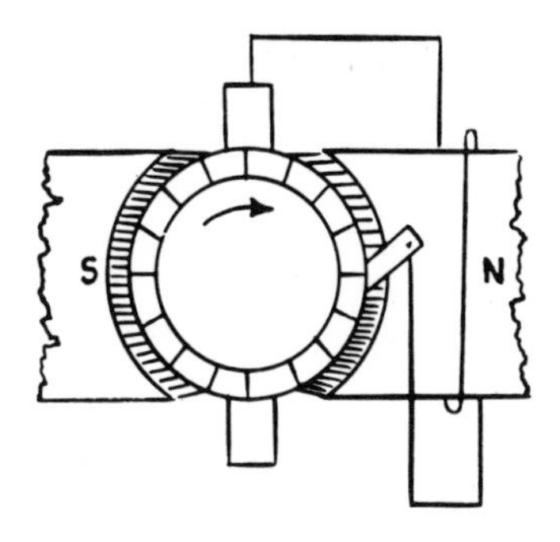

E-31. The reaction of the magnetic field is used to control the output of third brush generators.

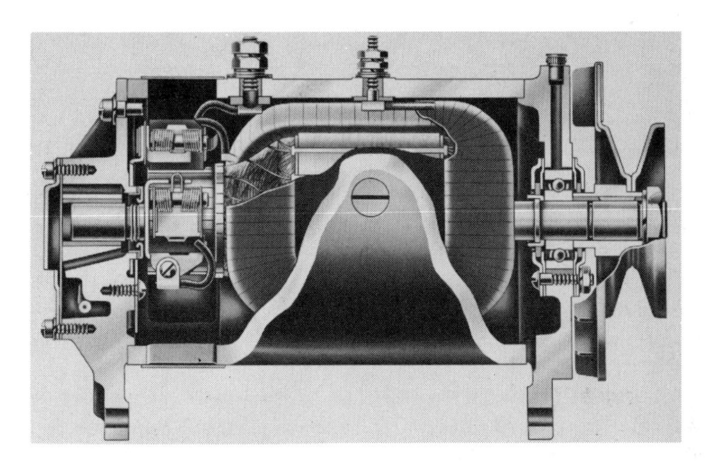

E-32. Sectional view of third brush generator.

armature is rotating, Fig. E-30. Armature coils passing through this denser field will be generating higher voltage than those passing through the weaker portions of the magnetic field.

This reaction of the magnetic fields is utilized in controlling the output of third brush generators, Fig. E-31.

THIRD BRUSH GENERATORS

In the third brush generator, Fig. E-32, it will be noted that instead of both terminals of the shunt field windings being connected directly to the brushes, one end of the field winding is connected to the third brush, while the other end of the field winding is connected to the (-) main brush in the usual manner. The position of this third brush controls the voltage applied to the circuit and in that way controls the generator output. The explanation of this is as follows: Assume that the generator (A), Fig. E-33 is operating at 2000 r.p.m. and the voltage across the two main brushes is 8 volts. Then if one lead of a voltmeter is connected to one brush, and the other lead is held against the commutator at a point equivalent to the width of one commutator bar away from that brush, a slight voltage will be indicated. As this voltmeter lead is moved progressively around the commutator, the indicated voltage will increase gradually until it reaches the maximum reading at the other brush. In other words, the voltage across the main brushes of the generator is equal to the sum of the voltages between the adjacent commutator bars between the main brushes.

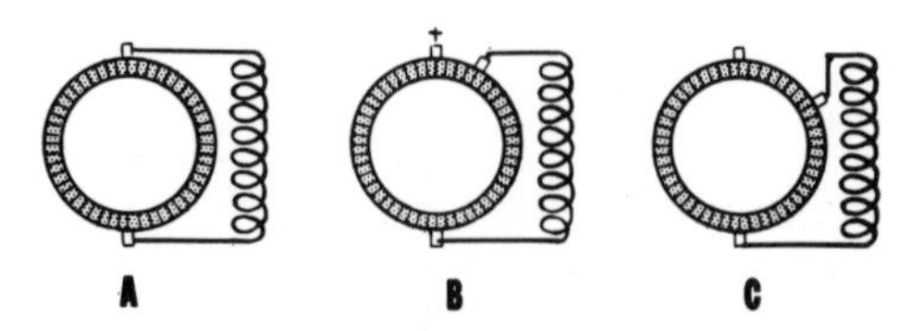

E-33. By varying the voltage applied to the field coils, the output of the third brush generator is changed.

In the case of the third brush, the voltage applied to the field circuit would be increased as the third brush is moved closer to the top brush, (B) in Fig. E-33, and would be decreased as it is moved away from the top brush, (C) in Fig. E-33. In service work it is more usual to relate the positioning of the third brush to the direction of rotation of the generator. Moving the third brush in the same direction as the armature rotates, will increase the voltage applied to the field and consequently increase generator output. Moving the third brush in the direction opposite to armature rotation will decrease the output.

The output of the generator is dependent on the number of lines of magnetic lines of force cut by the armature coils, and the rate at which they are cut. The magnetic lines of force are equal to the current flowing in the field and the number of turns of wire in the field coils. (The number of turns of wire, times the current in amperes is known as ampere-turns).

As the turns in the field coils are fixed, the magnetic lines of force can only be varied by changing the current flowing through the coils, and the current flowing through the coils is dependent on the voltage applied to them. Therefore, by varying the voltage applied to the field circuit by moving the third brush around the commutator, the strength of magnetic field is varied and the output of the generator is also varied.

The output of a third brush generator is therefore dependent upon the voltage applied to the field circuit, however, the armature voltage is dependent upon the resistance of the circuit to which it is connected. If the third brush generator should be operated without being connected to some electrical load, the generated voltage would rise to approximately 60 volts. The resulting current flowing through the field coils would be so high, that they would be quickly burned out. To protect the field coils from such a condition a protecting fuse is placed in the field circuit.

Third brush generators when used to charge starting batteries have the undesirable characteristic of providing a higher charging rate when the battery approaches full charge and a low charging rate when the battery is in a discharged condition, Fig. E-34. To a certain degree, this is controlled by the armature reaction previously discussed and gives satisfactory results for generators having an output not exceeding 20 amp. Another undesirable characteristic of a third brush generator is that maximum output is not reached until a relatively high speed is reached. However, at still higher speed, the output drops rapidly as shown in Fig. E-34.

SHUNT TYPE GENERATORS

Because of the wide range of speeds under which a generator operates, a shunt type generator would not have satisfactory voltage characteristics. In order to maintain a battery in a fully charged condition it is necessary that full charging current be supplied at as low a speed as possible.

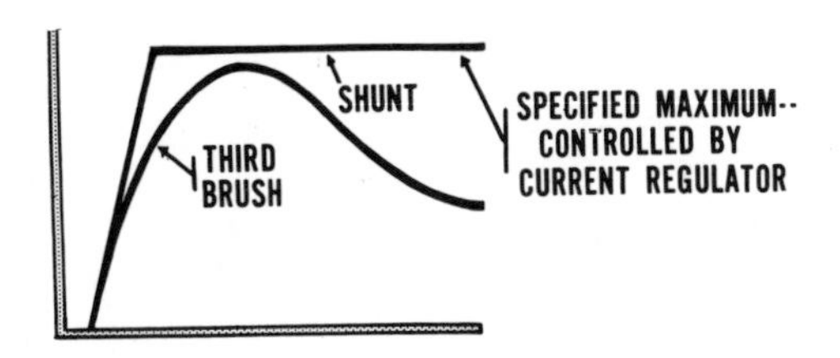

E-34. Comparison of the output of third brush and shunt wound generators.

If the low speed charging requirements were met in a conventional shunt type generator, then at high speeds, the charging current would be excessive, as the generated voltage is proportional to the product of the speed and the field strength. Therefore, as the speed of rotation increases, some means must be provided to reduce the field strength in order that the product of the speed and field strength remains constant, if the generator voltage is to be maintained within desirable limits.

One method of securing that condition is the third brush generator previously described. But as that is unsatisfactory for large outputs, external current and voltage regulators were developed for use with two brush shunt type generators.

There are two major types of internal circuits used on generators, these are shown in Fig. E-35 and Fig. E-36. These connections are largely dependent on the type of regulator used.

To understand the difference between the generators shown in Fig. E-35 and Fig. E-36, it is first necessary to explain briefly the operation of the regulator. This consists basically of spring loaded contact points and a resistance. The contact points are opened magnetically by means of a winding. When the points are open, the resistance is automatically connected in the field circuit, thereby reducing the amount of current flowing in that circuit. This in turn reduces the strength of the magnetic field and lowers the output of the generator. When the points are closed, the resistance is shorted out of the circuit so that the field current is increased and the generator output rises.

In the generator system shown in Fig. E-35, the regulator resistance is inserted between the field and the ground when the regular points are open. This system is called the "standard duty." In the heavy duty system shown in Fig. E-36, the regulator inserts resistance between the insulated side of the circuit and the field coil.

The terms "standard duty" and "heavy duty" are arbitrary terms and have no relation to the output of the units. Both types are made in both low and high output sizes. However, because of the difference in connecting the regulator in the field circuit, the regulators are not interchangeable.

Regardless of the system polarity or battery ground, it is necessary to trace all regulator circuits in one way. Circuits should always be traced by starting from the generator armature which is the source of supply. In the standard duty circuit, Fig. E-35, the field is traced from the insulated commutator brush, through the field coils, through the regulator to the

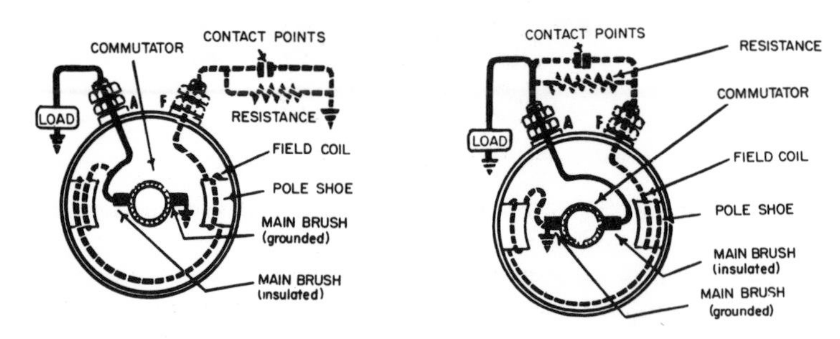

E-35. Standard duty type circuit of shunt generator. Note that the field coil is connected to the insulated commutator brush.

E-36. Heavy duty type circuit of shunt generator. Note that the field coil is connected to the grounded commutator brush.

ground and back to the grounded brush. In the heavy duty circuit, Fig. E-36, the field starts with the insulated commutator brush, then passes through the regulator, returns to the generator field terminal, passes through the field coils to the grounded commutator brush.

In practice the type of circuit is easily determined by inspecting the connections at the brushes and the field. If the generator field coil lead is connected to the insulated commutator brush, then the generator is of the standard duty type. If the generator field coil is connected to the grounded commutator brush, or to the frame of the generator, then the unit is of the heavy duty type.

INTERPOLE AND BUCKING FIELD GENERATORS

As previously pointed out, the generation of voltage and current is dependent on the number of lines of magnetic force, the number of coils or conductors in the armature and the speed of the armature. It was also pointed out that the magnetic field made by the field coils and the field set up by the armature, react on each other, strengthening the field at some points and weakening it at others. Furthermore, as the current through the armature and fields increase, there is a corresponding increase in the strength of the magnetic field and also greater distortion of the field.

One method of explaining this distortion of the normal magnetic field is to consider the armature conductors as turns of a coil. All of the conductors

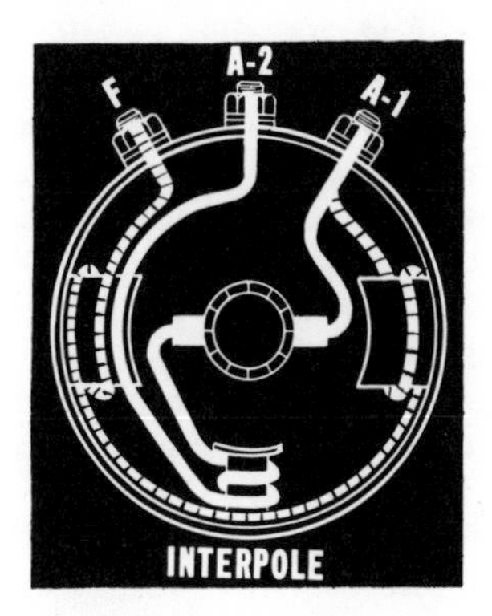

E-37. Diagram of generator with interpole.

are connected in series through the commutator and brushes and therefore, the generated current flows through all the turns.

The greatest voltage is generated in the conductors at the center of the poles, so that if the direction of current flow is checked by the commutator at that point, a magnetic field is created which is at right angles to the regular field. The combined magnetic fields of the armature and the field coils shifts in the direction of rotation and causes the current to be generated at the neutral commutating point.

If the coil being commutated is cutting lines of force arcing will occur at the commutator brushes which shortens brush and commutator life.

One method of neutralizing the magnetic effect of the armature coils is to provide an interpole, Fig. E-37. This is a small pole shoe, mounted between the regular field coils and provided with a winding of heavy bar copper. The heavy winding is required as all the current passes through the winding. The winding is made in a direction so that the magnetic field will be in opposition to that created by the armature. Since the current in the interpole is always equal to that in the armature, the right amount of correction is always provided.

On interpole generators, the commutator brushes are placed at the neutral position rather than in an advanced position as is the case with a

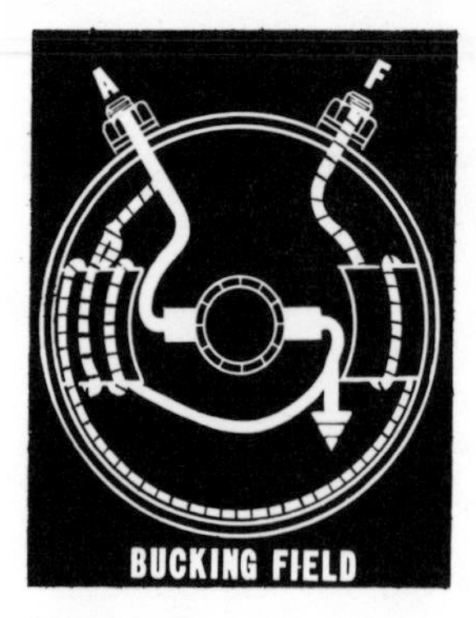

E-38. Note the additional winding on the field coil (left) which produces a bucking field.

simple shunt generator. And as the result of the accurate control of armature reaction, there is no brush arcing, and brush life is much greater than that of similar generators without an interpole.

Another method of controlling the magnetic field is by what is known as a bucking field, Fig. E-38. This, as the name implies, is an additional field winding which sets up a field in opposition to, or bucking, the normal field. Such a construction is of advantage in generators which are operated through a large range of speeds.

With a conventional generator, the voltage will continue to increase as the speed increases. On the bucking field generator a shunt coil is wound on one field coil and is connected directly across the brushes of the armature. As this winding is in the reverse direction to the normal field winding it has an opposing magnetic effect. At low speeds, when the normal field is strong, the opposing effect is small. But at higher speeds, when the current in the regular field circuit is reduced by the voltage regulator, the opposing effect is greater than the residual magnetic field. Thus the current flow through the field coils can be controlled by the regulator and a normal voltage is maintained.

E-39. Turning down the commutator of an armature on a lathe.

Some generators may use both interpole and a bucking field as a means of controlling voltage.

GENERATOR SERVICING, TESTING

To obtain maximum life from a generator it is important that regular inspection and maintenance procedure be followed. Periodic lubrication, where required; inspection of brushes and commutator and checking of brush spring tensions are essential. In addition, it is important that electrical connections be checked.

The first step in the generator inspection is to make sure that all the electrical connections are tight and making good electrical contact. Also

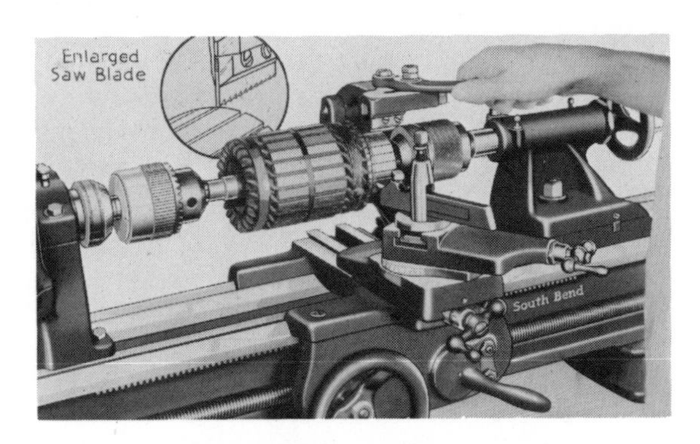

E-40. Undercutting the mica on a commutator with a special attachment on a South Bend lathe.

make sure that the drive pulley is tight on the shaft and the mounting bolts are tight. The generator drive belt should be checked to make sure that it is in good condition and is adjusted to the proper tension.

Remove the cover band if the generator is so equipped and inspect the commutator, brushes and electrical connections. If the commutator is dirty or rough, it may be sanded with No. 00 sandpaper. Emery cloth should never be used on a commutator. To sand a commutator, wrap the end of a flat piece of soft wood with a strip of No. 00 sandpaper, and with the generator in operation hold the sandpaper against the commutator. Move the sandpaper back and forth so that the entire area of the commutator is sanded.

If the commutator is rough and pitted, the generator should be disassembled, and the commutator turned down on a lathe, Fig. E-39. In addition the mica, Fig. E-40, should be under cut so that it is 1/32 in. below the surface of the commutator bars.

After inspecting and sanding the commutator, the interior of the generator should be blown clean with compressed air. If the brushes are worn down to one-half their original length they should be replaced. The amount of wear can be determined by comparison with a new brush. Make sure that the new brushes are free in the brush holders. New brushes should be sanded so that they conform to the curvature of the armature. This is accomplished by placing a strip of No. 00 sandpaper between the armature and the brush. Then with light pressure on the brush the sandpaper is withdrawn.

The tension of the brush spring is important, for if the tension is too great, rapid brush and commutator wear will result. If the brush spring tension is too weak, arcing at the brushes will result, which in turn causes rapid brush and commutator wear. A generator that has been operated at excessive loads will overheat and in extreme cases the temperature may be sufficient to cause the brush springs to lose their strength. Such a condition will usually be revealed by a burned or blue appearance of the spring. Such springs should be replaced.

Inspect the inner surface of the generator cover band for tiny globules of solder. If any solder is found it is an indication that the generator was producing excessive current and the solder used in connecting the armature wires to the commutator bars has melted. In such cases, the armature should be replaced or the connections resoldered, Fig. E-41.

E-41. Soldering armature coils to commutator risers.

GENERATOR RELAYS

GENERATOR CUT-OUT RELAY

In order to prevent the battery from discharging through the generator when the engine is stopped, a cut-out relay, Fig. E-42, is placed in the circuit. This relay closes the circuit between the generator and the battery, when the generator speed is high enough to develop sufficient voltage to charge the battery. It also opens the circuit when the generator speed is too low to develop charging voltage.

As shown in Fig. E-43, the cut-out relay is provided with two windings assembled on a single core. One winding consists of a few turns of heavy wire which is in series with the charging circuit, while the other winding is a shunt winding of many turns of fine wire which is shunted across the generator.

The windings and core of the cut-out relay are assembled in a frame and a flat steel armature with a contact point is attached to the frame by a

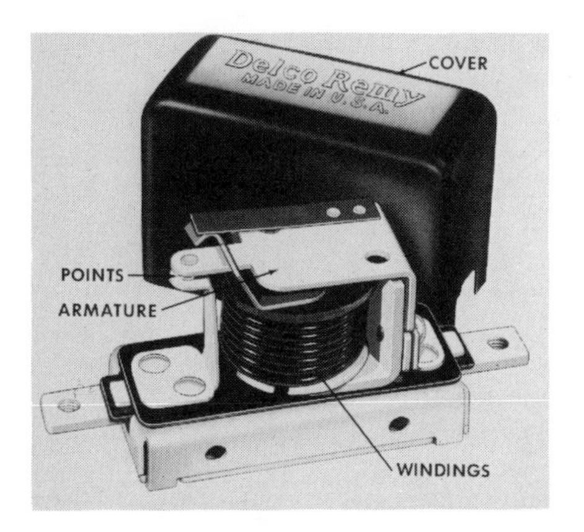

E-42. Typical cut-out relay.

flexible hinge. When the generator is not turning fast enough to develop sufficient charging voltage, the armature contact point is held away from the stationary point by the tension of a flat spring.

When the generator builds up sufficient voltage to charge the battery, the

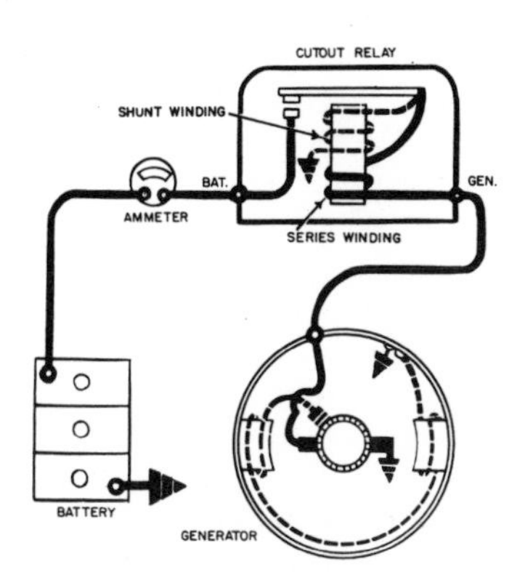

E-43. Windings and connections of cut-out relay.

current flowing through the windings of the cut-out relay will produce sufficient magnetism to pull the armature toward the relay core. This will close the relay contact points, completing the circuit between the battery and the generator.

The current passes through the series winding in the proper direction to add to the magnetism which holds the armature down. When the generator

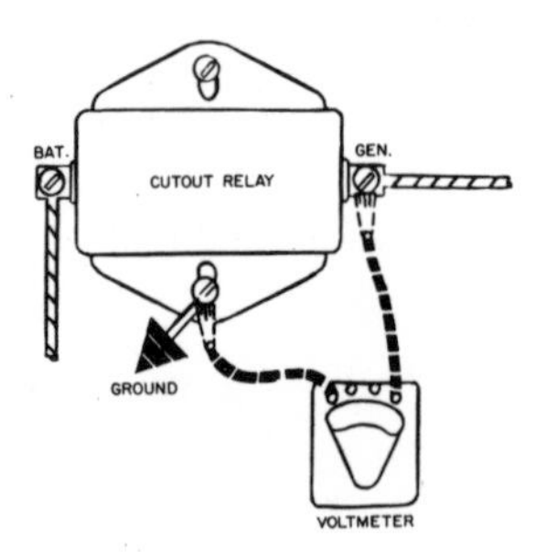

E-44. Connections for checking voltage at which cut-out relay points close.

speed drops, current will flow from the battery to the generator. This reverse flow of current through the series winding causes a change in the magnetic field. However, the magnetic field of the shunt winding remains the same with the result that the magnetic field is weakened and the flat spring pulls the armature away from the core and the contact points are opened. This opens the circuit between the generator and the battery.

CUT-OUT RELAY ADJUSTMENT

The cut-out relay requires three checks and adjustments. These are air gap, point opening and voltage required to close the contacts. When adjusting the air gap and the point opening it is necessary to disconnect the battery.

The air gap is the space between the armature and the core and is measured when the armature is held down so that the contact points are closed. To adjust, loosen the adjusting screws and raise or lower the armature until the desired gap is obtained. Be sure that the points are in alignment and that the adjusting screws are tightened when the adjustment is completed.

The point opening or gap is adjusted by bending the upper armature stop.

A voltmeter is needed to check the voltage at which the points of the cut-out relay close. The voltmeter is connected from the "Gen" terminal of the relay, Fig. E-44, to the relay base or gound. When making the test the generator speed is increased slowly until sufficient voltage is produced to close the relay contacts. To adjust the closing voltage, bend the armature spring post, bending it up to increase the closing voltage and down to lower the closing voltage. After each adjustment, the generator should be stopped and then its speed increased slowly to check the closing voltage.

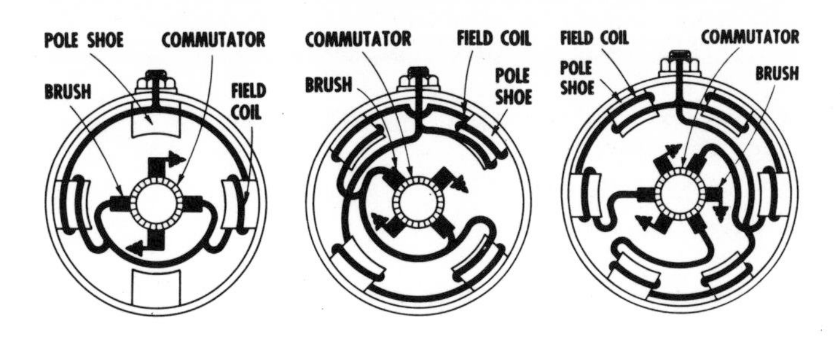

E-45. Schematic diagrams of various types of starting motors. Left: two-pole, four-brush series wound motor. Center: four-pole, four-brush series wound motor. Right: six-pole, six-brush series wound motor.

The manufacturer's specifications should be followed closely when making any of these adjustments.

STARTING MOTORS

All electric cranking motors in current use are much the same in design and consist essentially of the drive mechanism, the frame, armature, brushes and field winding. The armature is supported on bearings which in most cases are of the sleeve type. The number of field poles and brushes is varied in accordance with the power requirements, Fig. E-45.

The cranking motor or starter is a special type electric motor designed to operate under a heavy overload and, for its size, produces great power. This, however, it can do for a short time only, for in order to produce high

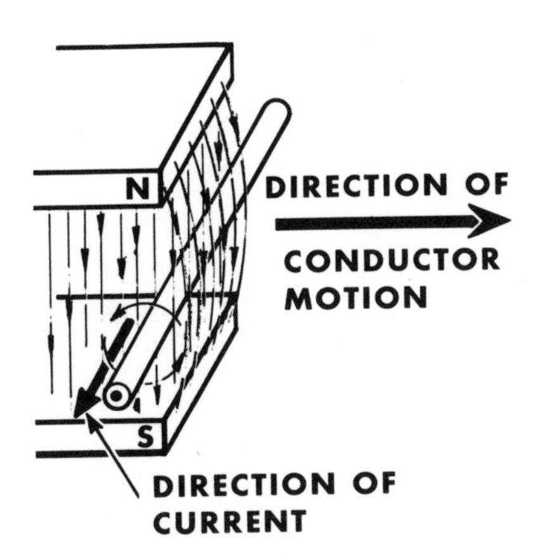

E-46. Voltage is induced in a conductor moved through a magnetic field. Magnetic lines of force are shown in dotted line.

power, large current (200-300 amp.) is used. High current creates considerable heat, and if continued for any length of time will cause considerable damage. For that reason a starting motor should not be used for more than 30 seconds at a time and at intervals of about two minutes to permit the heat to escape. This will prolong the life of both the starting motor and the battery.

STARTING MOTOR OPERATION

The principle of operation of a starting motor is based on the fact that magnetic fields tend to attract each other and magnetic fields of the same polarity will repel each other. In Fig. E-46 is shown a sketch of a magnetic field in which a single conductor is placed. With current flowing through the conductor in the direction shown by the arrow, a magnetic field will surround the conductor and the direction of the magnetic field is shown by the circular arrow. The interaction of the two fields of magnetic force will tend to move the conductor as illustrated.

The reason for this is that the magnetic field set up by the current in the conductor opposes the magnetic field on the right side of the conductor,

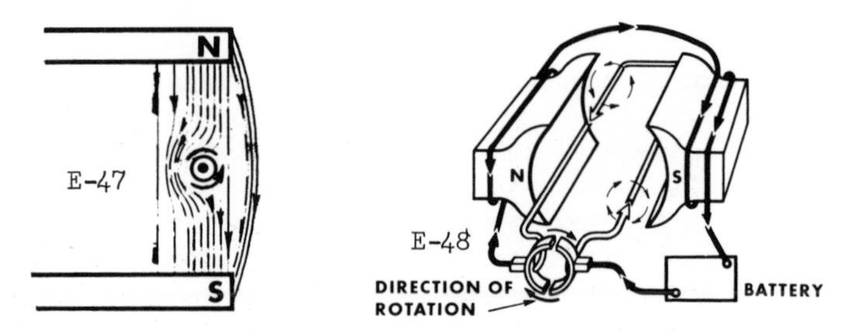

E-47. Distortion of magnetic field ahead of conductor moved through field which is productive of voltage. Magnetic field is in dotted line.

E-48. Simple electric motor. Magnetic field surrounding conductors in armature is shown in dotted line.

but aids or strengthens the field on the left side of the conductor. The magnetic lines of force are, therefore, distorted as shown in Fig. E-47 and a force is exerted toward the right on the conductor.

This tendency of the conductor to move is changed to rotary motion by placing the conductor on an armature that is free to rotate. This is illustrated in Fig. E-48. The armature or rotating part is provided with two semi-circular commutator bars to which are connected the ends of the conductor. The magnetic field in which the conductor rotates is strengthened by passing current through the windings (field windings) which surround the poles. Current is supplied by the battery and flows through the armature windings and the field coils. The current flowing through the armature winding causes circular magnetic fields to surround the conductors. In the left-hand side of the winding, Fig. E-48, the current is flowing toward the reader while the current in the right-hand side of the winding is flowing away from the reader. This causes the conductor to rotate in a clockwise direction.

In an actual motor the armature is wound with many turns of wire. All starting motors are of the series-wound type. That is, the armature and field coils are in series. Such motors provide maximum torque and will start under full load. Shunt-wound motors have low starting torque and are used where constant speed is desired.

While all starting motors are of the series-wound type, some have two field poles, while others have four or six field poles as shown in Fig. E-45.

STARTER SERVICE

To inspect the starting motor, the cover band should be removed and the condition of the commutator and brushes noted. If the commutator is dirty it should be cleaned with a strip of No. 00 sandpaper, which is held against the commutator while the armature is rotating. To prevent the motor from overheating, it should not be operated for more than 30 seconds at a time. If the commutator is rough, pitted, or out-of-round, or if the

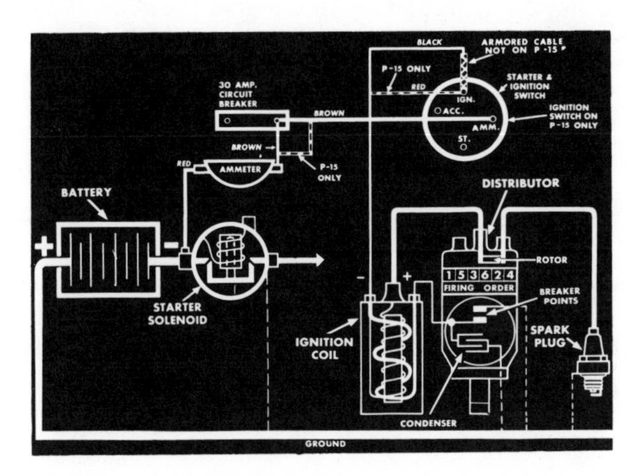

E-49. Wiring diagram of typical battery ignition system.

mica is high, the starting motor should be disassembled and the commutator reconditioned in a lathe. Mica on starting motor commutators should be undercut 1/32 in. If there are spots of solder on the interior surface of the cover band, it indicates that the motor has overheated due to excessively long periods of cranking. This may cause open circuits at the commutator riser bars and consequent failure. Each time an open-circuited bar passes under a brush, severe arcing will occur so that the commutator bar will be badly pitted.

Brushes should make good clean contact with the commutator and should have the specified spring tension. Brushes should also have free movement in the brush holders and if worn more than one-half their length, they should be replaced.

IGNITION

THEORY OF OPERATION

The ignition system on an internal combustion engine provides the spark which ignites the combustible mixture in the combustion chamber. There are two major types of ignition systems: the battery system, and the magneto.

BATTERY IGNITION SYSTEMS

The ignition system operating from a battery, consists of the battery, ignition coil, distributor, condenser, ignition switch, spark plugs, and the necessary low and high tension wiring. A wiring diagram of a typical ignition system is illustrated in Fig. E-49.

The purpose of the ignition coil, Fig. E-50, is transforming or stepping up the 6 or 12 volts from the battery to the high tension voltage of approximately 20,000 volts required to jump the spark plug gap located in the combustion chamber.

E-50. Ignition coil.

The ignition distributor has several functions. It opens and closes the primary ignition circuit, it distributes the high tension current to the respective cylinders of the engine and also has a mechanism which controls the point at which the breaker points open, thereby advancing or retarding the spark in accordance with engine requirements.

The purpose of the ignition condenser, Fig. E-51, is to reduce arcing at the breaker points and thereby prolong their life.

The spark plug, Fig. E-52, provides the gap in the combustion chamber across which the high tension electrical spark jumps to ignite the combustible charge.

The purpose of the ignition switch is to connect and disconnect the ignition system from the battery so that the engine can be started and stopped as desired.

When the ignition switch is closed, Fig. E-49, and the ignition distributor contacts also closed, current will flow from the battery, through the primary of the ignition coil, the distributor contact (breaker) points to the ground connection and back to the battery. The current flowing through the primary winding of the ignition coil produces a magnetic field in the coil. When the distributor contact points open, the magnetic field collapses and the movement of the magnetic field induces current in the secondary

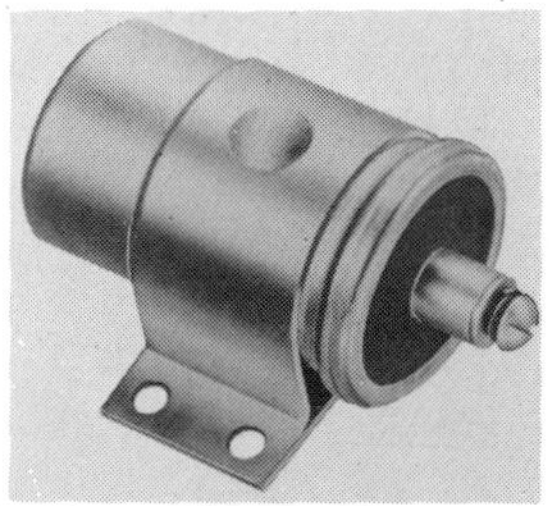

E-51. Ignition condenser with mounting bracket.

winding of the coil. As there are many more turns of wire in the secondary than there are in the primary, the voltage is increased up to 20,000 volts. The distributor then directs this high voltage to the proper spark plug where it jumps the gap. The heat of this spark ignites the fuel in the combustion chamber.

IGNITION COILS

The ignition coil, Fig. E.50, is a pulse transformer composed of a primary and a secondary winding and core of soft iron. The primary

E-52. Spark plug of the double electrode type.

winding is made up of approximately 200 turns of relatively heavy wire and the secondary winding may have as many as 22,000 turns of fine wire,

Fig. E-53. The usual construction is to have the secondary winding wound around the soft iron core and the primary winding surround the secondary. The purpose of the core is to concentrate the magnetic field. This assembly is usually placed in a steel case with a cap of molded insulating materials which carries the terminals. Many coils have their windings immersed in oil. This is done to improve insulation and reduce the effects of moisture. In addition such coils can better withstand corona effects and heat.

When the ignition switch, Fig. E-49, is closed and the distributor contact points are closed, the current flows through the primary winding of the ignition coil. The current produces a magnetic field around the coil windings. However, this does not occur instantly as it takes time for the current and consequently the magnetic field to reach its maximum. The value is determined by either the resistance of the coil winding or the length of time the distributor contacts are closed. In general, the current does not reach the maximum as the contacts remain closed for such a short time, particularly at higher engine speeds.

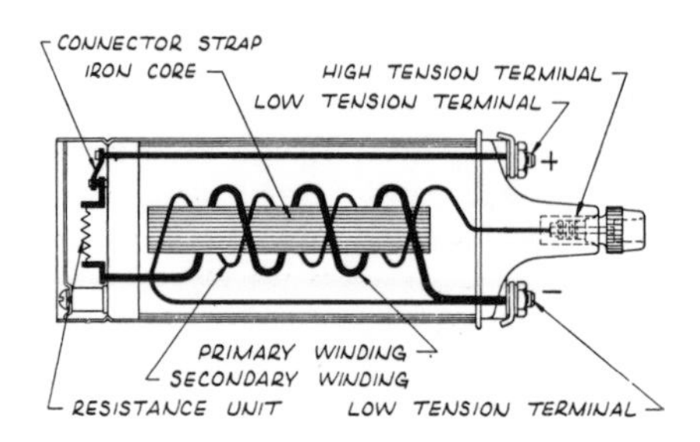

E-53. *Details of ignition coil, showing the primary and secondary windings and terminals.*

When the breaker points begin to open, the primary current will tend to continue flowing. This is a natural condition in a winding which is increased by means of the iron core. Without an ignition condenser, the induced voltage causing this flow of current would establish an arc across the contact points and the magnetic energy would be consumed in this arc. As a result the contact points would be burned and normal ignition would be impossible. The condenser prevents this arc by providing a place for the current to flow, thus quickly checking the flow of current. As a result of this action, the magnetic field produced and sustained by the current flow will quickly collapse. It is this rapid collapse of the magnetic field, cutting the windings of the coil, which induces the high voltage in both the primary and secondary windings.

IGNITION CONDENSERS

Condensers are made of alternate sheets of metal foil and insulation. The sheets of foil are of slightly smaller area than the insulating sheets

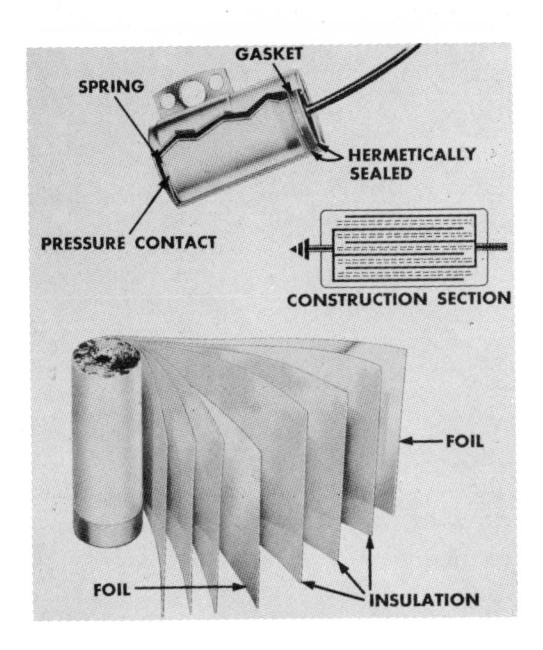

E-54. Construction details of Delco-Remy ignition condenser.

and, as shown in Fig. E.54, alternate sheets of foil are connected on the terminal of the condenser, while the remaining sheets of foil are connected together to provide the other terminal. The condenser is connected directly across the distributor contact points.

In order to eliminate the possibility of moisture entering the condenser, they are hermatically sealed. Any moisture present will greatly reduce the insulating qualities of the sheets of paper separating the sheets of foil. Tests have shown that really dry insulation in a condenser will have as much as 1,000 times the life as insulation that is only partly dried.

The capacity of a condenser is measured in microfarads and is proportional to the total area of the foil and inversely proportional to the thickness of the insulating sheets which are called the dielectric. In other words, the thinner the dielectric the greater the capacity of condenser. Ignition condensers usually vary in capacity from .15 to .25 microfarad.

Loosened or corroded connections will increase the series resistance of a condenser which will cause it to be slow in taking a charge. This in turn causes high voltage and arcing at the distributor contact points. In general a resistance up to .5 ohm does not seriously affect ignition performance.

IGNITION DISTRIBUTORS

The ignition distributor is designed to make and break the primary ignition circuit and also to distribute the high tension current to the proper spark plug at the correct time. It is driven at one-half crankshaft speed on four cycle engines and is usually driven by the camshaft, though in some cases an accessory shaft is used. On a two cycle engine the distributor shaft would revolve at the same speed as the crankshaft.

Detailed construction of the ignition distributor varies considerably with different manufacturers. Basically it consists of a housing into which the distributor shaft and weight base assembly are fitted with suitable bearings. In most cases, these bearings are of the bronze bushing type, though heavy duty distributors frequently employ ball bearings. In low-priced distributors, the shaft will turn directly in the cast iron housing of the distributor.

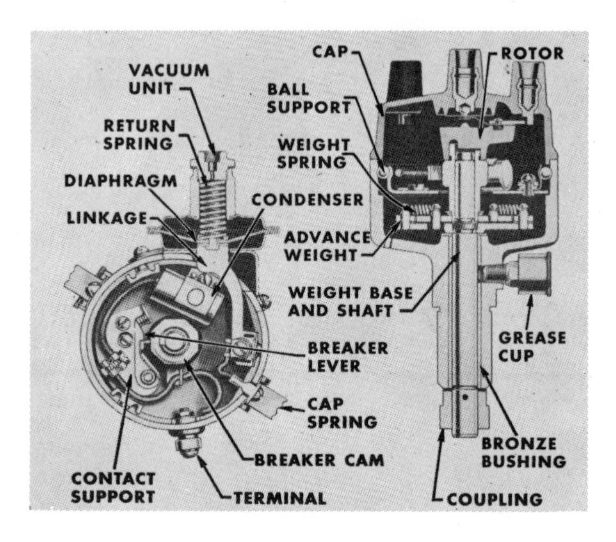

E-55. Details of typical Delco-Remy distributor.

A Delco-Remy design is shown in Fig. E-55. In this, centrifugal spark advance weights are pivoted on studs in the weight base and are free to move against calibrated weight springs which connect them to the advance cam and breaker cam assembly. The advance cam and breaker cam assembly is a slip fit on top of the distributor shaft and rotates with the shaft as it is actuated by the advance weights. Lateral movement of the weights advances the cam assembly in relation to the shaft as speed is increased. The breaker plate carries the breaker lever, contact support and the condenser. (In many designs the condenser is mounted externally.)

When the breaker cam is rotated by the centrifugal advance mechanism, each cam lobe passes under the breaker lever rubbing block. This causes the breaker points to separate. As these are connected in series with the primary winding of the ignition coil, current will pass through that circuit when the points are closed. When the points open the magnetic field collapses and a high tension voltage is induced in the secondary winding of the ignition coil.

The usual design is to provide one lobe on the breaker cam for each cylinder of the engine. As a result, every revolution of the breaker cam will produce one spark for each cylinder of the engine.

After the high tension surge is produced in the ignition coil by the opening of the breaker points, the current passes from the coil to the center terminal of the distributor cap which is mounted on top of the distributor housing. From that point it passes down to the rotor which is mounted on top of the breaker cam and revolves with it. The current passes along the rotor, and jumps the minute gap to the outer cap electrode under which the rotor is positioned at that instant. This outer cap electrode is in turn connected by high tension wiring to the spark plug. As the rotor rotates, it distributes current to each of the cap terminals in turn.

In order to obtain efficient operation of an internal combusion engine, throughout the range of speed and operating conditions, it is essential that the spark occur at the correct instant. That instant will vary according to engine load and speed. Mechanism is, therefore, provided to automatically

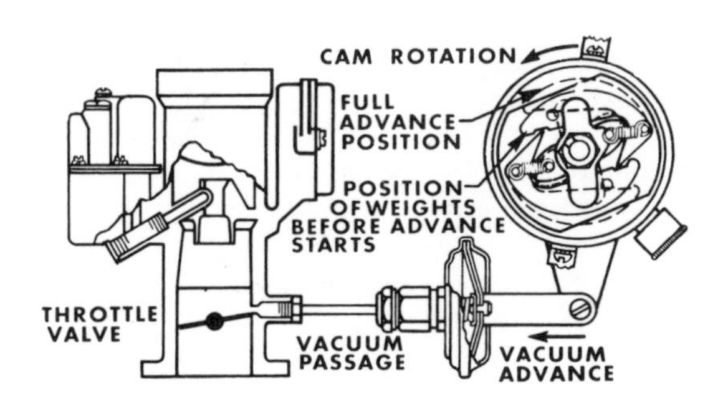

E-56. Diagram showing details of centrifugal and vacuum advance mechanism. (Delco-Remy)

advance and retard the spark as conditions require. Either or both of two methods are provided: these are centrifugal force and engine vacuum.

When the engine is idling the spark is usually timed to occur just before the piston reaches the top of the compression stroke. Under idling conditions or, when driving at a sustained speed under part throttle conditions, cylinders take in only part of the full charge. As a result, compression pressures are relatively low, and as a consequence combustion is slow and must be started earlier. At higher engine speeds, there is a shorter interval of time for the mixture to ignite and expand. Therefore, in order to obtain the maximum amount of power at high speeds, it is necessary to have the spark occur slightly earlier in the engine cycle. This is accomplished by means of the centrifugal advance mechanism, Figs. E-55 and E-56, which is assembled on the distributor housing immediately below the plate that carries the ignition breaker arm. The mechanism consists of two weights, which the centrifugal force developed by the rotating shaft tends to throw outward against the tension of springs. The faster the distributor shaft rotates, the greater the centrifugal force, and the greater the movement of the advance weights. The movement of the weights is transmitted to the breaker cam so that the cam is rotated to an advanced position in respect to the distributor drive shaft. In other designs, the cam is integral with the distributor shaft, and the movement of the centrifugal weights will rotate the breaker plate around the axis of the distributor shaft.

The amount of centrifugal advance required varies considerably for each make and model of engine and is determined experimentally on a dynamometer. Under part throttle operation, the intake manifold vacuum is high and, therefore, a smaller amount of mixture is sucked into the engine and compression pressure is low. With lower pressures, the mixture does not burn as rapidly, and to obtain maximum efficiency under such conditions, the spark should be advanced more than that obtained by the centrifugal mechanism. This additional advance is obtained by means of the vacuum advance mechanism.

VACUUM ADVANCE

The conventional vacuum advance mechanism, Fig. E.56, utilizes the vacuum in the intake manifold to provide the additional spark advance required under part throttle operation and has a spring loaded diaphragm connected by linkage to the ignition distributor. The spring loaded side of the diaphragm is airtight and is connected by tubing to a point on the atmospheric side of the carburetor throttle, when the throttle is in the idling position. With the throttle in the idling position, there is virtually zero vacuum at the point where the vacuum spark control connection is made. However, as soon as the throttle is opened, it swings past the opening of the vacuum passage and the vacuum can then act on the diaphragm of the spark advance mechanism. This causes the diaphragm to deflect and its motion is transmitted by linkage to the distributor. In some designs, the distributor is rotated on its mounting, while in other designs the breaker plate is rotated.

The amount of movement is of course proportional to the amount of vacuum. At any particular engine speed there will be a definite amount of spark advance resulting from the operation of the centrifugal advance mechanism, plus an additional amount of advance resulting from the vacuum advance mechanism.

IGNITION DISTRIBUTOR SERVICE

In addition to proper timing of the spark, the spark inside the cylinder must be HOT and FAT if the engine is to start easily and run well.

If a battery ignition system is used, it is obvious that there must be sufficient current available from the battery. A semi-discharged battery will be unable to furnish sufficient voltage for ignition purposes. Even with a fully charged battery there may be a loss of current in the primary circuit. A weak primary current will result in a weak spark from the secondary or high tension current.

The primary circuit consists of the battery, low tension winding of the coil, breaker points in the distributor, condenser and all the wires, switches and connections required. With all these items in one circuit it is obvious that resistance from loose or dirty connections can exist at several places to choke the flow of current.

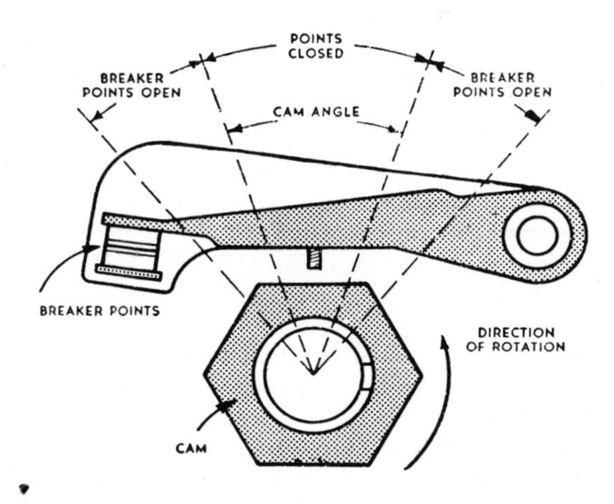

E-57. The cam angle controls the coil saturation.

Battery terminals become corroded, wires become loose in terminals, contacts wear in switches, corrosion will occur on ground wire terminals, on contact points and breaker plate. All these things reduce primary voltage. Coils and condensers sometimes burn out or become grounded. Equipment is available for testing these units.

In addition to these mechanical and electrical defects, adjustment of the contact points has a definite effect on secondary current strength. This is because the strength of the magnetic field in the coil depends on the saturation, or amount of time the current flows in the primary winding.

The current flows in the coil primary winding only while the distributor contact points are closed. This period of time is known as the contact angle, cam angle or degrees of dwell. See Fig. E-57. This cam angle also has a direct bearing on the capacity of the condenser.

When the cam angle or closed period is too long, the increased time the current flows through the points will have a tendency to cause them to burn. It also creates too much condenser effect. When the length of dwell is too short, the coil does not receive complete saturation, and there is also a tendency toward insufficient condenser effect.

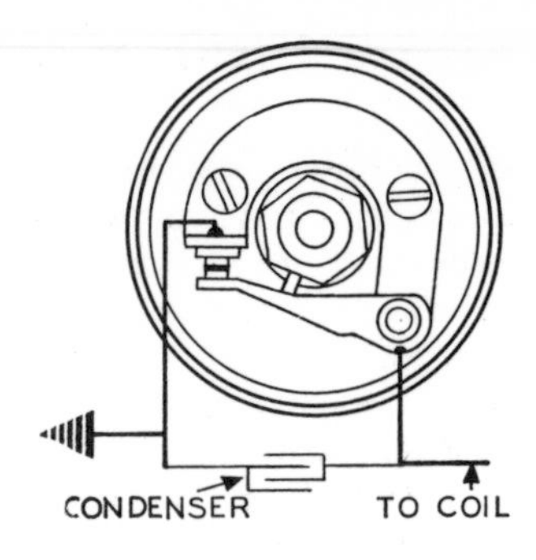

E-58. To avoid arcing between points, a condenser is connected across them.

The manufacturer recommends a definite setting of the contact point gap and this should be followed.

CONDENSERS

The distributor cam and breaker arm are designed to separate the points rapidly, provided the points are properly adjusted and the tension is correct on the breaker arm spring. Thus the current which magnetizes the coil is cut off very abruptly when the points open, and therefore the magnetic field will collapse.

This collapse of the magnetic field in the coil, which induces a high tension current in the secondary, also induces a high tension current in the primary winding. The induced current in the secondary winding may exceed 20,000 volts, while the induced current in the primary winding probably does not exceed 250 volts.

However, 250 volts is enough to cause the current to arc across the contact points when they are opened and cause them to burn. It also slows down the speed with which the magnetic field collapses and thus weakens the spark induced in the secondary winding. To avoid this arcing between the points, a condenser is connected across the points (see Fig. E-58).

The condenser thus provides a quick exit for the induced high tension current in the low tension winding and provides a storage "tank" in which to hold this induced current momentarily while the secondary discharges to the spark plug. After the spark occurs at the spark plug the condenser discharges back into the primary circuit.

It is obvious that under such carefully balanced electrical action it is important to have a condenser of correct capacity rather than just any condenser. The capacity of the condenser depends upon the area of the plates in the condenser, the spacing between the plates and the kind of insulating material between the plates.

Special condenser testers are available which will check the condenser for insulation breakdown, low insulation resistance, high series resistance and capacity. If the test indicates any defect whatever, the condenser should be replaced.

Even if the condenser functions satisfactory on test it should be of correct capacity to balance with the rest of the ignition system. Condenser capacity is measured in units known as microfarads. The larger the capacity in microfarads the more current it can store, and more time is required to charge it to capacity.

This capacity is important, and a condenser of improper capacity will be indicated by the condition of the contact points. If there is a pit or crater in the contact and a corresponding peak or hill on the other, lack of balance is indicated. This hill and crater effect is caused by the transfer of the tungsten metal from one contact to the other. The direction in which the metal transfers indicates the remedy.

For instance, if the metal transfers from the negative to the positive point, as shown in Fig. E-59, it indicates a condenser of insufficient capacity. Additional remedies for persistent cases is to shorten the con-

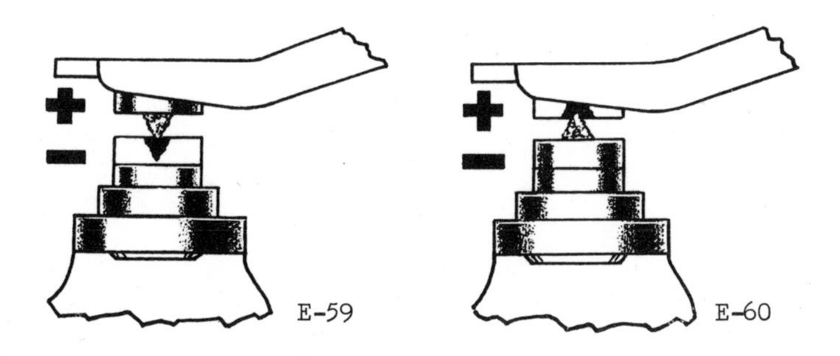

E-59. A point condition such as shown here indicates a condenser of insufficient capacity.

E-60. This point condition indicates a condenser of excessive capacity.

denser lead; separate the distributor-to-coil low and high tension wires; move these wires closer to ground; remount the coil directly on a good ground if it depends on a wire for ground.

If the material transfers from the positive to the negative contact, as shown in Fig. E-60, it indicates a condenser with excess capacity. Additional remedies are: move distributor-to-coil wires closer together; move these wires away from ground; lengthen condenser lead.

Contact points will also burn as a result of high voltage; improper adjustment; the presence of oil or other insulating matter; loose or dirty condenser ground; loose or dirty condenser lead terminal connection.

High voltage can result from improperly adjusted or inoperative voltage regulator or from an excessively advanced third brush on third brush generators without voltage regulation.

If the contact opening is too closely adjusted, the resultant cam angle is too large and the points stay closed too much of the operating time. This excess current causes heating and burning of the points.

Oil or crankcase vapor working up into the distributor will deposit an insulating film on the point surfaces and cause them to burn. This is often caused by clogged crankcase breathers which generate enough crankcase pressure to force oily vapor into the distributor. This is easily detected, as a smudgy line of soot will be deposited on the distributor breaker plate parallel with and below the contact points.

Many shops make a practice of replacing the condenser with every set of points installed. If the points show no hill and crater effect, a condenser of the same capacity as the old one is used. If the used points indicate unbalance, a condenser of greater or lesser capacity, as required, is installed iwth the new points.

If not arbitrarily replaced at the time new contacts are installed, the condenser should always be tested and replaced if any doubt exists.

CONTACT POINT ADJUSTMENT

Precise adjustment of the contact point separation is of paramount importance. This separation is measured in thousandths of an inch, of course, and the dimension is furnished by the manufacturer.

It is obviously ridiculous to attempt to adjust the contact points within a few thousandths of an inch if the distributor shaft or cup is worn several thousandths.

The clearance between the shaft and housing can be readily checked by mounting a dial gauge on the distributor cup with the dial plunger resting against the side of the shaft. If the clearance exceeds .005 in., new bushings should be fitted.

In those distributors having a centrifugal advance of the type where the cam is mounted on a stub shaft which floats on the upper end of the distributor shaft, this stub shaft should be removed before measuring the

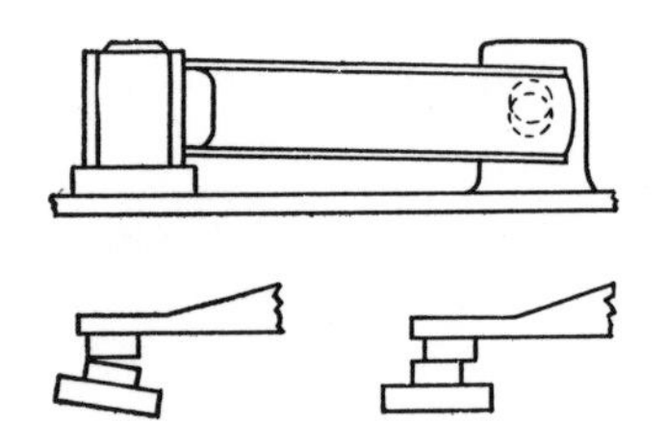

E-61. Various types of point misalignment.

clearance. There will be some clearance between the inside of the stub shaft and the outside of the distributor shaft, as this stub shaft must not bind on the distributor shaft. This normal small amount of clearance may be ignored, however, as the cam has a tendency to center itself around the shaft when in operation due to the pull of the weights.

Of course there should be no abnormal amount of looseness in the stub shaft or in the advance weights or pins. Like any other reciprocating mechanical part, they must move freely without undue looseness.

E-62. Magneto as mounted on Kohler engine. A—Stop button. B—Bearing plate. C—Pole shoes. D—Magneto coil. E—Magneto rotor. F—Condenser.

With the distributor shaft and cup in good mechanical condition, it should be possible to adjust the contacts to the correct specification and obtain the correct cam angles. In this connection, it is important to have proper alignment of the contact points. There are several different types of misalignment illustrated in Fig. E-61.

When bending the parts to obtain correct alignment between the contacts, it is desirable, when possible, to bend the bracket of the stationary contact rather than the contact arm - most particularly near the contact insert. Bending the contact arm is the easier way, but, in some cases, this may loosen the bond between the arm and contact and create a high resistance condition which is indeed difficult to diagnose.

MAGNETOS

A magneto is a self-contained device which generates and distributes electricity for igniting the combustible mixture in the combustion chamber of the internal combustion chamber. The magneto not only generates the electricity, but it also steps up the low voltage to a high tension voltage and distributes it to the various cylinders at the correct instant. It does this without the aid of a battery. Some magnetos are of the low tension type, generating a low voltage which is then stepped up to a high voltage by means of a separate coil. High tension magnetos produce voltage of sufficient value to jump the spark plug gap without any external coil.

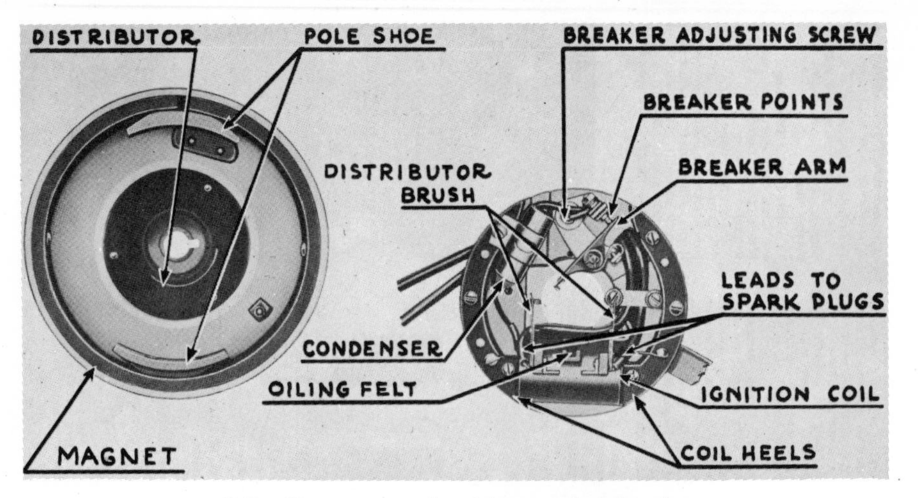

E-63. Magneto as used on Johnson outboard engine.

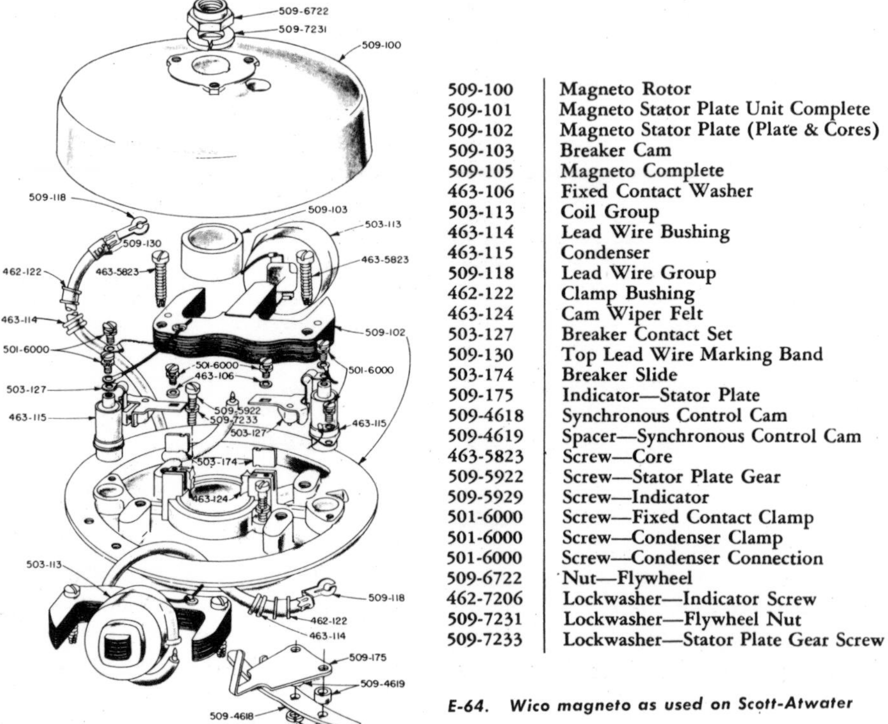

509-100	Magneto Rotor
509-101	Magneto Stator Plate Unit Complete
509-102	Magneto Stator Plate (Plate & Cores)
509-103	Breaker Cam
509-105	Magneto Complete
463-106	Fixed Contact Washer
503-113	Coil Group
463-114	Lead Wire Bushing
463-115	Condenser
509-118	Lead Wire Group
462-122	Clamp Bushing
463-124	Cam Wiper Felt
503-127	Breaker Contact Set
509-130	Top Lead Wire Marking Band
503-174	Breaker Slide
509-175	Indicator—Stator Plate
509-4618	Synchronous Control Cam
509-4619	Spacer—Synchronous Control Cam
463-5823	Screw—Core
509-5922	Screw—Stator Plate Gear
509-5929	Screw—Indicator
501-6000	Screw—Fixed Contact Clamp
501-6000	Screw—Condenser Clamp
501-6000	Screw—Condenser Connection
509-6722	Nut—Flywheel
462-7206	Lockwasher—Indicator Screw
509-7231	Lockwasher—Flywheel Nut
509-7233	Lockwasher—Stator Plate Gear Screw

E-64. Wico magneto as used on Scott-Atwater outboard engine as exploded.

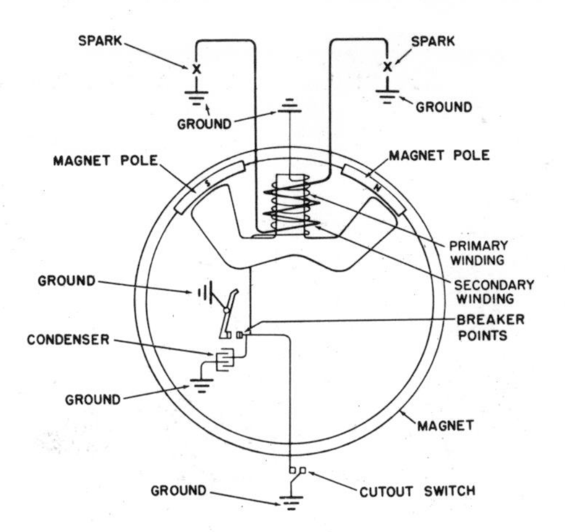

E-65. The magnets may be in the flywheel as shown here for an Evinrude outboard engine.

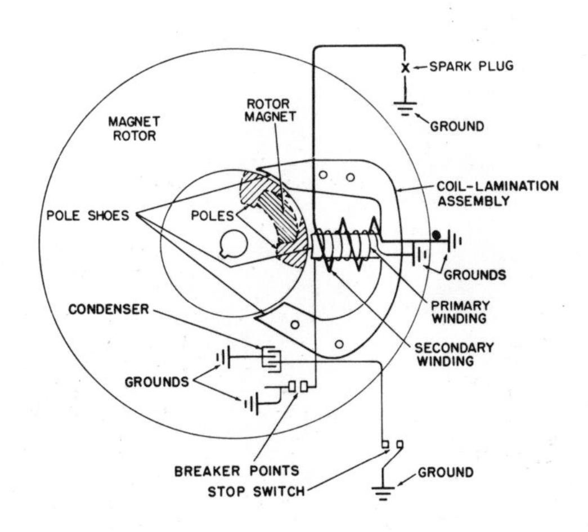

E-66. Another Evinrude has the magnets in a rotor as shown here.

MAGNETO IGNITION ADVANTAGES

Magneto ignition systems have several advantages. First of all they do not require any battery or other source of current. Secondly, the intensity of the generated voltage does not decrease with the engine speed, but increases.

Magnetos are particularly popular for internal combustion engines, where a battery is not needed for starting or lighting. See Figs. E-62 to E-66. The recent development of permanent magnets of greatly increased strength has materially improved their performance.

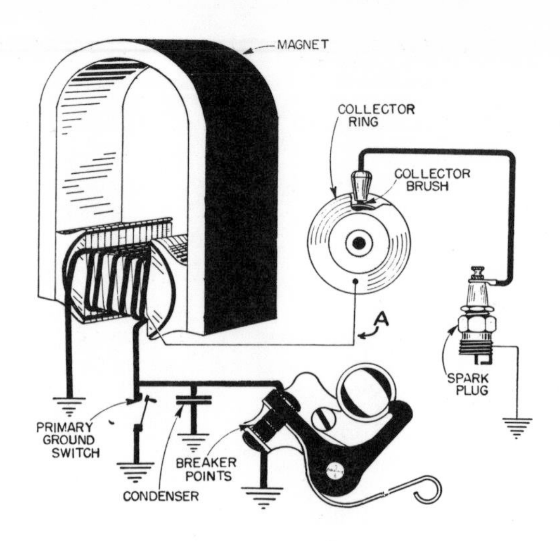

E-67. Diagram of shuttle wound high tension magneto. The lead to the high tension winding on rotor is shown at A.

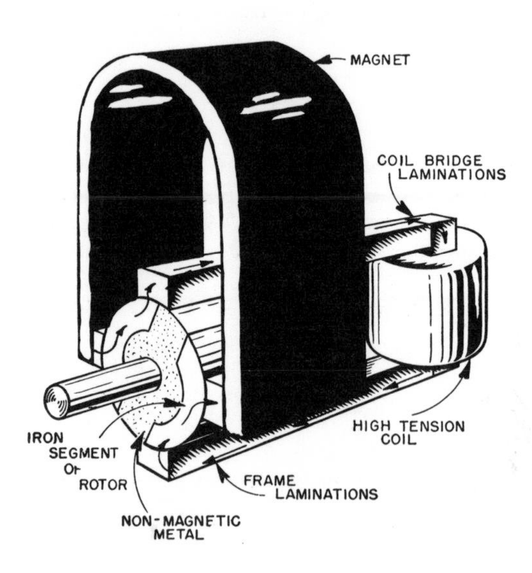

E-68. Rotary inductor type magneto.

PRINCIPLES OF OPERATION

As previously pointed out in the section devoted to the fundamentals of electricity, electricity can be generated by revolving a coil of wire in a magnetic field. In the conventional generator, the magnetic field is produced by passing some of the generated current through coils of wire (field coils) which in turn produce the magnetic field. In other words, the magnetic field is produced electrically. In the case of the magneto, the magnetic field is produced by means of permanent magnets. Until recently the magnets used in magnetos were made of high quality carbon steel. In approximately 1935, special alloy steels were developed which have greatly improved magnetic characteristics over the carbon steel formerly used. Magnets made of such special alloys are not only stronger for the same size, but also retain their magnetism for much longer periods. The alloys used on modern magnets are usually tungsten, chromium and cobalt.

TYPES OF MAGNETOS

There are two ways in which magnetos may be classified. Originally they were classified as to the type of current they produced - low tension or high tension. The low tension magneto developed a low voltage and required an external coil to step up the voltage. The high tension magneto incorporated the coil in the magneto itself.

The other method of classifying magnetos takes into consideration the portion of the magneto which is revolved. Magnetos which have the windings on an armature which is revolved in a magnetic field are known as shuttle wound magnetos, Fig. E-67. In the inductor type magneto, both the coil and magnet are mounted in stationary positions and movement of the magnetic field is obtained by breaking and re-establishing the magnetic field, Fig. E-68. The third type of magneto is known as the revolving magnet design. This has been made possible by the new magnetic steels and in this design the coil, together with a short magnetic circuit, is mounted in a stationary position and one or more magnets are revolved between the pole pieces of magnetic circuit. Some manufacturers also classify this construction as the induction type. Several types are described and illustrated in the section devoted to specific two and four cycle engines.

LOW TENSION MAGNETOS

The low tension magneto was the first type of magneto and is still used extensively on industrial engines. In this construction the permanent magnets are U-shaped, with the armature, carrying a single primary winding, revolving between the pole pieces.

The armature winding is connected to the primary winding of an ignition coil, and breaker points which revolve with the armature are timed to open the circuit at peak voltage. This interruption of the primary current produces a high tension current in the secondary winding of the coil which is carried back to the distributor rotor on the magneto where it is directed to the proper spark plug.

Breaker points on a low tension magneto can be connected either in series with the armature winding or in parallel. In the series connection, the magneto serves simply as a current source and the value of the current is relatively low, because the resistance of the primary winding of the coil is included in the circuit. However, when the breaker points are in parallel with the armature winding, a heavier current flows through the armature as the resistance of the primary winding of the coil is no longer included in the circuit. Then when the breaker points open, this heavy current surges through the primary winding of the coil with a strong inductive effect. The result is that the magnetic field of the coil is built up very rapidly.

HIGH TENSION MAGNETOS

The high tension magneto differs from the low tension magneto in that it generates high tension electricity within itself and distributes it to the various spark plugs. No external ignition coil is used, as in the case of the low tension magneto.

In the conventional high tension magneto, the armature is wound with primary and secondary windings, corresponding to the windings of an ignition coil, Fig. E-67. These windings on the armature revolve in the magnetic field set up by permanent magnets. As the coils or windings pass

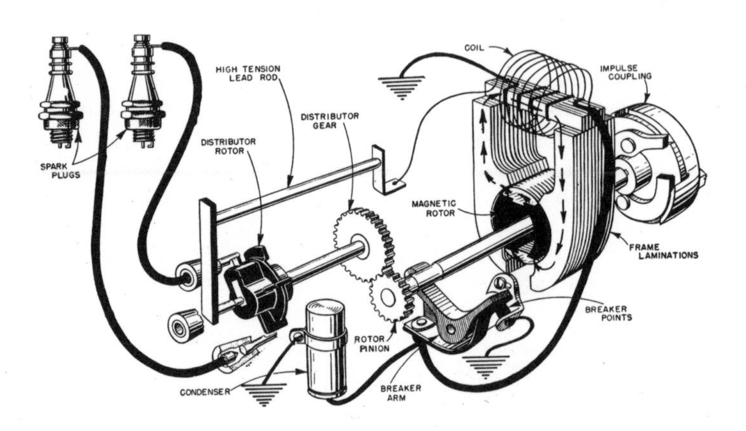

E-69. Schematic diagram of rotating magnet magneto.

through the magnetic field, current is generated and when it reaches its maximum, the breaker points (shunted across the primary winding) open. This induces a current in the secondary windings. As there are more turns of wire in the secondary than in the primary, the voltage is increased in value. The end of the secondary is connected to a collector ring. From there the high tension voltage passes to a distributor and from there to the individual spark plugs.

A variation of the original high tension magneto, in which the coil, condenser and breaker points were rotated, is to rotate a portion of the primary winding, while the remainder of the primary, together with the secondary, contact points, and condenser are stationary. The rotating portion of the primary is wound on the armature and is connected through a collector ring to the stationary primary. The primary circuit is completed through the breaker points to the ground.

High tension magnetos are provided with a safety gap which is shunted across the terminal of the high tension winding and the ground. In this, the insulation of the secondary winding is protected from excessive voltage, which would occur if a wire should become disconnected from a spark plug and there would be an incompleted circuit. A spark would then occur at the safety gap, and excess strain on the secondary insulation would be avoided.

ROTARY INDUCTOR MAGNETOS

In the rotary inductor type magneto, Fig. E-68, both the magnet and coil are stationary and current is induced in the primary winding by rotating one or both legs of the magnetic circuit. When only one leg of the magnetic circuit is broken, the magnetic flux in the coil alternates from maximum to minimum, but does not undergo complete reversal when both legs of the magentic circuit are interrupted.

ROTATING MAGNET MAGNETOS

The introduction of the more powerful permanent magnets of special alloy steel made possible the design of magentos in which the magnet was revolved. Such magnetos are known as rotating magnet magnetos and have virtually replaced the original design with stationary U-shaped magnets.

In the rotating magnet design, the coil, condenser and breaker points are stationary with the result that the design is simplified, of more sturdy construction, and moving connections are eliminated. In addition, tests and repairs are more easily made. Smaller and more compact units are also made possible with reduction in cost.

A schematic drawing of a rotating magnet magneto is shown in Fig. E-69. Rotation of the magnetic rotor produces an alternating magnetic flux or field which cuts the stationary primary winding each time it increases and decreases. As a result, alternating electric currents are induced in the primary circuit during the period the circuit is completed through the closed breaker points. As the density of the magnetic field varies, the strength of the current induced in the primary circuit also varies and reaches a maximum value each time a complete magnetic flux reversal occurs in the magnetic circuit.

The current induced in the primary winding produces a magnetic field which surrounds the secondary winding. This field reaches its maximum when the current in the primary winding reaches its maximum. At the instant of maximum current in the primary winding, the breaker points are caused to open by the action of the breaker cam. This stops the flow of current in the primary circuit and causes the collapse of the magnetic field. The collapsing lines of force then induce a current in the secondary circuit and, as the ratio of turns in the secondary is high compared to those in the primary, a high tension voltage is produced.

The self-induced voltage produced in the primary winding, resulting from the collapsing magnetic field, is absorbed by the condenser which is shunted across the breaker points. In effect this action promotes a more rapid collapse of the primary field and at the same time reduces arcing at the breaker points.

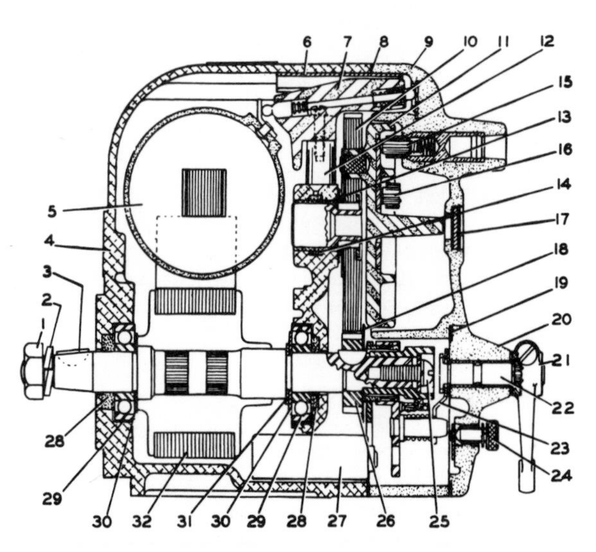

E-70. American Bosch type MJB rotating magnet magneto. (1) Nut, drive shaft. (2) Lockwasher. (3) Key. (4) Magneto housing. (5) Coil. (6) High tension conductor insulation. (7) High tension conductor. (8) Distributor plate gasket. (9) Distributor plate. (10) Distributor gear. (11) Distributor rotor. (12) Distributor gear bracket. (13) Distributor gear shaft bearing. (14) Bearing wick. (15) Distributor plate brush. (16) Distributor plate brush. (17) Observation window. (18) Indicating disc. (19) End cap gasket. (20) End cap. (21) Timing lever. (22) Timing lever shaft. (23) Timing lever bracket. (24) Short circuit screw. (25) Cam fastening screw. (26) Magnet rotor gear. (27) Condenser. (28) Felt washers. (29) Ball bearings. (30) Grease retaining washers. (31) Equalizing washer. (32) Magnet rotor.

An example of the rotating magnet magneto is American Bosch type MJB magneto, Fig. E-70. In this magneto the coil windings (5), condenser (27), and interrupter are stationary, while the magnets (32) are rotated. The screened ventilators on each side of the housing (4) and the fan action of the magnet rotor (32) insure constant change of air throughout the magneto. The ball bearings (29) supporting the magnet shaft are packed in high temperature grease and require no further attention for at least a year of normal operation. The distributor bushing (14) is of the oil-less composition type.

The type PA4, Bendix Scintilla magnet, shown in Fig. E-71, is of the rotating magnet type. High tension current is produced in the secondary winding as previously described. One end of the primary winding (12) is grounded to the magneto housing, while the other end is connected to the insulated contact point. When the contact points (20) are closed, the primary circuit is completed, permitting current to flow in the primary winding.

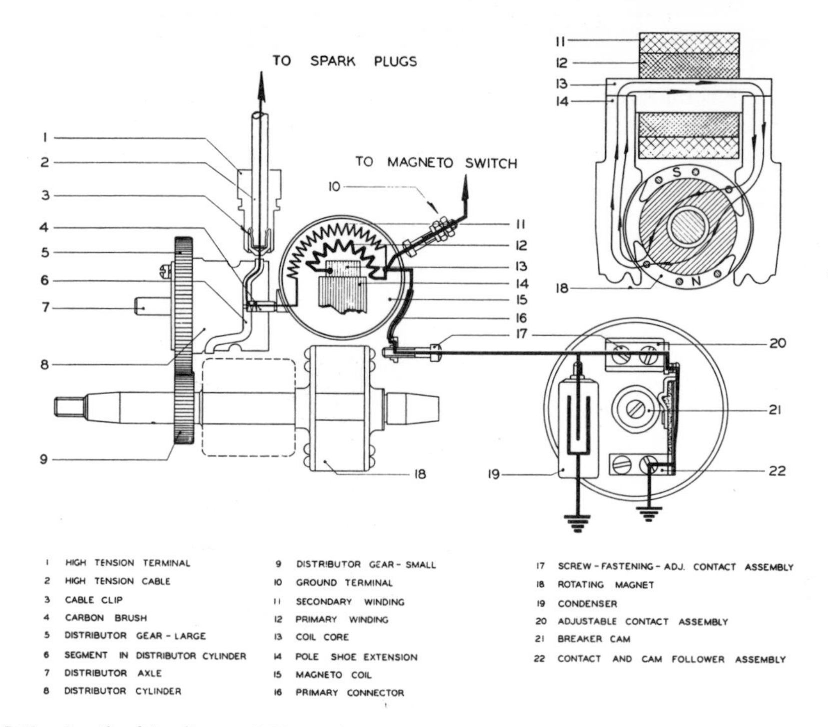

E-71. Details of Bendix type PA4, rotating magnet magneto, showing electric and magnetic circuits.

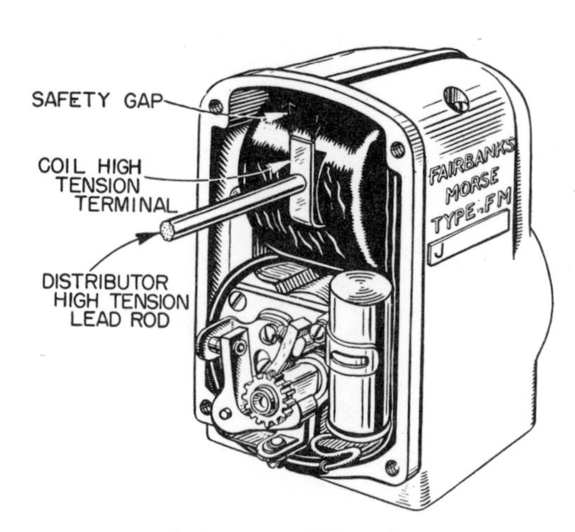

E-72. Fairbanks Morse type FM, rotating magnet magneto.

One end of the secondary winding (11) is connected to the insulated end of the primary winding, while the other end terminates at the high tension insert in the coil. High tension current in the secondary winding is conducted to the center of the distributor cylinder (6) by means of the carbon brush (4). From there it is conducted to the segments of the distributor cylinder and then to the electrodes of the high tension cable terminals (1). High tension cables then carry it to the individual spark plugs.

The ground terminal (10) on the type PA4 Bendix Scintilla magneto is electrically connected to the ignition switch. When the switch is in the "OFF" position, this wire provides a direct path to ground for the primary

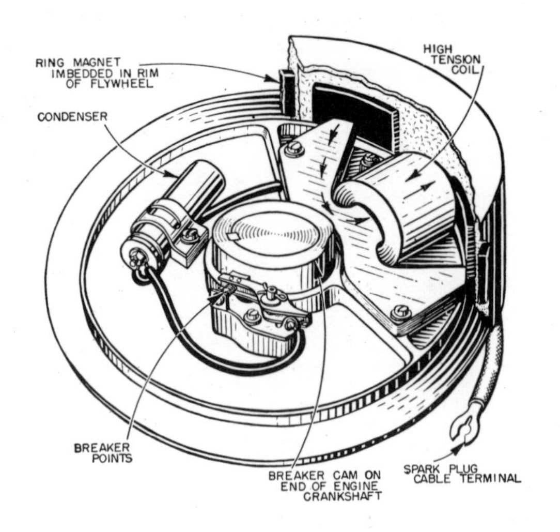

E-73. Flywheel type magneto.

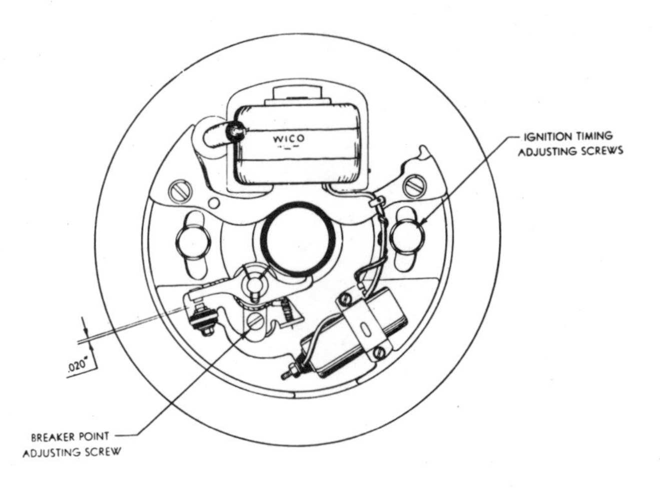

E-74. WICO magneto as used on Gladden series 40 engines.

current, preventing interruption of the current when the points open. As a result, high voltage will not be induced in the secondary circuit.

A Fairbanks Morse type FM magneto with cover removed is shown in Fig. E-72. Note gear for rotating magnet and breaker cam. These are built in a variety of designs for engines of various sizes and compression ratios.

FLYWHEEL MAGNETOS

Flywheel magnetos, Fig. E-73, are of the revolving magnet type and are used extensively for ignition on small internal combustion engines used on lawn mowers, garden tractors, outboard motors, etc. For the most part,

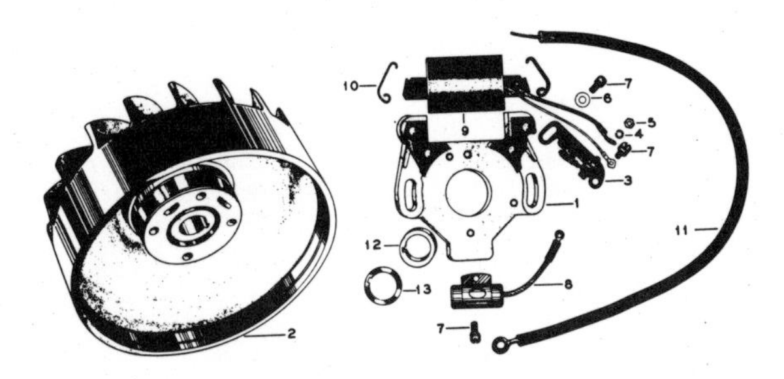

E-75. Bendix-Scintilla type KI-503 flywheel magneto for use on single cylinder engines. (1) Magneto mounting flange. (2) Flywheel and magnet assembly. (3) Breaker point assembly. (4) Lock washer. (5) Nut. (6) Washer. (7) Screw and lock washer. (8) Condenser. (9) Ignition coil. (10) Coil clamp. (11) High tension lead. (12) Breaker cam. (13) Washer.

flywheel magnetos are used on single cylinder engines, but are also used occasionally on two and four cylinder engines.

The theory of operation is similar to that of the rotary magneto. In the typical flywheel magneto the magnet is mounted on the outer rim of the flywheel which revolves around the stationary ignition coil, condenser and breaker point assembly. As the ends of the magnet pass by the pole pieces, an alternating magnetic flux is established through the ignition coil and current is generated in the primary circuit during the period that the breaker points are closed. A cam located on the crankshaft opens the points when the primary current is at a maximum. Interruption of the current causes the magnetic field to collapse, which in turn induces a high tension voltage in the secondary winding.

A WICO flywheel magneto for single cylinder engines is shown in Fig. E-74. A type HI-503 Bendix Scintilla magnet, also for use on single cylinder engines, is shown in Fig. E-75, and Fig. E-76 gives the details of a flywheel type magneto for two cylinder engines. This is also of Bendix Scintilla manufacture. Note that it consists basically of two complete ignition systems with individual coils, breaker points and condensers.

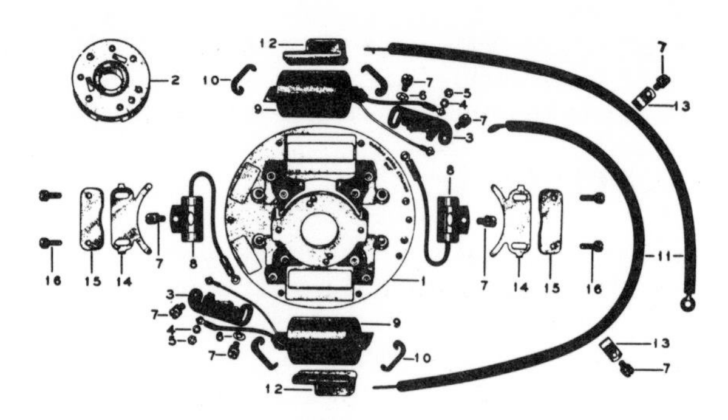

E-76. Bendix-Scintilla type K2A-1 flywheel magneto for two cylinder engines. (1) Magneto mounting flange. (2) Rotating magnet. (3) Breaker point assembly. (4) Lock washer. (5) Nut. (6) Washer. (7) Screw and lock washer. (8) Condenser. (9) Ignition coil. (10) Coil core clamp. (11) High tension lead. (12) High tension insulator. (13) Clamp. (14) Magneto flange tension spring. (15) Flange tension spring plate. (16) Screw and lock washer.

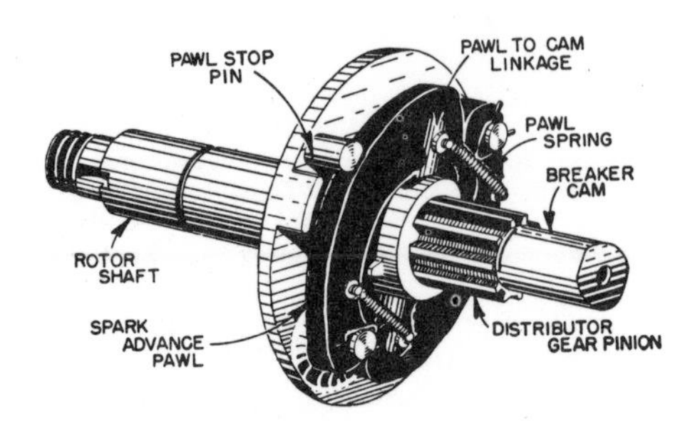

E-77. Details of spark advance mechanism as used on magnetos.

MAGNETO SPARK ADVANCE

In order to advance the timing of the spark in accordance with different engine speeds and loads, both manual and automatic spark advance are used on magnetos. However, the manual advance is virtually obsolete.

As the magneto produces an ignition spark at the instant the breaker points open, the spark timing can be advanced or retarded through a limited range by shifting the point at which the breaker points open. This is accomplished by rotating the plate on which the breaker points are mounted through an arc of approximately 10 degs. However, the amount of advance or retard that can be obtained by such a method is definitely limited, as the intensity of the ignition spark decreases rapidly as the points are opened farther away from the point of maximum current.

Automatic spark advance on magnetos is obtained by means of a centrifugally controlled spark advance rotor, Fig. E-77. This depends for its action on two spring loaded pawls which are held close to the center of the rotor at low speeds and gradually swing outward as engine speed increases. Outward movement of the pawls is transferred by linkage to the breaker camshaft with the result that the cam changes its relative position in respect to the drive shaft. In that way the spark timing is advanced. The degree and rate of spark advance is controlled by a pawl stop and the strength of the springs holding the centrifugal weights.

SPARK PLUGS

The spark plug in a spark ignition engine provides the gap across which the high tension voltage jumps, creating a spark which ignites the compressed mixture of air and fuel. The first spark plug was made in 1860 by a Frenchman named Lenoir.

The spark plug, Fig. E-78, consists of a central electrode which is connected to the ignition coil secondary through the distributor. The central electrode is insulated from the spark plug shell by means of a molded insulator resembling porcelain. Many spark plug insulators were

E-78. A spark plug manufactured by the AC Spark Plug Division of General Motors Corporation.

formerly made of mica. The side electrode protrudes from the bottom edge of the spark plug shell and is so positioned that there is a gap between it and the center electrode. This gap is known as the spark plug gap, the size of which is adjusted by bending the side electrode.

Spark plug gaps range from approximately .020 in. to .040 in. and they must be carefully set in accordance with manufacturer's specifications. The size of the gap is dependent on the compression ratio of the engine, and characteristics of the combustion chamber and the ignition system. In general, there is a trend toward wider spark plug gaps made possible by improved ignition systems. At one time a gap of .025 in. was virtually standard on all engines. Today, however, many manufacturers specify gaps of .030, .035, or .040 in. The advantage of the wider gap is that it includes more mixture than a narrow gap and consequently there is better opportunity to ignite it.

The shell of the spark plug is threaded so that it can be easily replaced. The following thread sizes are used: 1/2 in. pipe thread, 7/8 in., 10 mm., 14 mm., and 18 mm.

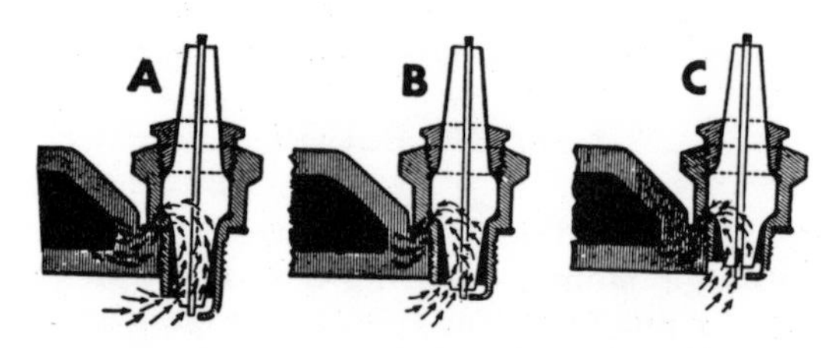

E-79. Illustrating the path that heat must take from the tip of the spark plug to reach the water jacket of the engine. The longer the path, the hotter the plug. Spark plug (A) is a hotter plug than plugs (B) or (C).

In addition to having the correct size thread, it is important that the spark plug extend into the combustion chamber the correct amount. The correct point for the spark plug electrodes in the combustion chamber is determined by the engine manufacturer. Installing plugs with a longer reach than specified will place the electrodes further in the combustion chamber. This may result in the valves or piston striking the spark plug. If a plug with a short reach is installed so that the spark plug electrodes become partly sheltered by the spark plug hole in the cylinder head, engine roughness and missing will probably result.

HEAT RANGE

Spark plugs must be designed so that the temperature of the firing end of the plug is high enough to burn off any carbon or other combustion deposits. But it must not get so hot as to cause preignition or deterioration of the insulator or electrodes. This is difficult as the temperature of the spark plug tip varies greatly with different engines and with different operating conditions.

The temperature of the spark plug insulator is dependent on the characteristics of the spark plug itself and also on the burning fuel in the combustion chamber. The latter temperature will of course vary with the design of the engine, compression ratios, cooling system, and air-fuel ratio.

As the tip of the spark plug absorbs heat from the burning fuel, the heat travels up the insulator to the spark plug shell to the cylinder head and then to the water jacket. The path the heat travels is shown in Fig. E-79. The heat absorbed by the insulator increases as the temperature in the combustion chamber increases. More heat will be absorbed as the area of the insulator exposed to the hot gases is increased. More heat will be absorbed by the spark plug shown on the left of Fig. E-79, than the one on the right as the area of its tip exposed to the combustion chamber is greater.

If the path the heat must follow to reach the cooling system is short, the tip will have a lower temperature than if the path is long. Plugs with long paths for the heat to travel are known as hot plugs, while spark plugs with short paths for the heat to travel are known as cold plugs.

In addition to the length of the path traversed by the heat in reaching the cooling system, the material of which the insulator is made and also its shape will affect its temperature. As a result, some spark plug insulators have a narrow neck just above the tip. Another design will have recessed tip sections which more readily follow temperature changes in the combustion chamber.

Engine designers select spark plugs which will give good performance for average conditions. However, if the engine is operated for long periods under approximately full load conditions, the standard equipment spark plug will operate at too high a temperature and preignition will result. It is, therefore, necessary to install a colder plug, which will carry off the greater heat more rapidly.

On the other hand, if the engine is operated for long periods of slow speed at part throttle opening, the standard equipment plug will tend to foul. That is, the insulator tip will become covered with carbon and other products of combustion. The result will be that the high tension voltage will leak across the accumulations (because of their lower resistance) rather than jump the gap at the electrodes. A hotter plug (one with a longer heat path) should then be used.

E-80. Illustrating a fouled spark plug.

SPARK PLUG FOULING

As pointed out in the preceding paragraphs on "Heat Range," there is a tendency for products of combustion to accumulate on the portion of the insulator of the spark plug within the combustion chamber, Fig. E-80. These products may be broadly classified as carbon fouling and lead fouling. In addition, oil fouling may occur in very badly worn engines.

Carbon fouling results primarily from extended low speed operation and when the carburetor mixture is excessively rich. Carbon fouling is usually relatively soft black soot which causes missing or roughness but which is easily removed from the spark plug.

Lead fouling results from the tetraethyl lead used in the fuel to improve its anti-detonating characteristics and is caused by extended high speed operation. Spark plugs with lead fouling will frequently operate satisfactorily at low and medium loads. But when full load is applied, missing will occur. This results from the higher temperatures melting the accumulations of lead salts, thus increasing their electrical conductivity so that the plug will be shorted out.

Lead compounds added to gasoline have a particularly bad effect on some spark plug insulators. They react with the silica in the insulator to form lead silicate glass which has a low melting point, and which at high temperatures, is a relatively good conductor of electricity. For that reason a spark plug may give satisfactory operation under light loads, but fail when full loads and high combustion chamber temperatures are reached.

In some cases of lead fouling, it is possible to operate the engine at a speed just below the point where missing will occur. Then by gradually increasing the speed (always keeping below the missing speed) it will be possible to burn off the lead fouling and full throttle operation attained.

Lead fouling will sometimes appear as a heavy crusty formation; in other instances it will be tiny globules. The form it takes will depend on fuel, operating conditions and time.

VOLTAGE REQUIRED TO JUMP GAP

There are many factors which will affect the voltage required to jump a certain gap. Among these factors may be included the shape of the electrodes forming the gap, the conductivity of the gasses in the gap, temperature, pressure, and the air-fuel ratio existing within the gap.

As pointed out in the section on distributors, the current delivered to the plugs is dependent on the current flowing in the primary, and this decreases as the engine speed increases. The voltage at the plug is also dependent on the cleanliness of the spark plug electrode. For example, an ignition system that is capable of delivering 20,000 volts to a clean plug may be able to deliver only one-half that amount to a plug that is partly fouled. This results from the fact that it takes appreciable time for the voltage to build up to a value where it can jump the plug gap. This is explained as follows: When the ignition breaker points are closed, energy is stored in the ignition coil in the form of the magnetic field. Then when the breaker points open, the magnetic field collapses, causing the high voltage. This high voltage is not reached instantaneously, but it is built up to a maximum and then drops to zero. This requires an appreciable length of time (electrically speaking) or about 1/20,000 second. Thus, the voltage increases until it reaches such a value that it is capable of jumping the gap at the spark plug. However, if the plug is partly fouled, some current will flow across the coating on the insulator. In other words, the accumulation on the insulator acts as a shunt across the gap. This loss of current reduces the peak voltage so that in the case of a badly fouled plug the voltage may not build up to a value that will jump the gap.

SPARK PLUG GAPS

Spark plug gaps do not remain constant, but increase in size, the amount of increase being dependent on length of time in service, chemical characteristics of the fuel, combustion chamber temperatures, and particularly the action of the electrical spark which tears off portions of the electrode. The electrical characteristics of the ignition system also affect the rate of wear of the spark plug electrodes.

Some engines operate better with wider spark plug gaps than others and many engineers are in agreement that the explanation is in the characteristics of the air-fuel mixture in the vicinity of the plug gap. The air-fuel mixture in different parts of the combustion chamber of different engines varies considerably. This is due to the form of the combustion chamber, the turbulence imparted to the mixture, and the amount of burned gases remaining in the combustion chamber from the previous cycle of operation.

Before installing a spark plug, it is important to make sure that it is clean (if a used plug is being installed) and that the gap is adjusted in accordance with the manufacturer's specifications. When adjusting the gap, the side electrode only should be bent. Never bend the central electrode, as that will crack the insulator.

After adjusting the gap, make sure that the threads of both the spark plug and the threads in the engine are clean and not encrusted with carbon and dirt. Also clean the surface of the cylinder head against which the spark plug gasket seats. This is important, for if dirt is present at that point, compression leaks may occur, and in addition, the dirt acts as a heat insulator and the spark plug will run hot and faulty operation results.

When tightening a spark plug, a torque wrench should be used. While most spark plugs should be tightened to 25 to 30 ft. lbs. torque, there are many exceptions and the manufacturer's specifications should be consulted. Spark plugs should be tightened only to the degree that the gasket is just crushed, and when spark plugs are replaced, new gaskets should always be used.

The external portion of the spark plug insulator, together with the terminal, should always be covered with a rubber nipple made for that purpose. This prevents accumulation of dust and moisture on the insulator which would permit the high tension voltage to leak across from the terminal to the ground shell or body of the plug. Without such nipples secondary voltage is greatly reduced.

CLEANING SPARK PLUGS

Special equipment is available for cleaning spark plugs. However, when the spark plug electrodes become worn, the spark plugs should be replaced as it takes a higher voltage to jump across worn electrodes even though the gap has been adjusted to the correct size.

STORAGE BATTERIES

A lead-acid storage battery, Fig. E-81, is provided to supply a source of power for cranking the internal combustion engine. At the same time it provides the necessary electrical energy for the ignition system.

The lead-acid storage battery is not a storage tank for electricity, but is an electro-chemical device for converting chemical energy into electrical energy. The amount of electrical power in the storage battery is determined

E-81. Typical starting battery, 6-volt, used for starting and lighting.

by the amount of chemical substances in the battery and when these substances have been used up, they are restored to their original chemical condition by passing an electric current through the battery.

Each cell of a lead-acid storage battery will produce approximately 2 volts regardless of the cell size. For a six-volt battery three cells are therefore provided and for a twelve-volt battery there are six cells. In each case the cells are connected in series.

Each cell contains an element which is composed of a negative-plate group and a positive-plate group, Fig. E-82. The plate is formed of lattice-like grids of an alloy of lead and antimony and the grids are filled with special lead-oxide pastes. These pastes after processing to make them solid, but porous, become the active materials of the battery after it has been charged.

The amount of current that can be produced by a storage battery is determined by the active area and weight of the materials in the plates and

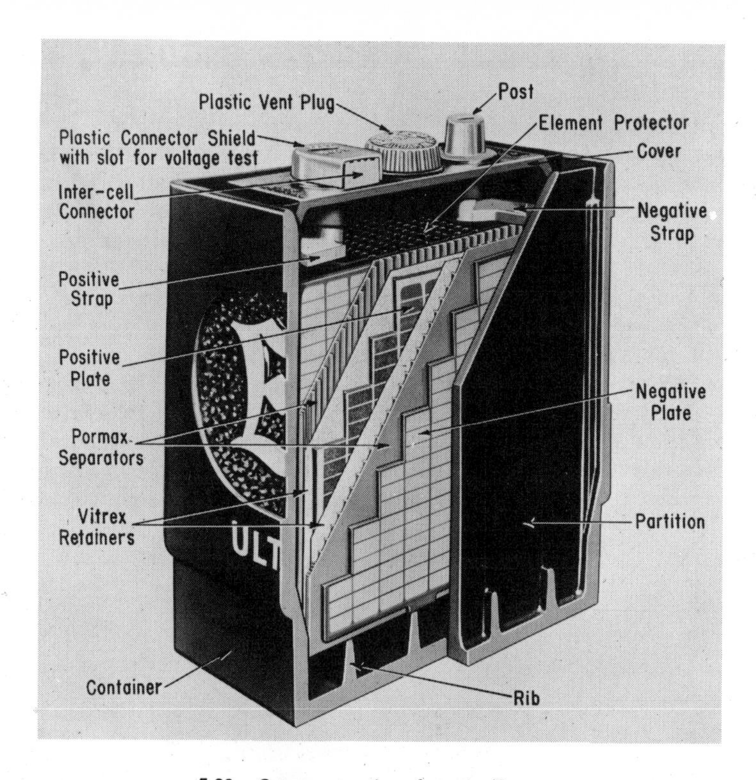

E-82. Cut-away section of starting battery.

by the quantity of sulphuric acid in the electrolyte. After most of the available active materials have been activated, the battery can produce little or no current and is said to be discharged. Before it can provide current again it is necessary to restore the battery plates to their original chemical condition. This is accomplished by passing an electric current, from an external source, through the battery. This charging current must flow through the battery in a direction opposite to the current flow from the battery. This results in a reversal of the discharge chemical reactions in the storage battery so that the chemicals are restored to their original active condition.

The construction of lead-acid storage battery is relatively simple. The positive and negative plates, Fig. E-83, consists of special active materials contained in cast grids of lead-antimony alloy. These grids are rectangular, flat, lattice-like castings with relatively heavy frames and a mesh of vertical and horizontal wires. The positive plates contain lead peroxide which is chocolate brown color, while the negative plates contain sponge lead which is gray in color.

Each cell of a storage battery is made of alternate positive and negative plates and a plate group is made by welding (lead burning) a number of plates of the same polarity to the plate strap. The plate strap also includes a vertical terminal post so that the cell can be connected to the other cells forming the battery. Plate groups of opposite polarity are interlaced so that negative and positive plates alternate. Usually negative plate groups contain one more plate than the positive plate group within the same cell. As a result there will be a negative plate on both sides of the plate group. The reason for this is that the chemicals forming the negative plates are not as active as those forming the positive plates. By providing the additional area, the chemical activity of the positive and negative plates are more nearly equalized. Each cell will, therefore, have an uneven number of plates and storage batteries are known as 13, 15, 17, etc. plate batteries. The greater the number of plates, or plate area, the greater the capacity of the cell and the greater the current that will be available.

To insure against adjacent plates touching each other, separators are placed between them. These separators are made of sheets of porous non-conducting material such as chemically treated wood, porous rubber, resin

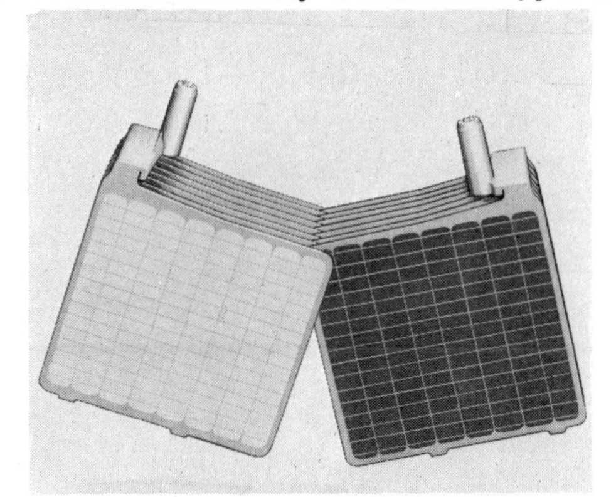

E-83. Negative (left) and positive (right), storage battery plates (Willard), showing how the plates alternate. Note also the "feet" on the bottom edge of the plates which rest on the element rests formed on the bottom of the battery container.

impregnated fiber and glass fiber. Separators usually have ribs on one side facing the positive plate. This provides greater volumes of acid next to the positive plate and improves efficiency by increasing acid circulation. Some separators are also designed to aid in the reduction of loss of active material from the positive plate.

Battery separators must be chemically resistant to sulphuric acid and at the same time be mechanically strong. They must be porous enough to permit free passage of the electrolyte and at the same time prevent the active chemicals in the plates from touching each other through expansion.

The group of positive and negative plates are placed in each cell of the battery case. The lower edges of the cell groups rest on ribs or element rests, Fig. E-82, and the space between the bridges are known as sediment chambers, where loosened material from the plates may accumulate without short circuiting the plates.

The battery container or case, in which the groups of plates are held is of the one piece molded type, usually of hard rubber or bituminous composition. In addition to withstanding the action of sulphuric acid, it must be mechanically strong and not be affected by wide variations in temperature.

With the plates in place in the battery case, cell covers of molded hard rubber or similar material are fitted over the terminal posts of the plate groups. Vents are provided in the covers, so that the cells can be filled with electrolyte and, periodically, with water that has been lost through evaporation. In addition, the vents permit gases to escape.

There are many different types of vent caps. Some of the caps of recent design have materially reduced evaporation of water, so that it requires replenishment only at long intervals.

After the covers are installed, the individual cells are connected together in series and finally asphaltic sealing compound is poured around the edges of the covers so that leakage is prevented.

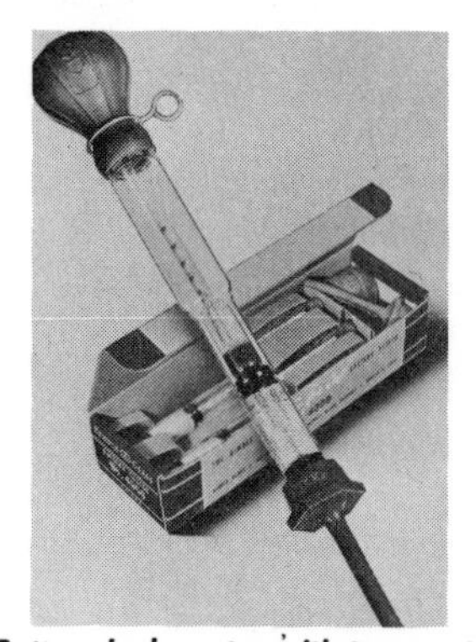

E-84. Battery hydrometer with temperature correction.

ELECTROLYTE

After the battery is completely assembled, it is filled with the electrolyte. In lead-acid storage batteries this is a fairly concentrated solution of sulphuric acid and water having a specific gravity of 1.290 at 80 deg. F. Specific gravity is the relation of the weight of a liquid to an equal volume of water. Therefore, when an electrolyte has a specific gravity of 1.290 it is 1.290 times as heavy as an equal volume of water, when both liquids are at the same temperature.

The specific gravity of a solution is measured by a hydrometer, Fig. E-84. This consists of a glass tube with a bulb syringe for sucking up samples of the electrolyte. Within the glass tube is a calibrated float. The depth to which the float sinks is a measure of the specific gravity of the solution. The float sinks further in solutions having a low specific gravity than it does in solutions having a high specific gravity.

The float is made of glass with a scale and its weight is accurately

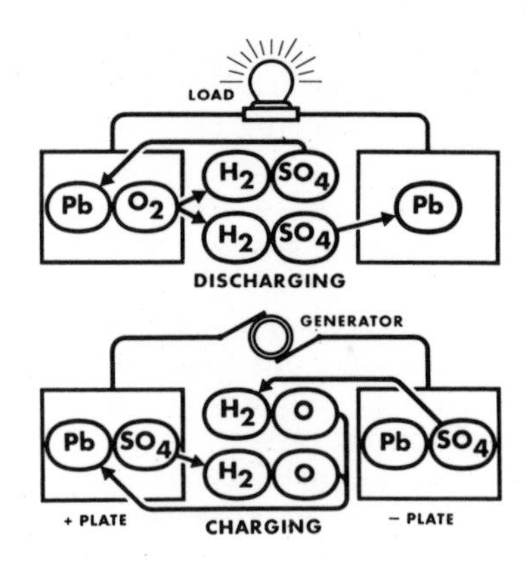

E-85. Chemical action in a lead storage battery.

determined by the manufacturer so that it will give an exact indication of the specific gravity of the solution.

As the temperature affects the specific gravity of a solution, it is therefore necessary to take the temperature at the same time the specific gravity is taken. The more expensive hydrometers have a built-in thermometer so that the temperature can be measured and the necessary correction made. The temperature correction amounts to about .004 specific gravity for every 10 deg. F. change in temperature. Basically for every 10 deg. F. of electrolyte temperature above 80 deg., four gravity points (.004) must be added to the gravity reading. This compensates for the loss of gravity caused by the expansion of the solution as its temperature increases. For every 10 deg. of electrolyte temperature below 80 deg., four gravity points must be subtracted from the gravity reading. This compensates for the gain in gravity due to the contraction of the liquid as its temperature decreases.

CHEMICAL ACTION

The chemical actions that take place during charging and discharging of a lead-acid storage battery are shown in Fig. E-85. In a charged condition, the positive plate material is essentially pure lead peroxide, the chemical symbol of which is PbO_2. This has a chocolate brown color. The active material of the negative plate is spongy lead, the chemical symbol being Pb, and is gray in color. The electrolyte is a solution of sulphuric acid, H_2SO_4, and water. The voltage of the cell depends upon the chemical difference between the active materials and slightly upon the concentration of the electrolyte.

When an electric load is connected to the battery, current will flow and this current is produced by the chemical reactions between the active materials of the two kinds of battery plates and the sulphuric acid. As shown in Fig. E-85, the oxygen in the PbO_2 combines with the hydrogen,

H_2, from the sulphuric acid to form water, H_2O. At the same time the lead, Pb, in the lead peroxide combines with the SO_4, portion of the sulphuric acid to form lead sulphate, $PbSO_4$.

A similar action takes place at the negative plate where the lead Pb of the negative active material combines with the SO_4 of the sulphuric acid to form $PbSO_4$, lead sulphate.

So, while there is an electric load on the battery, lead sulphate is formed on both positive and negative plates in the battery, and the electrolyte becomes diluted with water.

As the discharge continues, the accumulation of lead sulphate in the plates and the dilution of the electrolyte brings the chemical reactions to a halt. At low rates of discharge (small current), the reactions are more complete than at high rates, as more time is available for the materials to come into contact. When the chemical action can no longer take place, the battery is said to be discharged.

During charge, the chemical reactions are basically the reverse of those which occur during discharge. The $PbSO_4$, Lead sulphate, on both plates is split up into Pb and SO_4, Fig. E-85, while the water H_2O is split into hydrogen H, and oxygen O_2. The passage of the charging current, which is in the reverse direction to the discharging current, forces the SO_4 from the plates and combines with the H_2 to form H_2SO_4, sulphuric acid. At the same time the oxygen O_2, enters into chemical combination with the lead at the positive plate to form PbO_2.

The specific gravity of the electrolyte decreases during discharge for two reasons. Not only is the sulphuric acid used up, but new water is formed. As the water is formed at the positive plates and diffuses slowly through the electrolyte, the positive plates are more likely to be damaged during freezing weather. When the battery is fully charged, the specific gravity of the solution increases, sulphuric acid is formed, and water is used up. As a result there is little danger of a fully charged battery freezing.

Specific gravity of the electrolyte may continue to rise for some time after a battery has been quick charged, as the newly formed acid requires time to diffuse from the plates to the electrolyte. Specific gravity readings taken while a battery is gassing will be erroneously low.

BATTERY VOLTAGE AND CAPACITY

The open circuit voltage of a fully charged storage battery cell is 2.1 volt for acid of approximately 1.280 sp. gr. That is true regardless of the number of plates in the cell or their area. The voltage is determined only by the character of the chemicals in the plates and the specific gravity of the electrolyte. A six-volt battery will therefore be made up of three cells.

The capacity, that is the amount of current it will deliver, depends on the number and area of the plates in the cell and also on the amount of acid present. In other words, cells having a large number of plates will deliver more current than cells having a smaller number.

Battery capacity drops rapidly as the temperature is reduced. The reason for this is that the battery is an electro-chemical device and, as is the case with virtually all chemical actions, it is aided by heat. For example, if the capacity or cranking power of a battery at 80 deg. is given as 100 per cent, at 32 deg., the capacity will be only 65 per cent and at 0 deg. only 40 per cent.

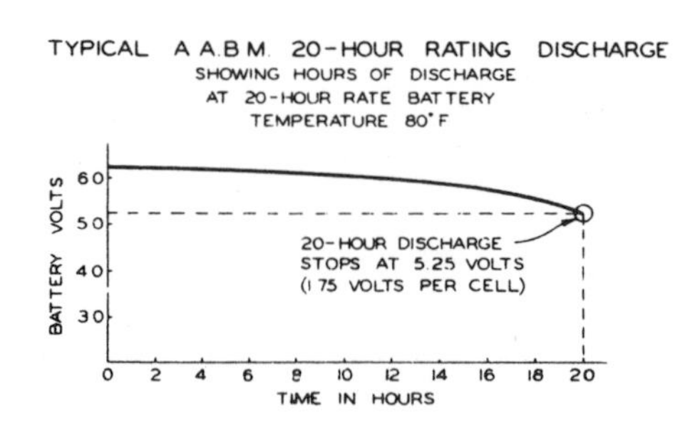

E-86. 20 hour discharge chart.

BATTERY RATINGS

There are two ratings for starting and lighting batteries which have been incorporated in the standards of the Society of Automotive Engineers, the Association of American Battery Manufacturers and the United States Government.

The 20 hour rating in ampere hours indicates the lighting ability of the battery. The fully charged battery is brought to a temperature of 80 deg. F. and is then discharged at a rate equal to 1/20 of the published 20 hour capacity in ampere hours. For example, a battery rated by the manufacturer as a 6-volt 100 A.H. capacity would be discharged at 1/20 of 100 or 5 amp., until the voltage has dropped to 5.25 volts. The number of hours required for the discharge, multiplied by the rate of 5 amp., is its 20 hour rating.

To methods are given for expressing the cranking ability of a fully charged battery at low temperature.

A. The terminal voltage of a fully charged six-volt battery taken five seconds after the start of a discharge of 300 amp. with an initial electrolyte temperature of 0 deg. F., Fig. E-86.

B. The number of minutes required for a six-volt battery to reach a terminal voltage of 3.0 volts when discharged at 300 amp. with an electrolyte temperature of 0 deg. F., Fig. E-87.

BATTERY TESTING

Checking the condition of a battery with a hydrometer should not be done immediately after water has been added to bring the electrolyte to the

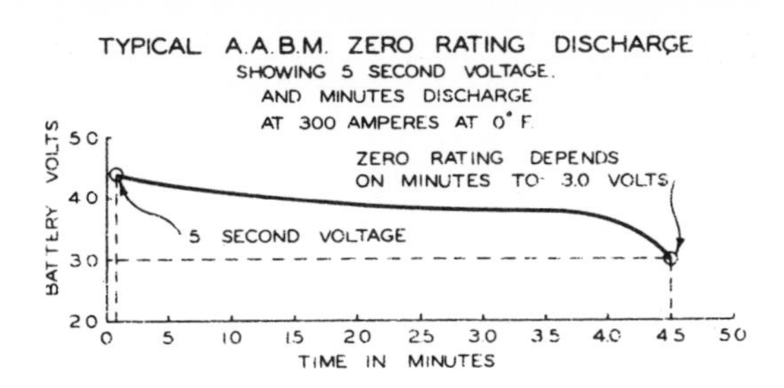

E-87. Showing battery voltage with 300 amp. discharge.

desired level. Such measurements should be made before the water is added in order to obtain a representative sample. If the level is too low to obtain a sample, water should be added as needed and then after the battery has been operated for a sufficient time to thoroughly mix the water with the electrolyte, the sample should be taken with the hydrometer.

Hydrometer readings should not be taken while the battery is gassing as this would affect the accuracy of the reading.

As previously pointed out, when checking the specific gravity of a cell, it is also necessary to check the temperature of the electrolyte and make the necessary correction.

BATTERY CHARGING

Only direct current can be used for charging storage batteries and some method must be provided for controlling the amount of charging current. Before placing a battery on charge, the exterior of the battery and the terminals must be cleaned. In addition, the electrolyte must be brought up to the desired level. When charging batteries, the positive lead from the charger is connected to the positive terminal of the battery, and the negative lead from the charger is connected to the negative terminal of the battery. It is extremely important that the connections be correctly made, otherwise the battery will be ruined. If several batteries are to be charged at the same time and connected in series, the positive terminal of one battery should be connected to the negative terminal of the next battery. The positive terminal of the end battery of the series is then connected to the positive terminal of the charger, and the negative terminal of the series of batteries is connected to the negative terminal of the charger.

The terminals of storage batteries are marked so that they can be easily distinguished. The positive terminal is usually marked with a "P," "Pos," or "+." Negative terminals are marked "N," "Neg." or "-." In addition the positive terminal of the battery is larger in diameter than the negative terminal. In case the markings have been erased, the polarity can be determined by dipping leads from the battery in a weak solution of sulphuric acid. More gas bubbles will collect around the negative lead than around the positive. The same procedure can be used to determine the polarity of the charger.

Most commercial electricity is of the alternating type. In such cases it is, of course, necessary to convert the alternating current to direct before it can be used for battery charging purposes. The usual methods used in converting alternating to direct current are motor-generators, tungar bulb rectifiers and dry disc type rectifiers.

The constant current method of charging batteries is one method that is used extensively. That method is particularly advantageous where the condition of the battery is not known.

The charging rate varies with different conditions; however, a safe rate would be equal to 1/2 of the number of plates in the cell. For example, the charging current in amperes of a 13 plate cell would be 6 1/2 amp., for a 17 plate cell, 8 1/2 amp. When several batteries of different sizes are connected in series for charging, the charging current is determined by the size of the smallest battery in the series.

During charge, the temperature of batteries should be watched carefully. Should the temperature approach 110 deg. F., the charging rate should be reduced.

Many storage batteries are fitted with filler plugs of the non-overfill type. In such cases, the electrolyte may be forced from the cell during charge when the vent plugs have been removed, so that a hydrometer reading can be taken. This tendency can be overcome by placing a small stick in the vent hole so that the non-overfill device is held in the open position while taking hydrometer readings.

Vent plugs on batteries with non-overfill devices should be screwed tightly in place during charge.

To check the progress of the charge, hydrometer readings should be taken every hour. The battery is fully charged when the cells are gassing freely and there is no increase in hydrometer reading for three successive hourly readings. Excessive charging will damage the battery, particularly the positive plates. Depending on the charging rate, most batteries can be charged in 12 to 16 hours. Batteries with sulphated plates will require a longer period.

Constant Potential chargers, as the name implies, maintain the same voltage on the batteries throughout the period of the charge. As a result, the current is automatically reduced as the battery approaches full charge. Batteries in good condition will not be damaged by this method of charging. However, a badly sulphated battery may not come up to charge when the Constant Potential method is used. With this method of charging, battery temperature may rise rapidly, and it is therefore important that frequent checks be made of the temperature.

High Rate Battery charging is a relatively new method. Prior to 1945 only low charging rates were advocated as it was believed that high rates would damage the battery plates. However, by using a high rate charge, batteries can be charged in approximately 30 minutes. As a result, the method has become popular as it permits charging the battery while the customer waits.

Trickle Chargers are designed to charge batteries at a rate of approximately 1 amp. They are used primarily for maintaining display and stocks of batteries in a fully charged condition. While the charging rate is extremely low, batteries can be damaged if left on a trickle charge for long periods. Common practice is to leave the batteries on a trickle charge during the day and take them off charge during the night. In that way danger of severe overcharging is eliminated.

REVIEWING THE STARTING, LIGHTING, IGNITION SECTION

1. Explain what is meant by the electron theory.
2. Give a definition of the term "ohm."
3. In electrical measurement there are three basic units. Can you name them?
4. What are the three types of electrical circuits? Make a simple diagram to illustrate each.
5. The electrical unit for measuring work is known as ______________.
6. Watts = volts x joules. True or false?
7. Discuss some of the effects of magnetism. When similar poles of two magnets are placed close together, do they repel each other, or are they attracted to each other?
8. Which retains magnetism best - soft steel or hard steel?
9. What is an electromagnet?
10. In constructing an electromagnet, the strength of the magnetic field is increased by __________.
11. How does a solenoid differ from an electromagnet as just discussed?

GENERATORS

1. The generator consists of what two principal parts?
2. Discuss the principles of operation.
3. The armature consists of __________.
4. May batteries be charged with alternating current?
5. A combination of series and parallel field winding is known as a ________________ winding.
6. On a third brush generator what is the procedure for increasing the output?
7. Name some objections to using the third brush generator.
8. There is a method of controlling the magnetic field known as a bucking field. Explain what we mean by this term.

GENERATOR RELAYS, REGULATORS

1. Why is a cut-out relay placed in the generator circuit?
2. On the cut-out relay, what adjustments are required.

STARTING MOTORS

1. Starters in current use consist essentially of what parts?
2. In operation, the rotation of the starting motor causes ______________.
3. What is the principle of operation of a starting motor?

IGNITION

1. Name the major types of ignition systems.
2. The modern ignition system operating from a battery consists of ____________________.
3. What is the purpose of:
   (a) Ignition coil?
   (b) Distributor?
   (c) Condenser?
4. Name the two principal methods used to automatically advance and retard the spark.

SPARK PLUGS

1. Describe a typical spark plug.
2. What is the ordinary cause of spark plug fouling by carbon? By lead?
3. Discuss some conditions which affect spark plug gaps.
4. What precautions should be taken when adjusting the gap and installing spark plugs?

MAGNETOS

1. What is a magneto?
2. How does it operate?
3. Does a magneto require the aid of a battery?
4. State the main difference between low tension and high tension magnetos.
5. In the magneto how is the magnetic field produced?
6. What development resulted in a great improvement in magnets?
7. By what characteristics are magnetos classified other than as low tension or high tension?
8. Define a shuttle wound magneto.
9. What is an inductor type magneto?
10. How does the revolving magnet design differ from the other two types?
11. Explain in detail how the low tension magneto operates.
12. Name some examples of the low tension magnetos in current use.
13. Give a detailed explanation of the principle of the high tension magneto.
14. What do you understand by the term "rotary inductor magneto?"
15. What made possible the introduction of the rotating magnet magneto?
16. Describe its principal characteristics.
17. What is a flywheel magneto?
18. What kinds of spark advance are used on magnetos?
19. Tell how spark timing on magnetos is obtained.

STORAGE BATTERIES

1. The lead-acid battery is a "storage tank" for electricity. True or false?
2. The amount of electrical power in the storage battery is determined by ________________

REVIEW QUESTIONS

3. Each cell of a lead-acid battery will produce about __________ volts.
4. Describe the construction of a typical storage battery cell.
5. What determines the amount of current that can be produced by a storage battery?
6. What is electrolyte?
7. Discuss the chemical action that takes place during charging and discharging of a lead-acid storage battery.
8. On what basis are storage batteries rated?
9. How would you test the condition of a storage battery?
10. In charging batteries, should the positive lead from the charger be connected to the positive or negative terminal of the battery?

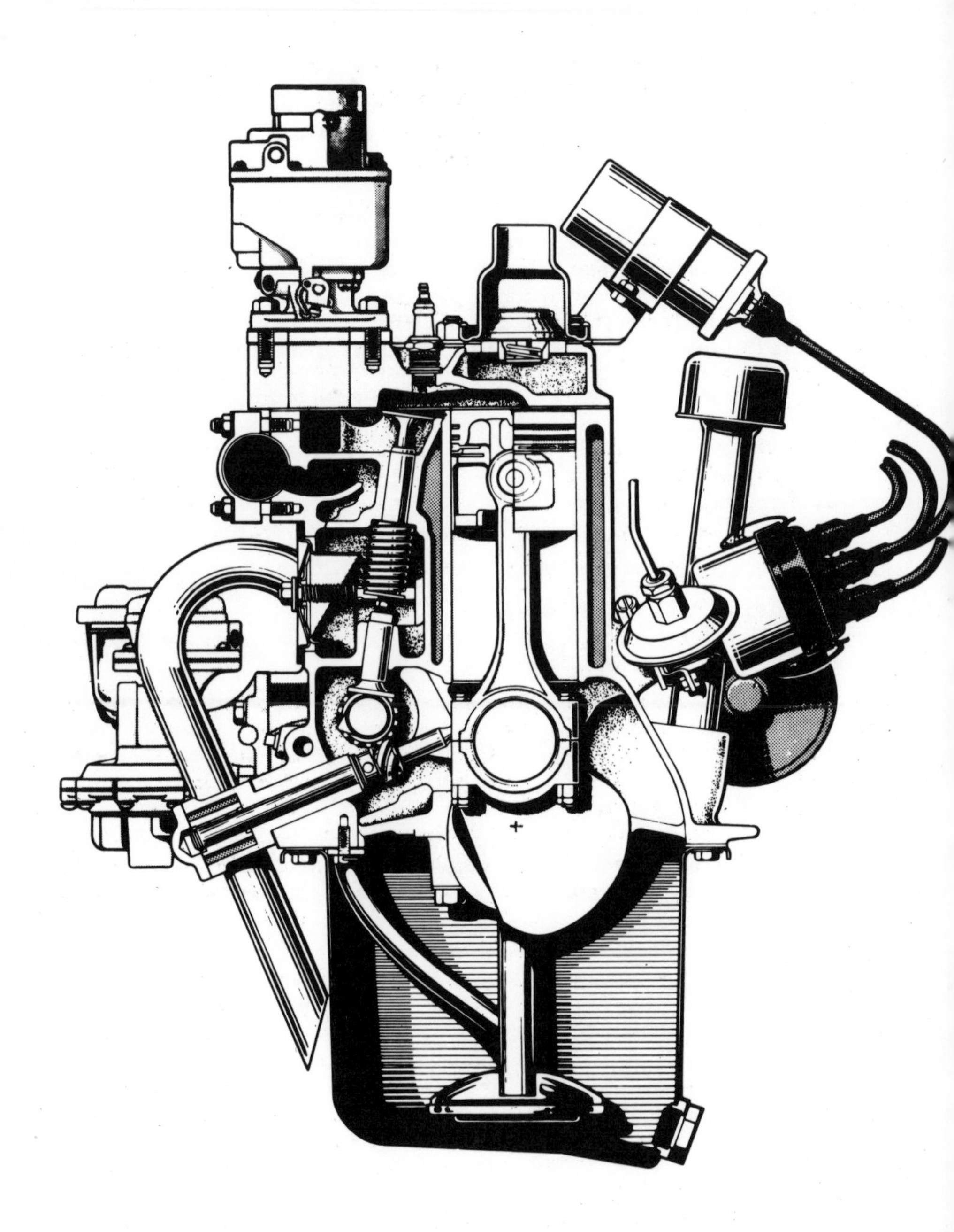

Small, water cooled, four cycle engines approach the design of automobile engines in many ways.

FOUR-CYCLE ENGINES

FOUR CYCLE WATER COOLED TYPES

Preceding chapters of this text have covered construction, service and repair of the four-cycle water cooled engine more completely than other types.

This for the reason that basic procedures of service and repair are applicable to all engines. Now we can readily cover the minor differences between water cooled and air cooled types. These variations are more easily understood after a sound basic knowledge is acquired from the preceding sections.

The typical water cooled engine is quite rugged in construction. The smaller air cooled engines are lighter in construction--particularly the two-cycle types--and parts are smaller and lighter. Therefore these parts must be handled more carefully.

Any excessive force used in disassembly, reassembly or repair operations is liable to result in bent, distorted or broken parts.

When repairing small engines it should be kept in mind that the parts are small, simple in design and relatively inexpensive. This means that many worn or damaged parts can be replaced with new parts at less cost than extensive repair operations. For example, if the crankshaft is worn on a six cylinder engine it might be worth while to regrind the journals and install undersize bearings. On a small one cylinder engine it might be better to install a new crankshaft.

As a further example, cylinder heads are often distorted or warped by careless tightening of head bolts, failure to use a torque-wrench or improper sequence of tightening. A six cylinder head from a water cooled engine could probably be ground down level on a surfacing machine at less cost than a new head.

If the warpage is slight, it could be trued up on a face plate, particularly if it is a single cylinder air cooled engine, as shown in a subsequent illustration. If badly warped, the most economical procedure might be the installation of a new head. In any case it is well to check before proceeding with extensive work.

In the following sections on the other three types of small engines we have relied to a large extent on carefully chosen illustrations and rather extensive captions to highlight the specific service requirements for each type of engine.

FOUR CYCLE AIR COOLED TYPES

The four cycle air cooled engine is used as a power source for lawn mowers, small tractors and every imaginable kind of light machinery.

These engines are remarkably sturdy and will operate for a considerable time unless damaged or abused by careless handling. One of the most frequent types of damage is broken cooling fins on cylinders and cylinder heads. These fins are of necessity thin and fragile and easily broken. Each broken fin results in lessened cooling capacity and also may cause distortion of cylinders or heads with resultant power loss and rapid wear.

Another common fault is broken vanes on the engine flywheel. These vanes serve as a fan to blow air over the cylinders and each break reduces the cooling system capacity. Of equal importance a broken vane serves to destroy the running balance of the engine thus causing vibration and rapid wear.

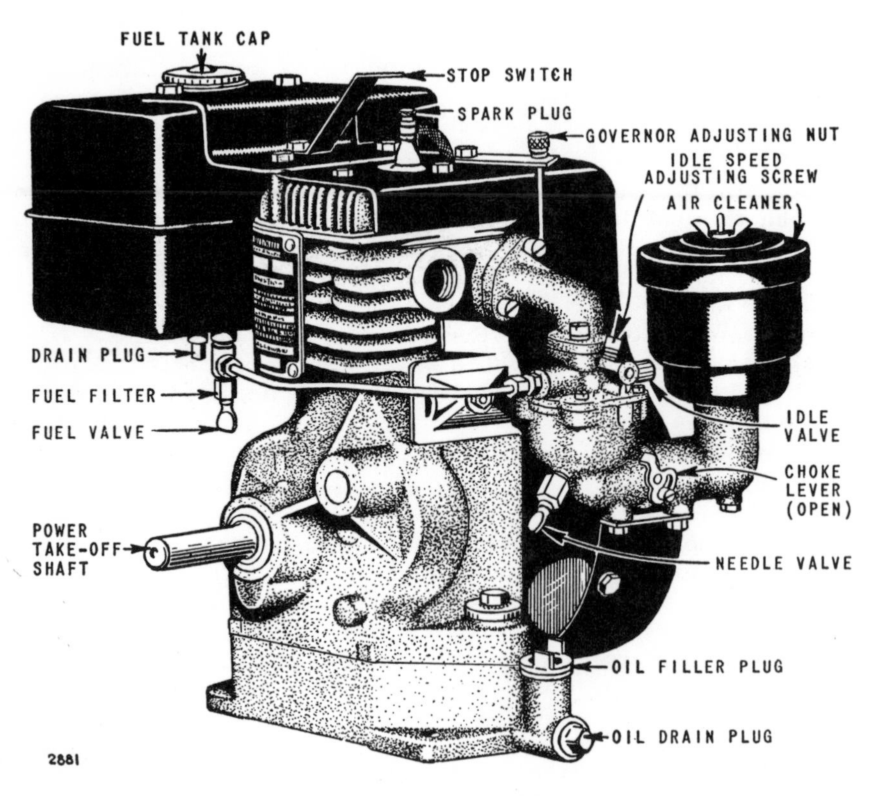

G-1. Typical single cylinder, four cycle, air cooled engine as made by Briggs & Stratton. This engine is fitted with a conventional updraft carburetor and built-in ignition system. The flywheel fan forces cooling air through the hood or cover over the cylinder cooling fins.

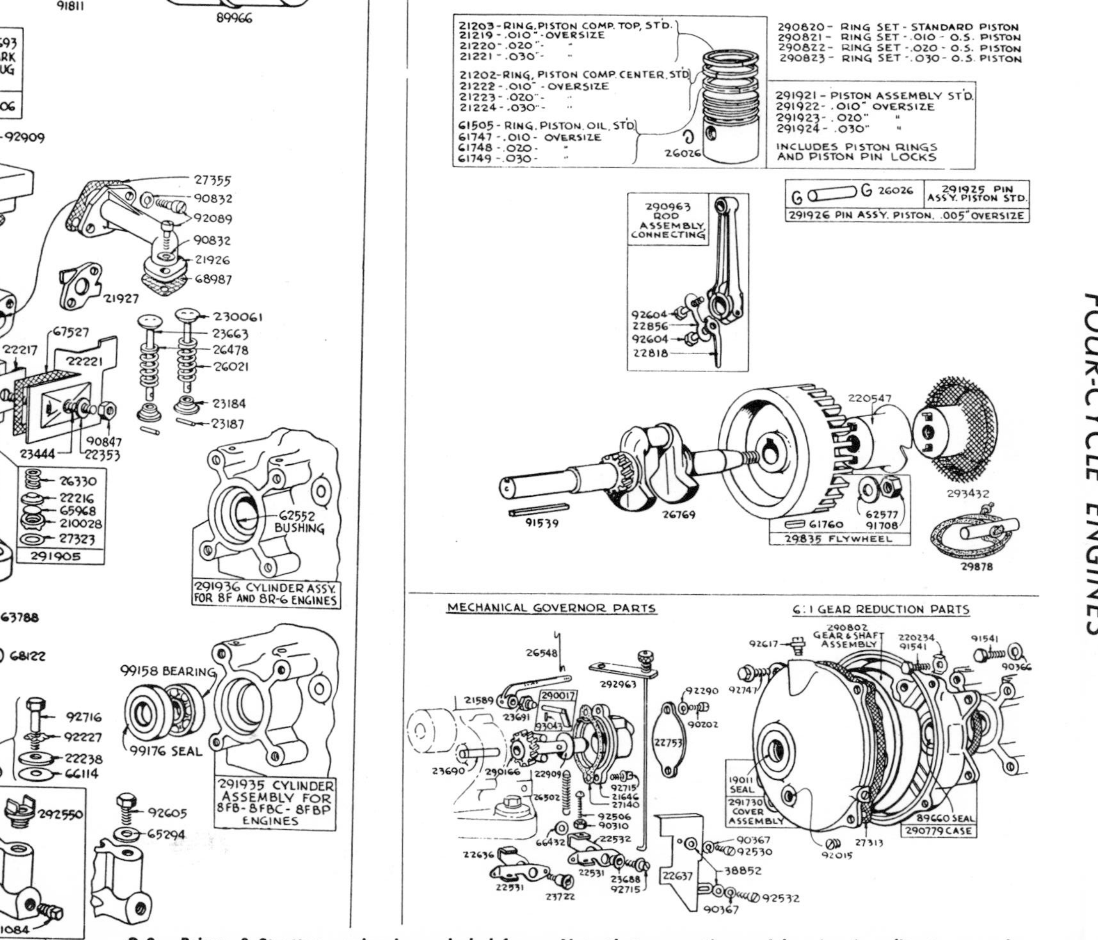

G-2. Briggs & Stratton engine in exploded form. Note that connecting rod bearing is split at an angle and also has a bolted on oil splasher.

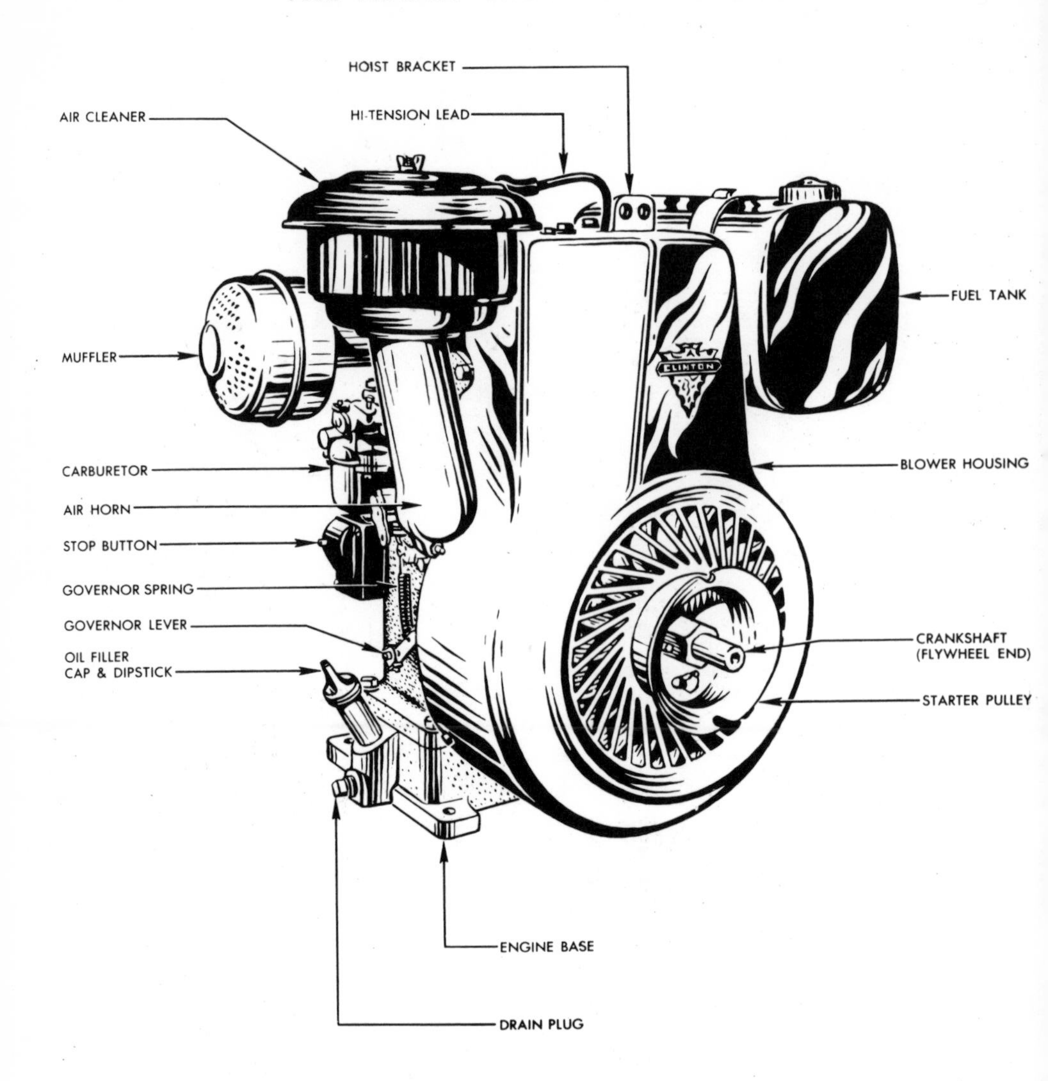

G-3. *Another typical single cylinder, four cycle, air cooled engine as made by Clinton. This view shows the cooling air control system in detail.*

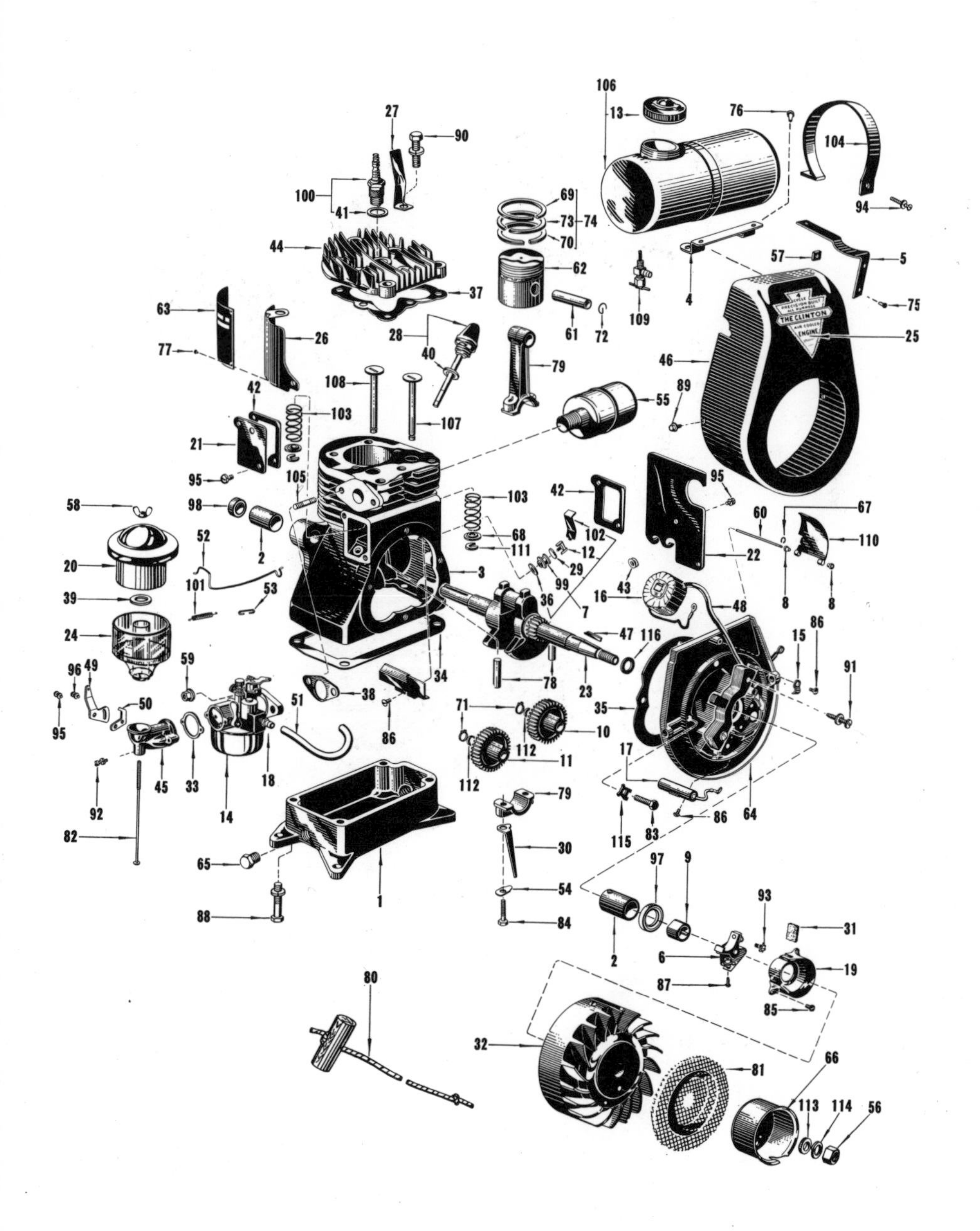

G-4. Clinton engine in exploded form. It will be noted that ignition system is enclosed within the fly-wheel.

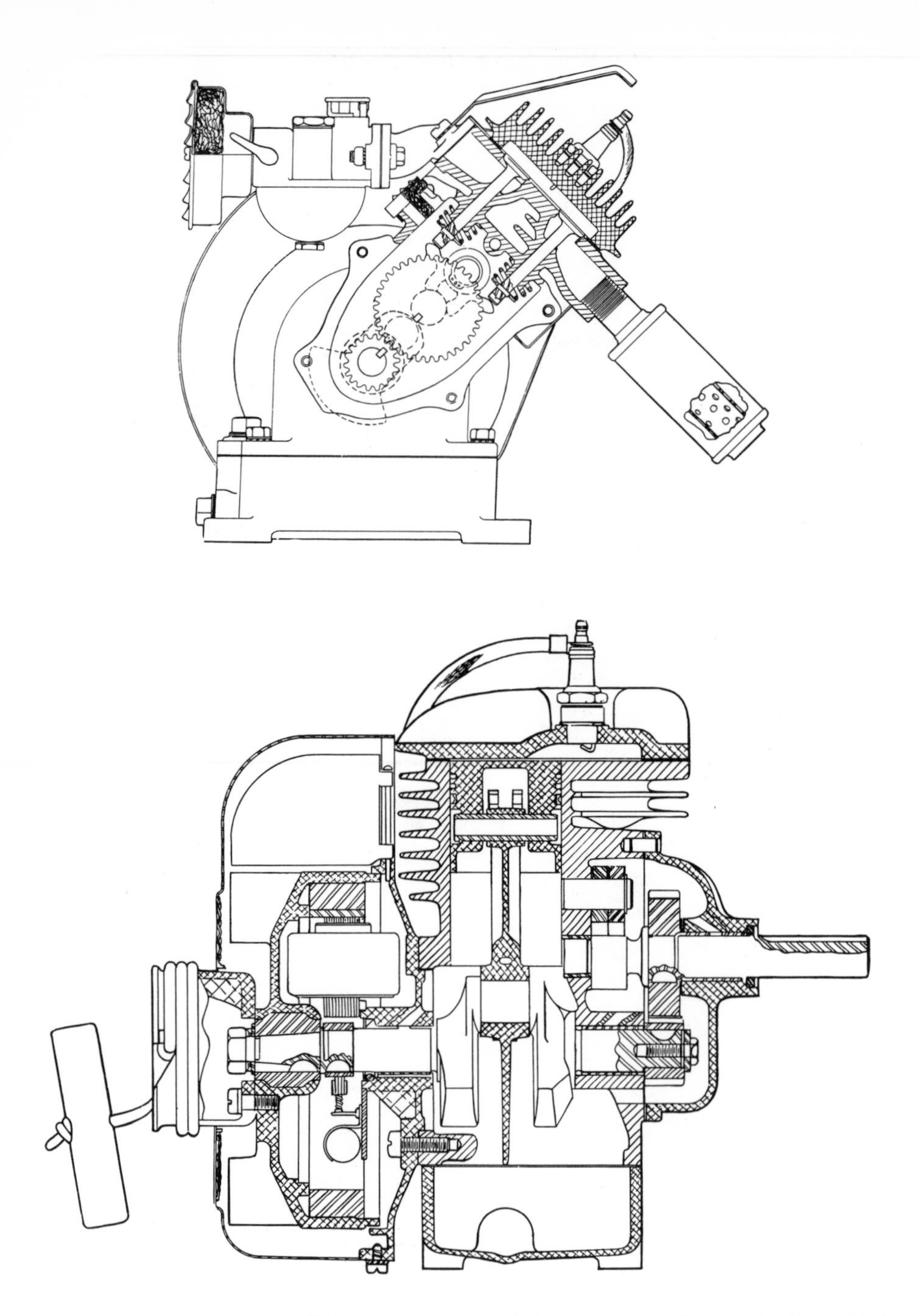

G-5. Cross sections of single cylinder, four cycle, air cooled engine as made by Reo. In this model the cylinder is placed at an angle instead of being vertical or horizontal.

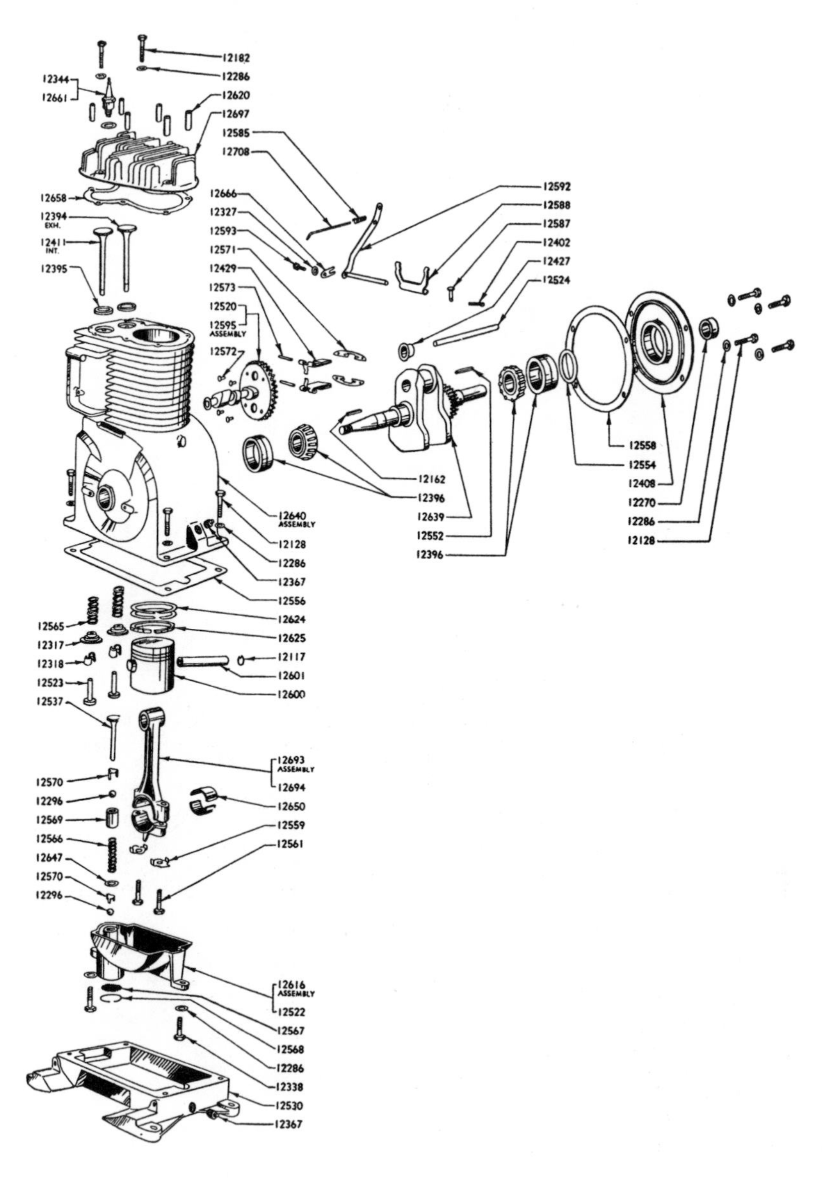

G-6. In this exploded view of a single cylinder, four cycle, air cooled engine as made by Gladden, note that main bearings are of the anti-friction type.

G-7. Four cylinder, 4-cycle, air cooled Wisconsin engine with 3 in. bore, 3¼ in. stroke, 91.9 cu. in. piston displacement. Engine develops 13 H.P. at 1400 r.p.m., 21.5 H.P. at 2400 r.p.m. Weight with stub shaft 295 lbs.

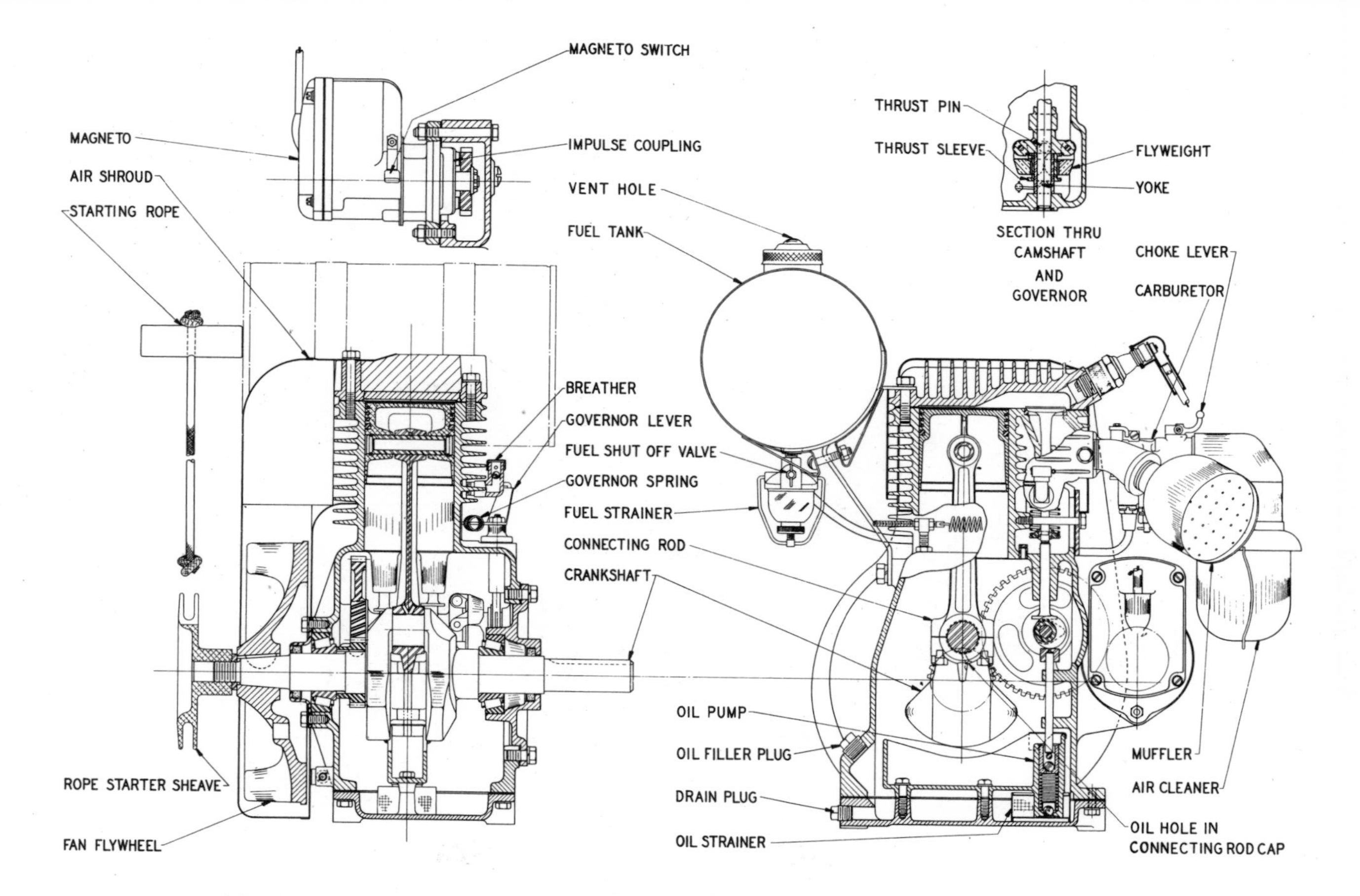

G-8. ***Cross sections of single cylinder, four cycle, air cooled engine made by Wisconsin. Note that main bearings are of the tapered roller type.***

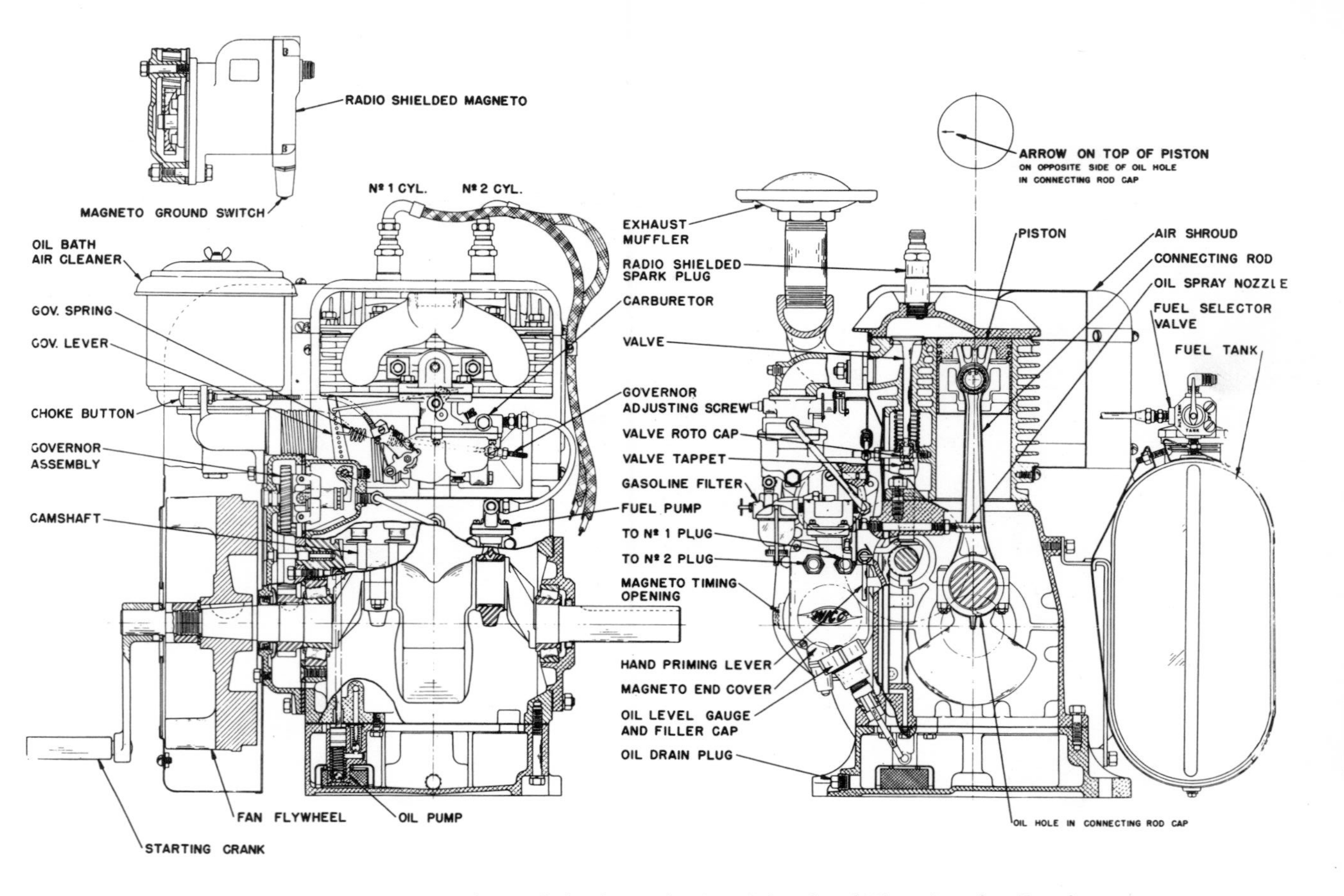

G-9. Cross sections of two cylinder, four cycle, air cooled engine of Wisconsin make. Note that magneto is a separate unit rather than being built into flywheel.

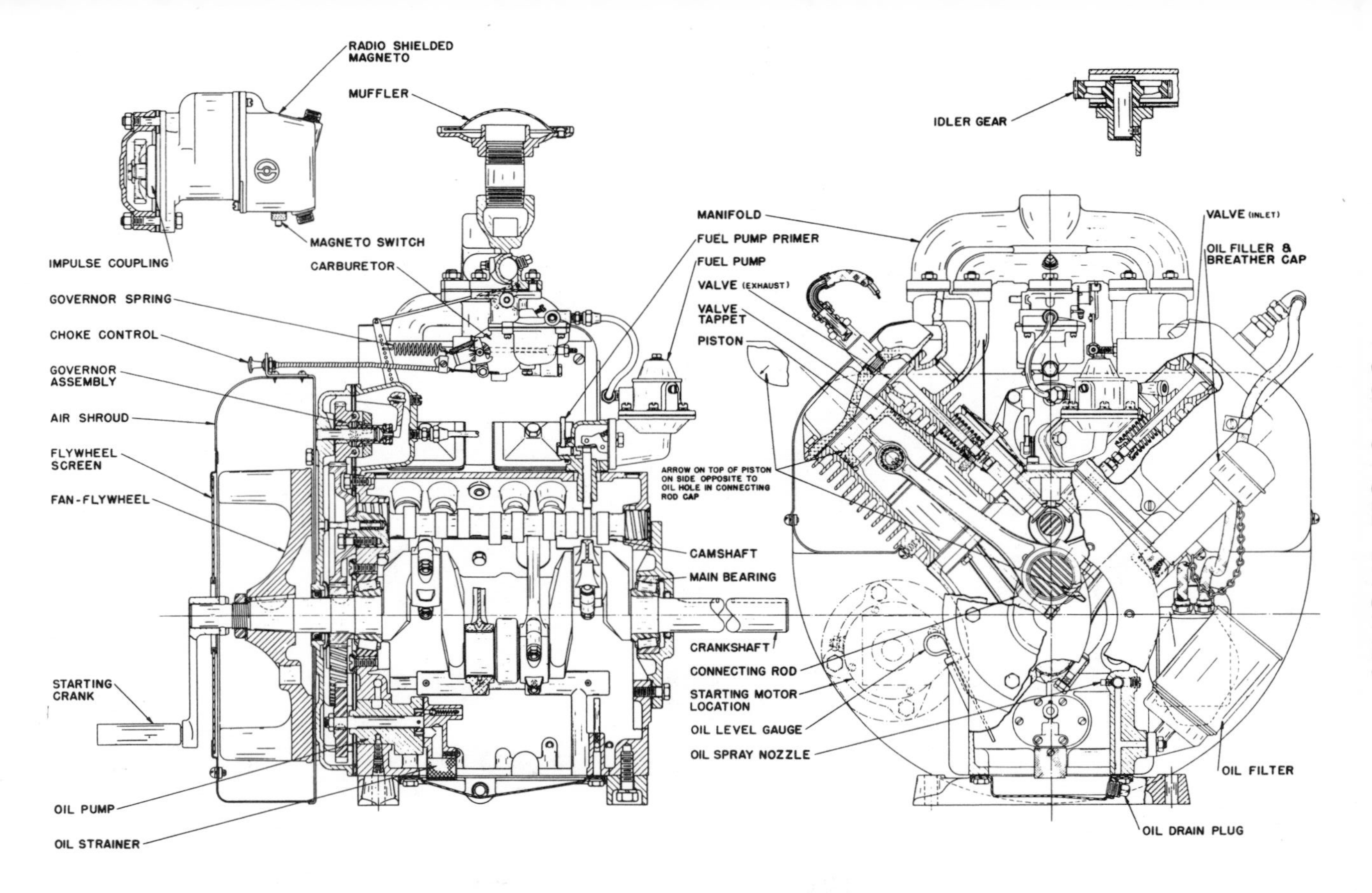

G-10. This Wisconsin four cylinder, four cycle, air cooled engine is built in Vee shape rather than having all four cylinders in line.

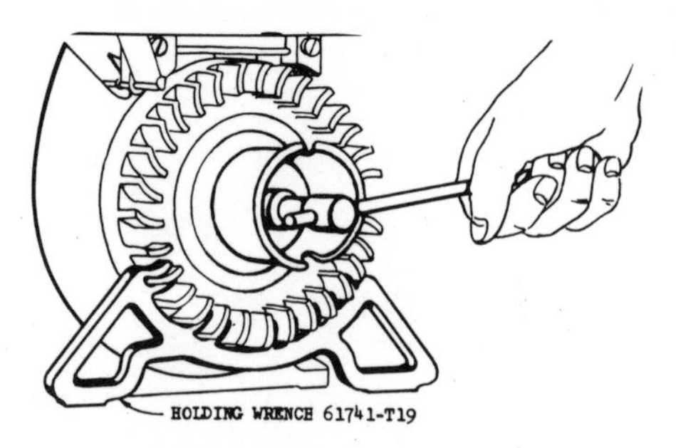

G-11. In order to get to the magneto, or disassemble the engine it is necessary to remove the flywheel on Briggs & Stratton engines. A special holding fixture is available from the factory to avoid injury to the fan vanes when removing or replacing the flywheel.

G-12. In an emergency wooden blocks can be used to hold the flywheel, but care should be taken to make sure the flywheel vanes are not damaged.

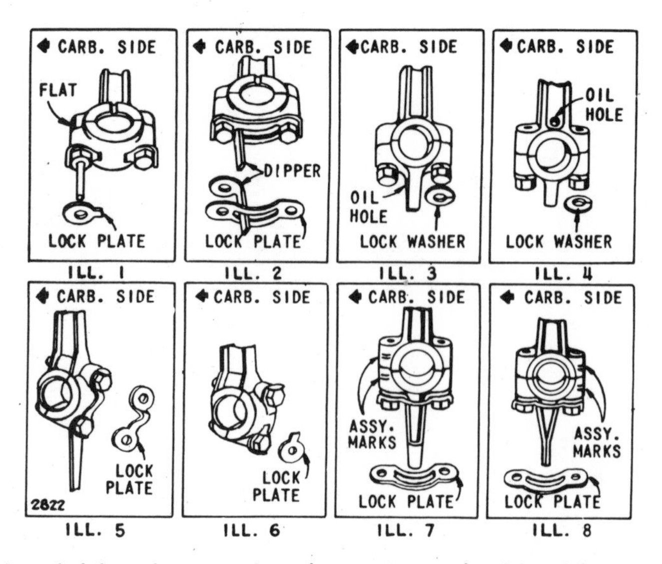

G-13. Several of the various connecting rod structures as used on Briggs & Stratton engines.

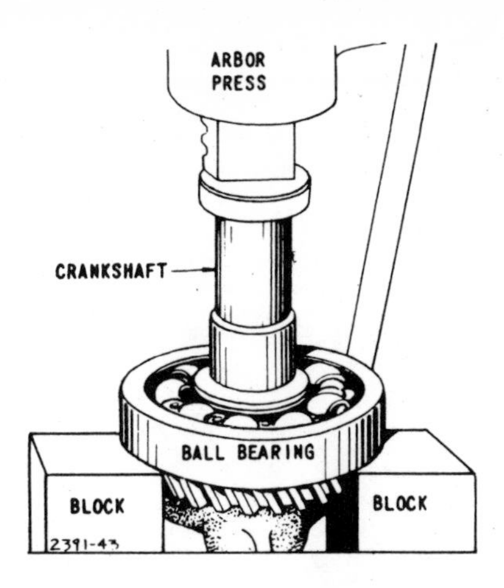

G-14. No part of an anti-friction bearing should be driven off or on the shaft with a hammer. The bearing should be solidly supported as near the shaft as possible and steady pressure exerted by a suitable press.

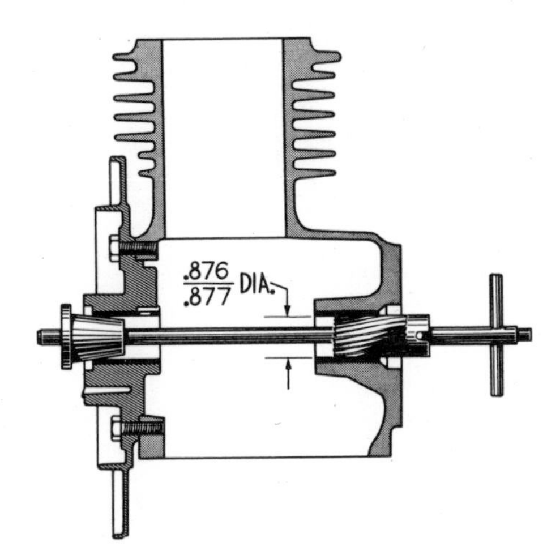

G-15. When main bearings are of the plain bushing type and must be reamed to fit the journal, it is essential to use an aligning type of reamer.

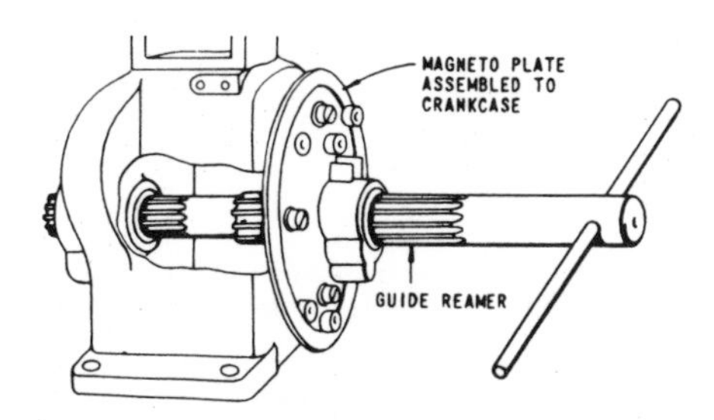

G-16. When reaming bearings mounted in a plate or crankcase flange, the plate must be bolted firmly in place to avoid misalignment.

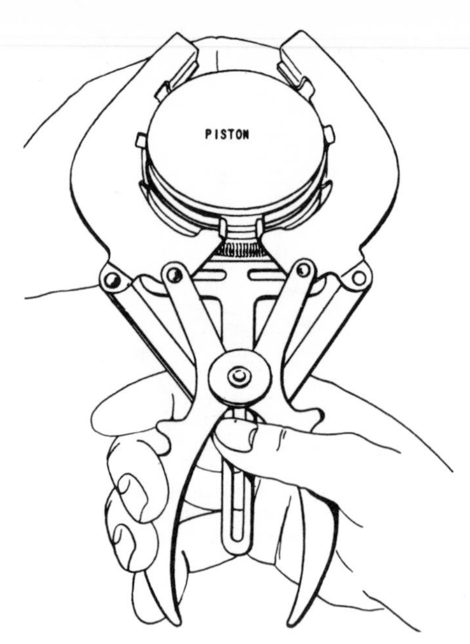

G-17. Piston rings used in small engines are of course small in diameter and easily distorted. If new rings are distorted they are worthless, so it is desirable to use a special tool when installing them on the piston.

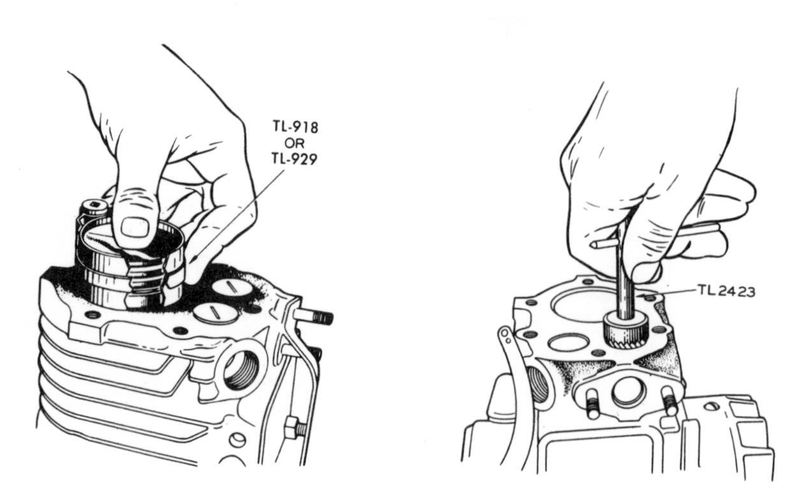

G-18. When the pistons are inserted in the cylinder, it is desirable to use a ring compressor or sleeve of suitable size to avoid damage to the sharp ring edges.

G-19. Special reamers are available and should be used to restore the valve seat surface to good condition.

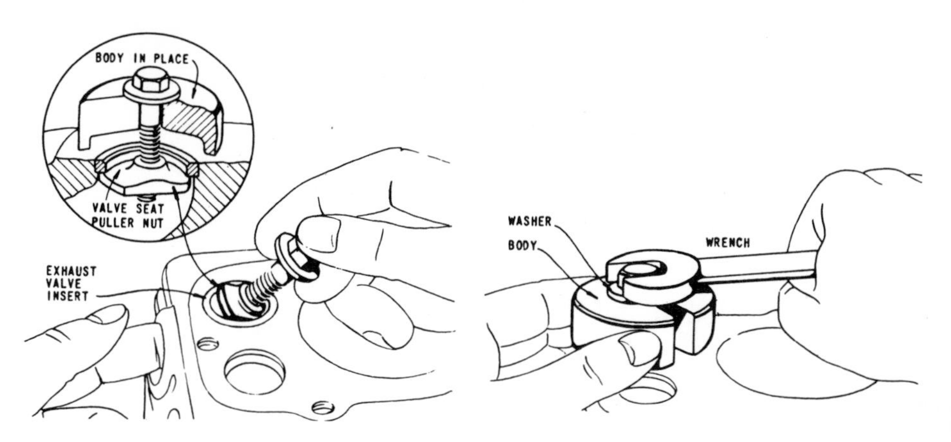

G-20. *On large engines, inserted valve seats are often broken out to remove them. On small engines, where the cylinder block is more fragile it is advisable to use special pullers to remove them.*

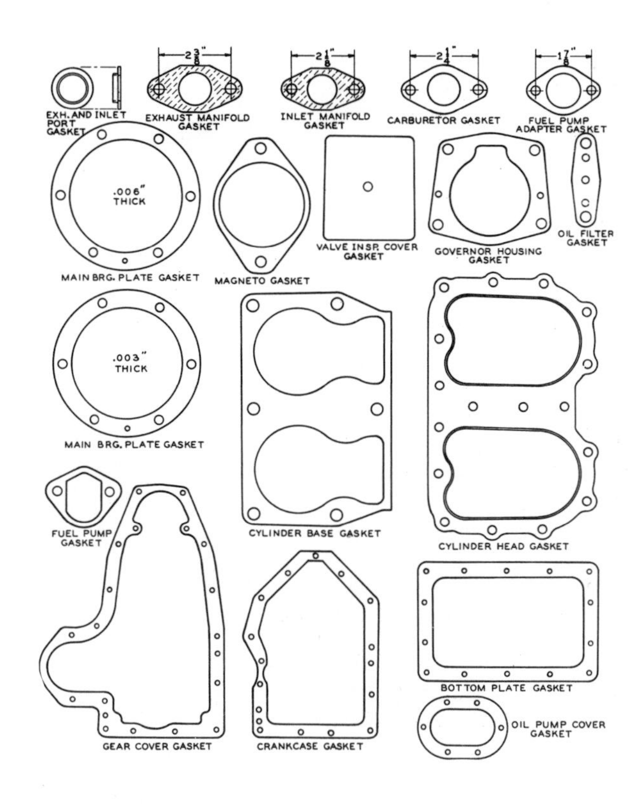

G-21. *Typical gasket set as supplied by engine manufacturer.*

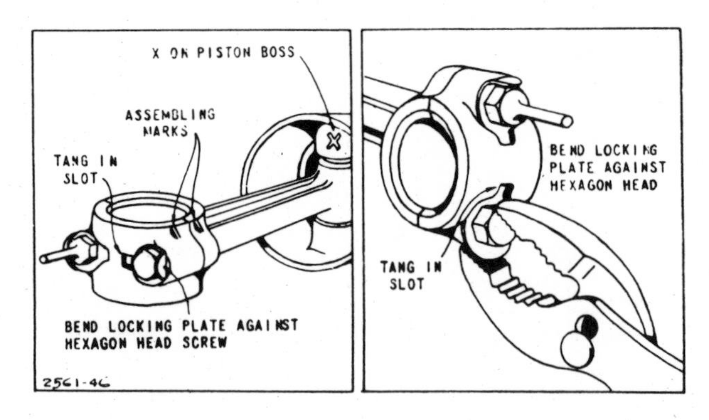

G-22. ***Where studs are used on connecting rod caps, it is essential to use new lock straps and bend the edge up securely.***

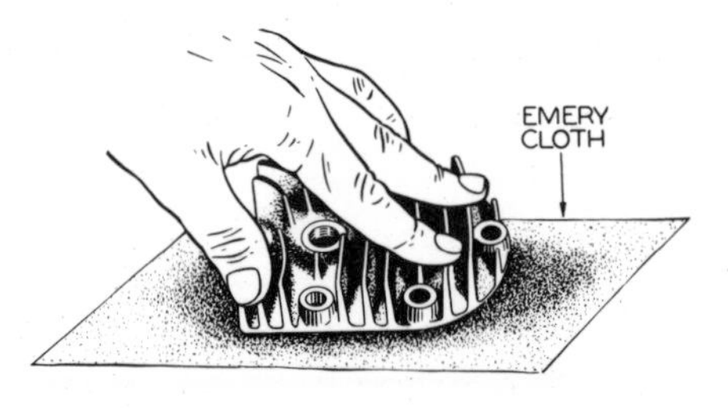

G-23. ***Small cylinder heads can often be resurfaced by placing a sheet of emery cloth on a piece of plate glass and using careful and even pressure. If badly warped, they should be replaced.***

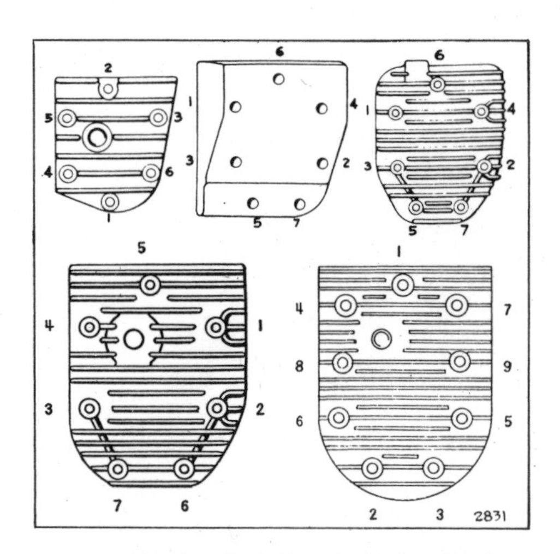

G-24. ***The cylinder head bolts should be evenly tightened with the aid of a torque-wrench. The correct sequence of tightening for various types of Briggs & Stratton cylinder heads is indicated here by numbers on the illustrations.***

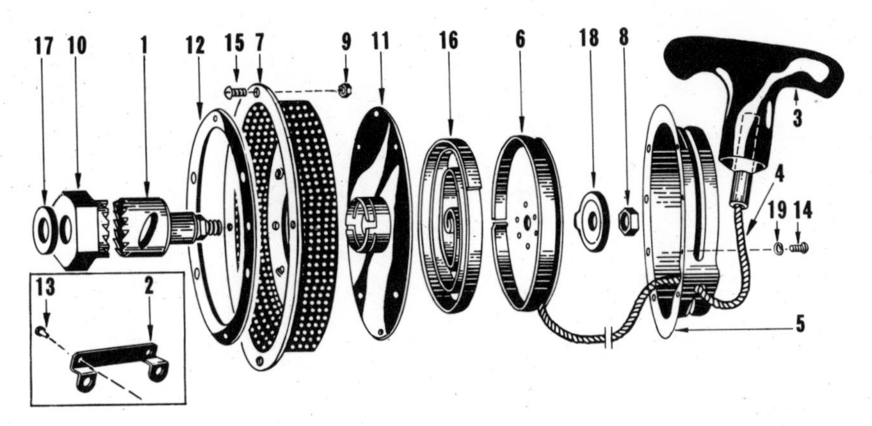

G-25. *Exploded view of rope pull starter mechanism as used on Clinton engine. This is known as a recoil type starter.*

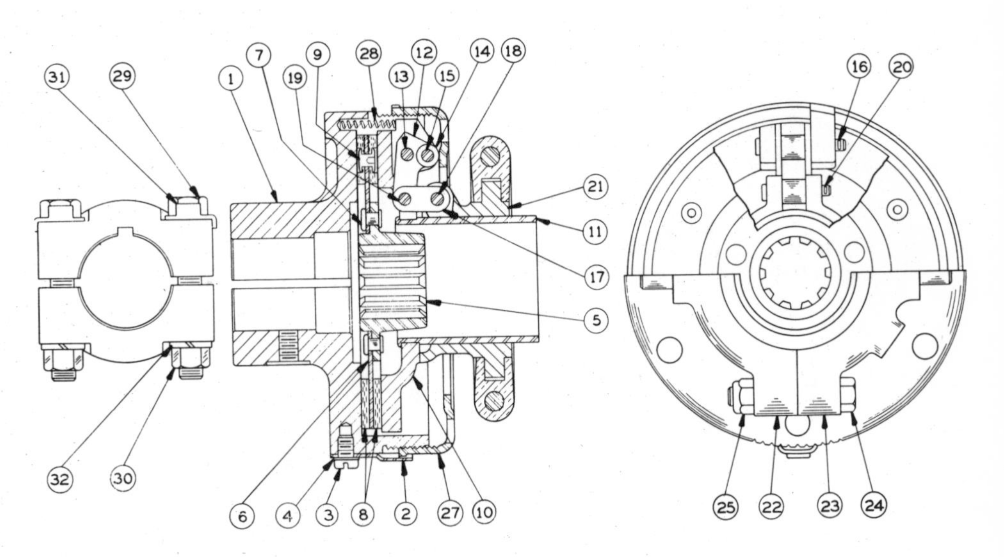

G-26. *It is often desirable to have a clutch on the engine to connect to the driven mechanism. This is a simple single plate design as used on one Wisconsin model.*

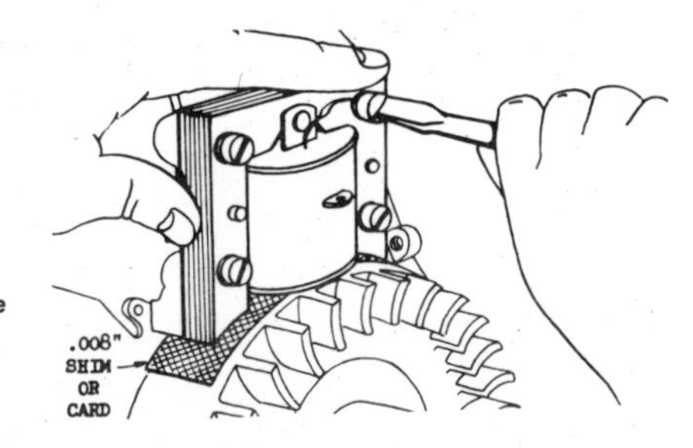

G-27. *Method of adjusting armature air gap on one type of magneto used on Briggs & Stratton engine.*

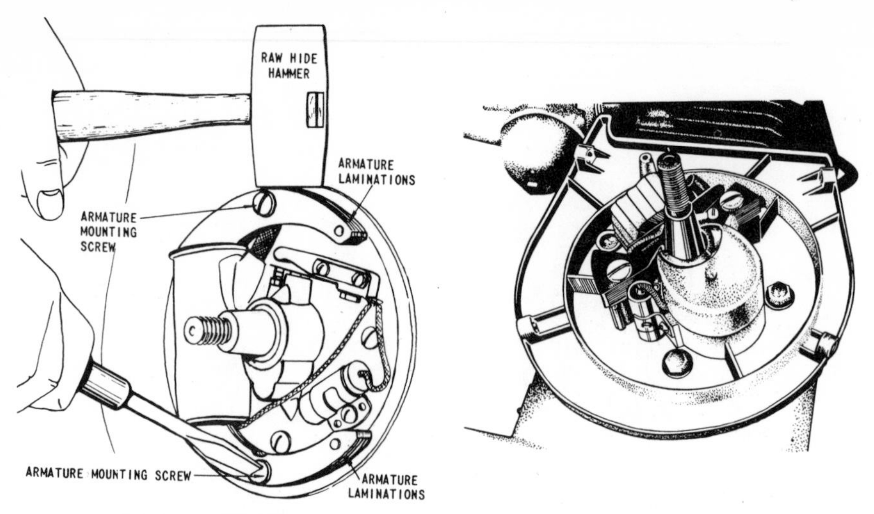

G-28. Slightly oversize holes permit slight movement of armature for position adjustment.

G-29. Phelon make of magneto as installed on Clinton engine.

G-30. Scintilla make of magneto as installed on Clinton engine.

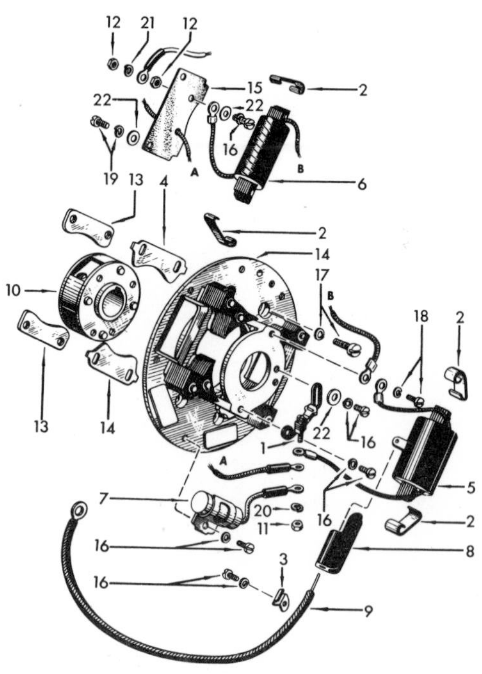

G-31. One type of Scintilla magneto as exploded to show all parts in related position.

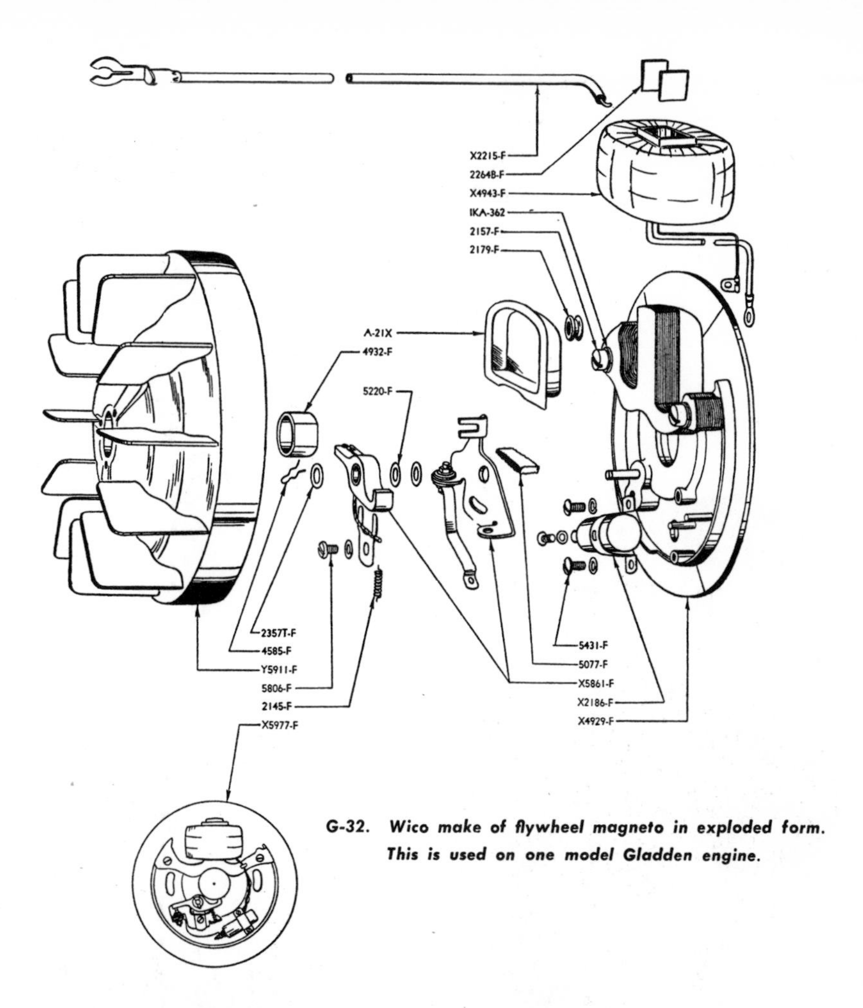

G-32. ***Wico make of flywheel magneto in exploded form. This is used on one model Gladden engine.***

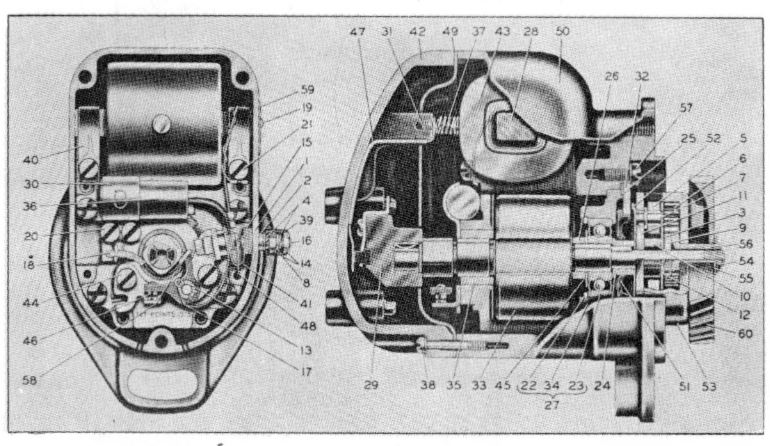

G-33. ***Wico gear driven magneto as used on four cylinder Wisconsin engine.***

G-34. Single cylinder, 4-cycle, air-cooled Wisconsin engine with 2⅝ in. bore and 2¾ in. stroke. Piston displacement is 14.88 cu. in. Engine develops 2.3 H.P. at 1600 r.p.m., and 5.6 H.P. at 3600 r.p.m.

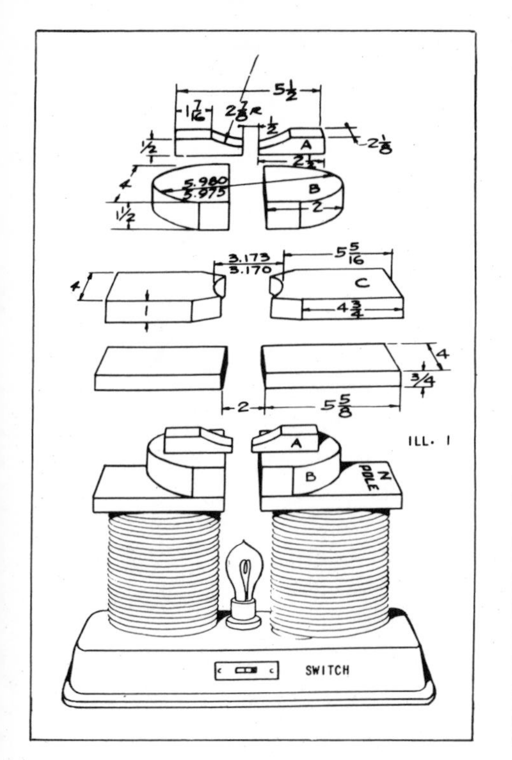

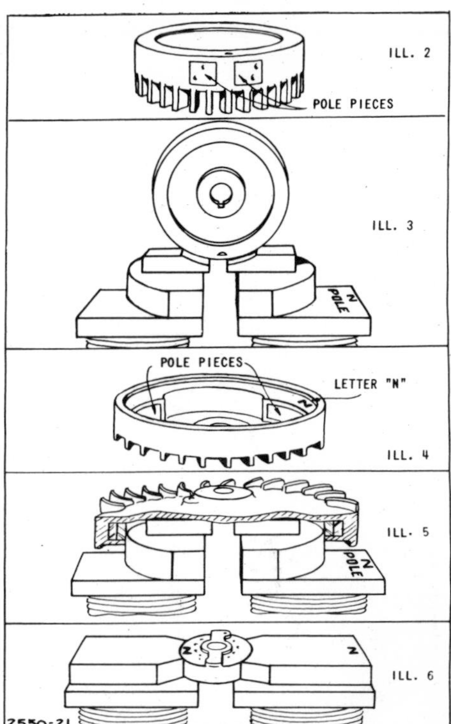

G-36. Magneto magnets whether of the flywheel, rotor or "U" type require occasional recharging. This requires special equipment as shown here.

G-37. Wiring diagram for electrical system used on four cylinder Wisconsin engine.

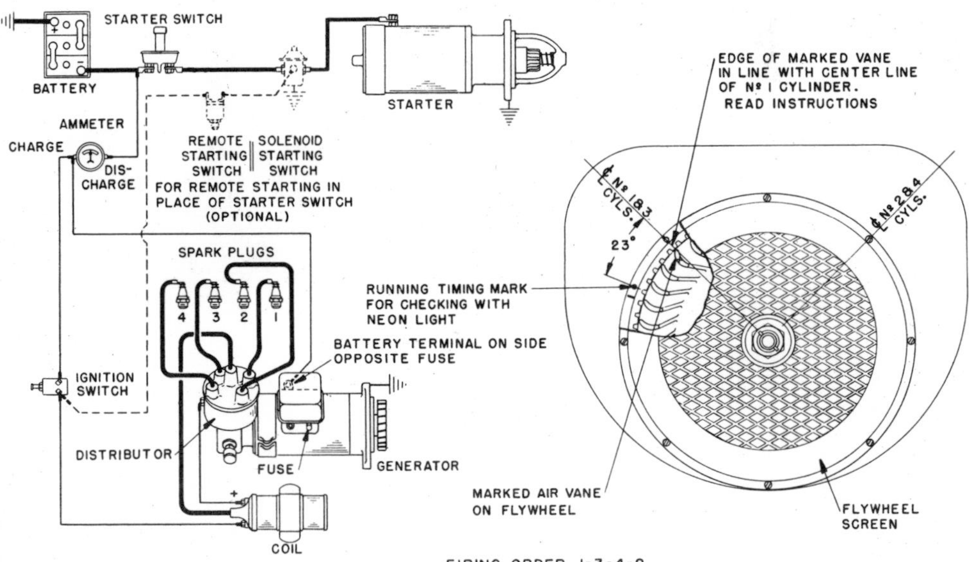

FIRING ORDER 1-3-4-2

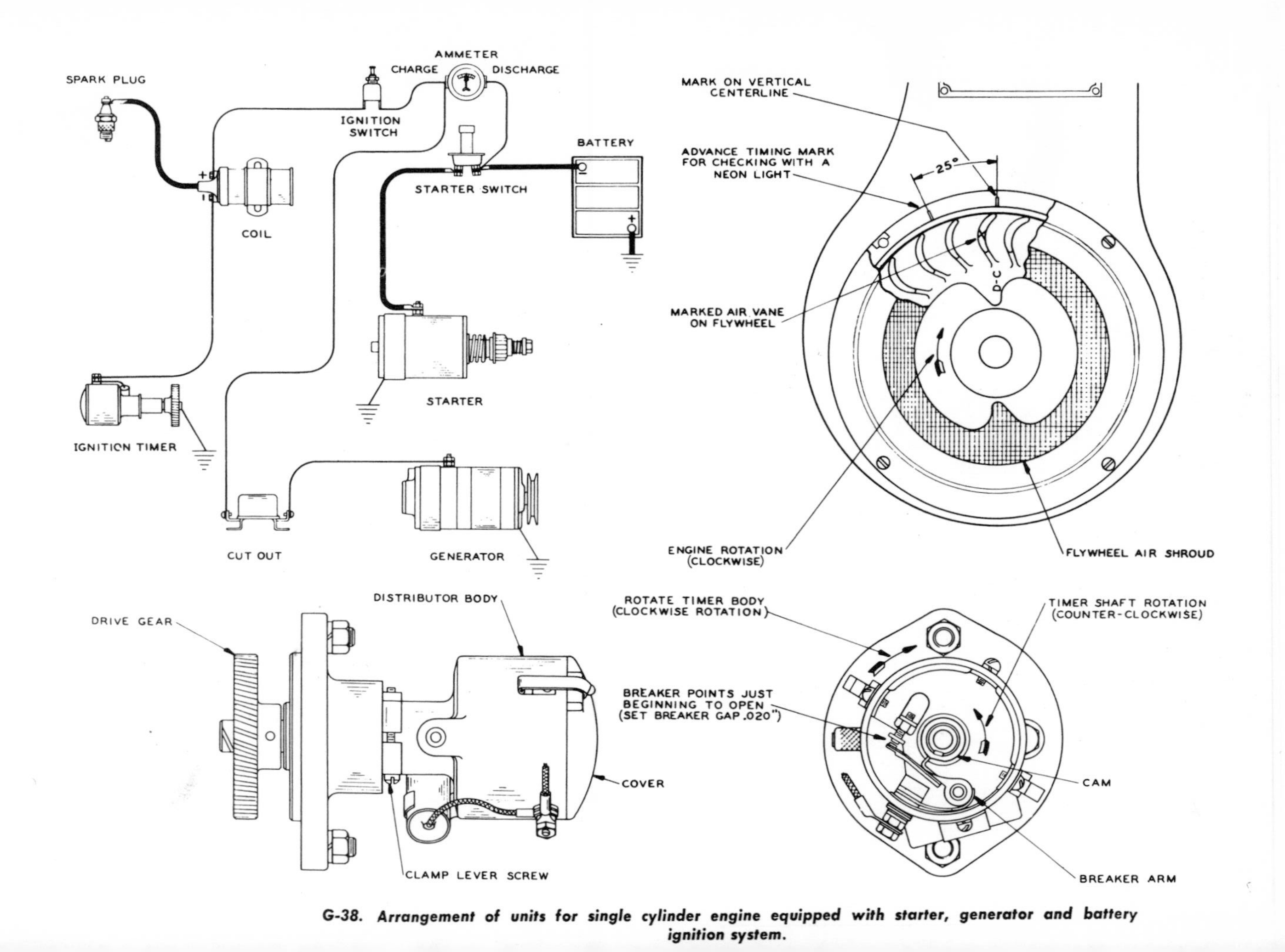

G-38. Arrangement of units for single cylinder engine equipped with starter, generator and battery ignition system.

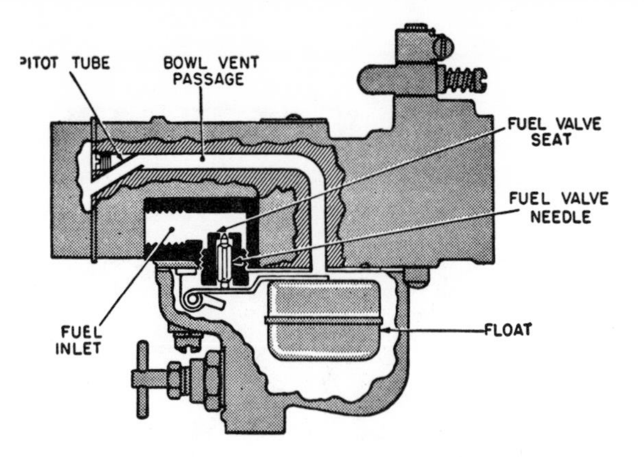

G-39. Fuel supply system of typical Zenith horizontal carburetor used on small engines.

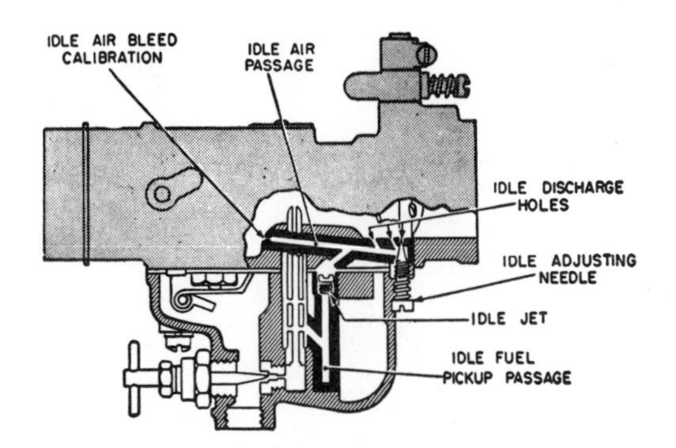

G-40. Idle system of Zenith horizontal carburetor.

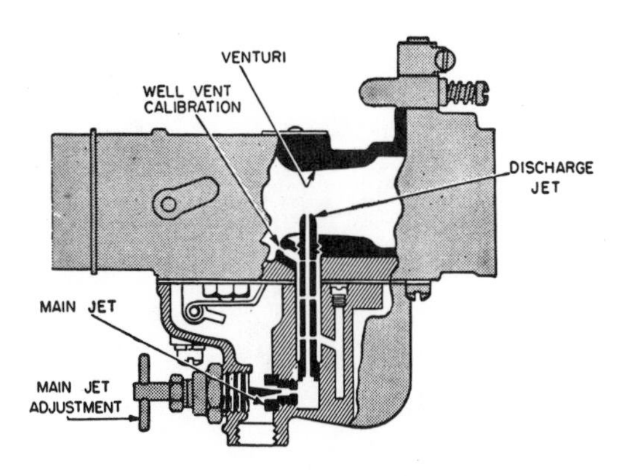

G-41. High speed system of Zenith horizontal carburetor.

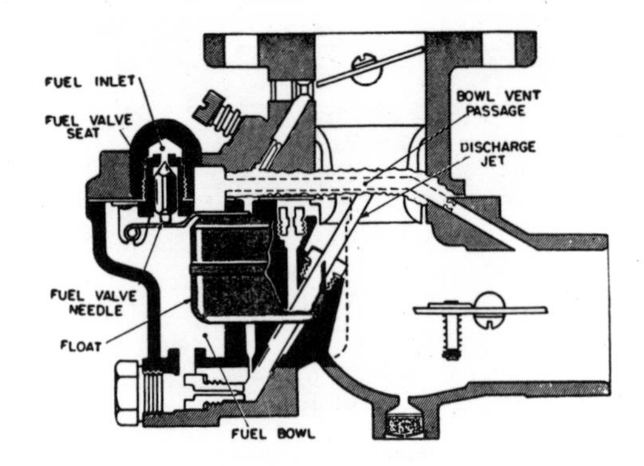

G-42. Fuel supply system of Zenith updraft type of carburetor used on small engine.

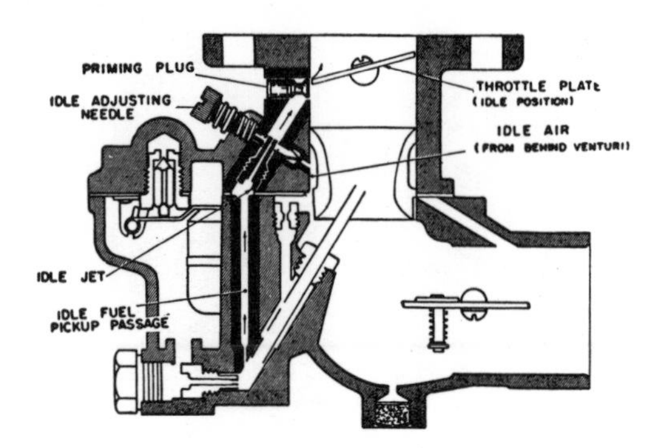

G-43. Idle system of Zenith updraft carburetor.

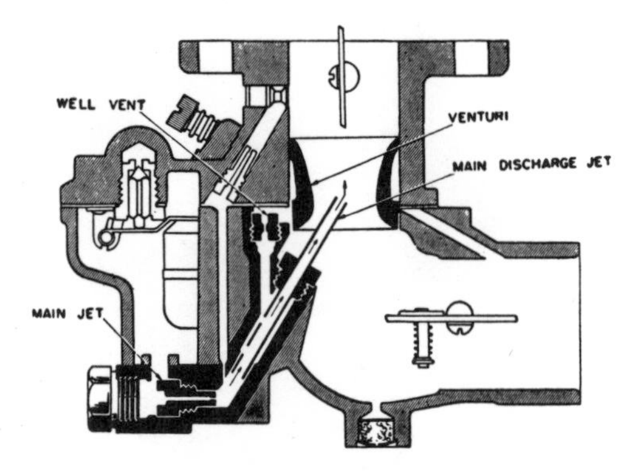

G-44. High speed system of Zenith updraft carburetor.

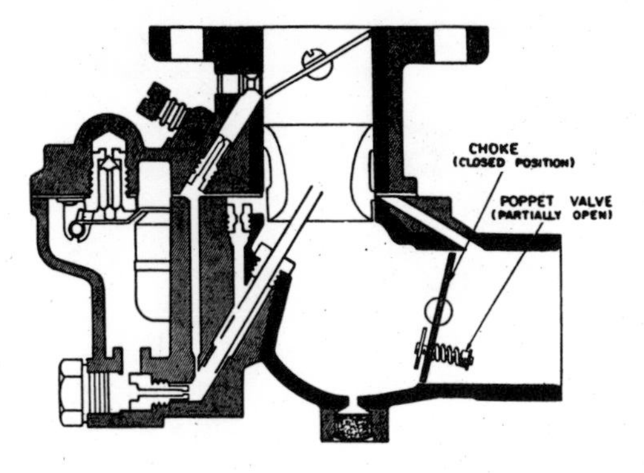

G-45. Choke system of Zenith updraft carburetor.

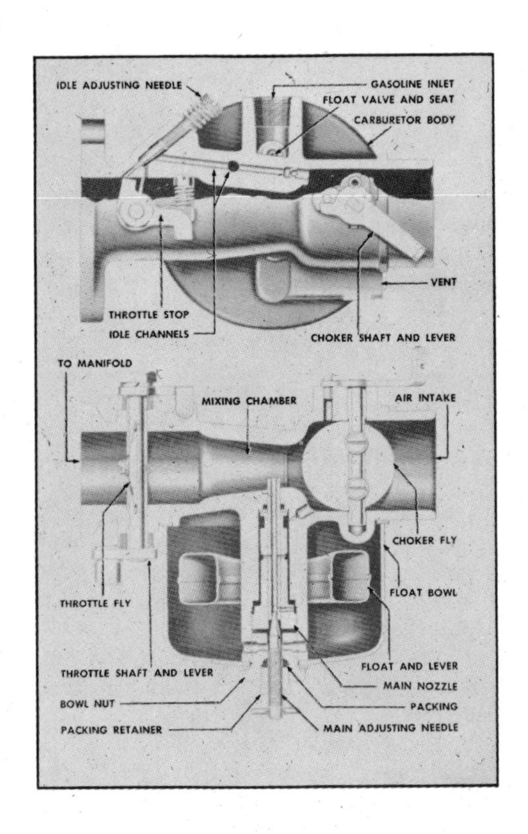

G-46. Partial cross sections of Marvel-Schebler carburetor as used on Wisconsin engine.

TWO-CYCLE ENGINES

TWO CYCLE WATER COOLED TYPES

Two cycle engines are light weight and compact. They are made in sizes up to 75 horsepower and larger. They may have one, two or more cylinders. Late models have electric starters and other accessories.

In working with these engines it must be borne in mind at all times that the parts are made as small and light as possible. Furthermore, aluminum and die cast metal is used because of its lighter weight. For these reasons the engines cannot be handled roughly. Distortion and breakage will occur if parts are improperly handled in repair operations.

For example, these engines use many anti-friction bearings of both the ball and roller type. The races, cups and balls or rollers of these bearings are almost as hard as glass and must not be hammered or punched when removed or replaced. Any sharp blow is liable to fracture or crack them and destroy their usefulness.

As these bearings must be completely free from any looseness, they are a tight fit in the housing and on the journal. When they are to be pulled out of a housing they should be firmly supported and pressed out as shown in the illustrations. This blocking is doubly important to prevent distortion of the aluminum or die cast plates or housings in which they are often mounted.

Quite often the bearing cone has an interference fit (the bearing bore slightly smaller than the shaft diameter) on the journal and in this case the bearing is heated in hot oil until it expands enough to slip easily over the shaft.

Another thing to be kept in mind when working with two cycle engines is the necessity for an air tight crankcase. It will be noted from the illustrations that the crankcase compartment is small and fits closely around the moving parts. It will also be noted that divisions in the crankcase are used to keep each cylinder separate.

This is necessary as the gas is compressed in the crankcase to force it into the cylinder ports. This of course means that the main bearing seals must be in good condition to prevent air leaks.

The same is true of gaskets. The surfaces must be smooth and free from warpage and the gasket uniform and tight. Incidentally it is well to use only the proper thickness of gasket to avoid misalignment. Some joints in some engines are lapped to fit and do not use a gasket. In such cases it may be desirable to use a suitable gasket compound on the surfaces when reassembling.

The following illustrations cover many of these special procedures. Also see comments under "Four Cycle Water and Air Cooled Engines".

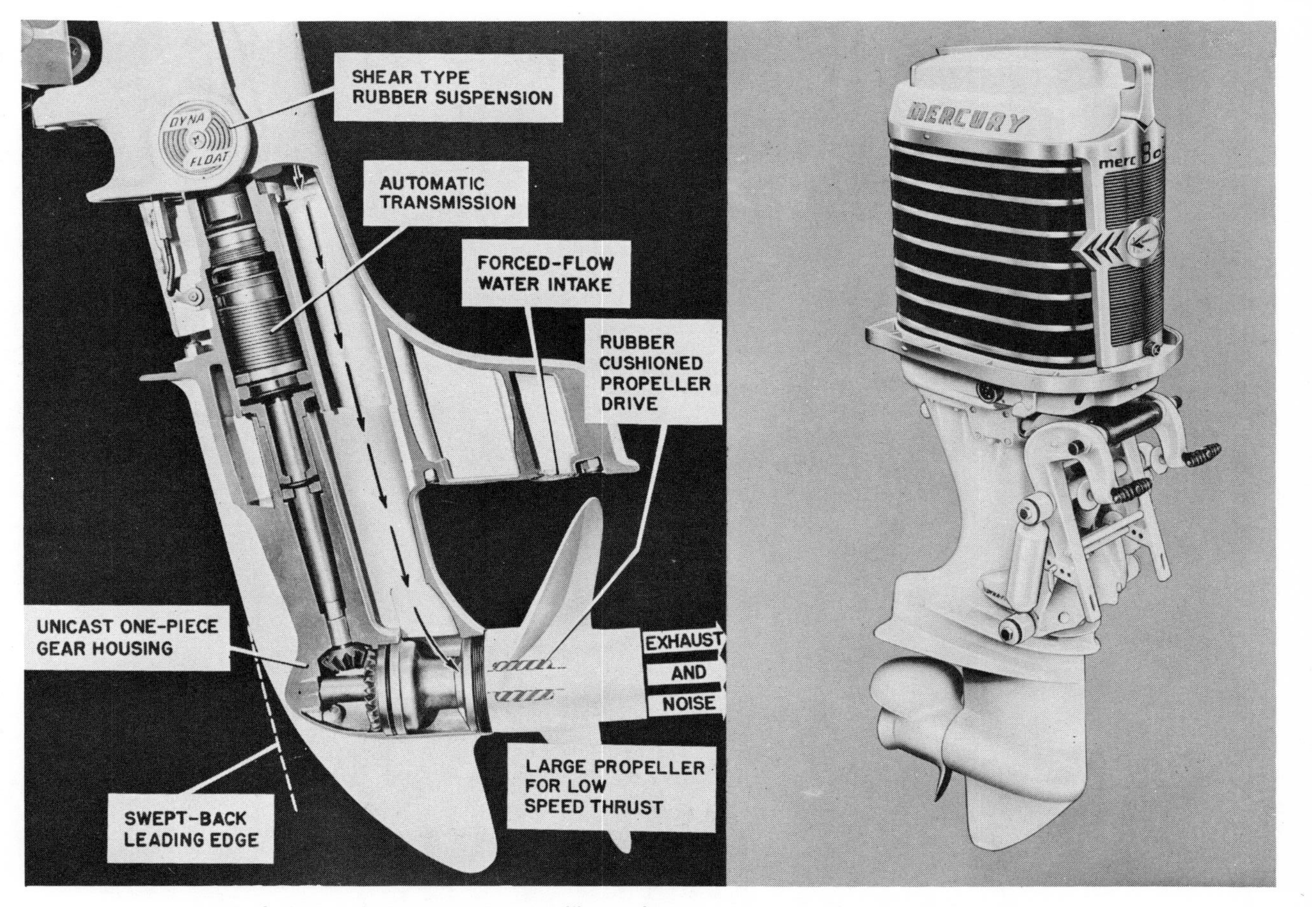

H-1. Left. Detail of engine exhaust muffling under water as used by Mercury outboard. Right. An example of high power outboards is furnished by this 80 h.p. engine having six cylinders in line.

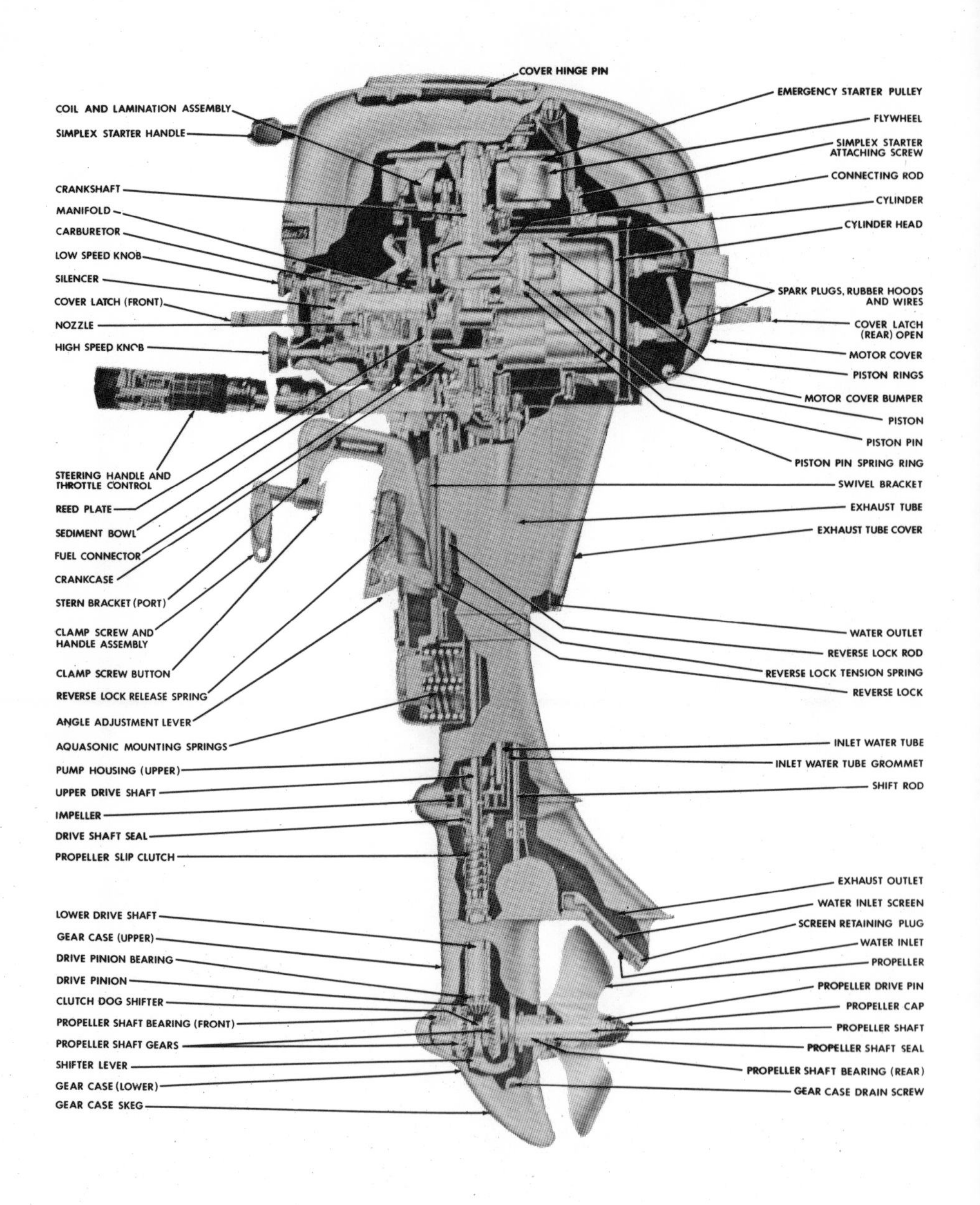

H-2. Evinrude two cylinder outboard partially cut away to show location and arrangement of all parts.

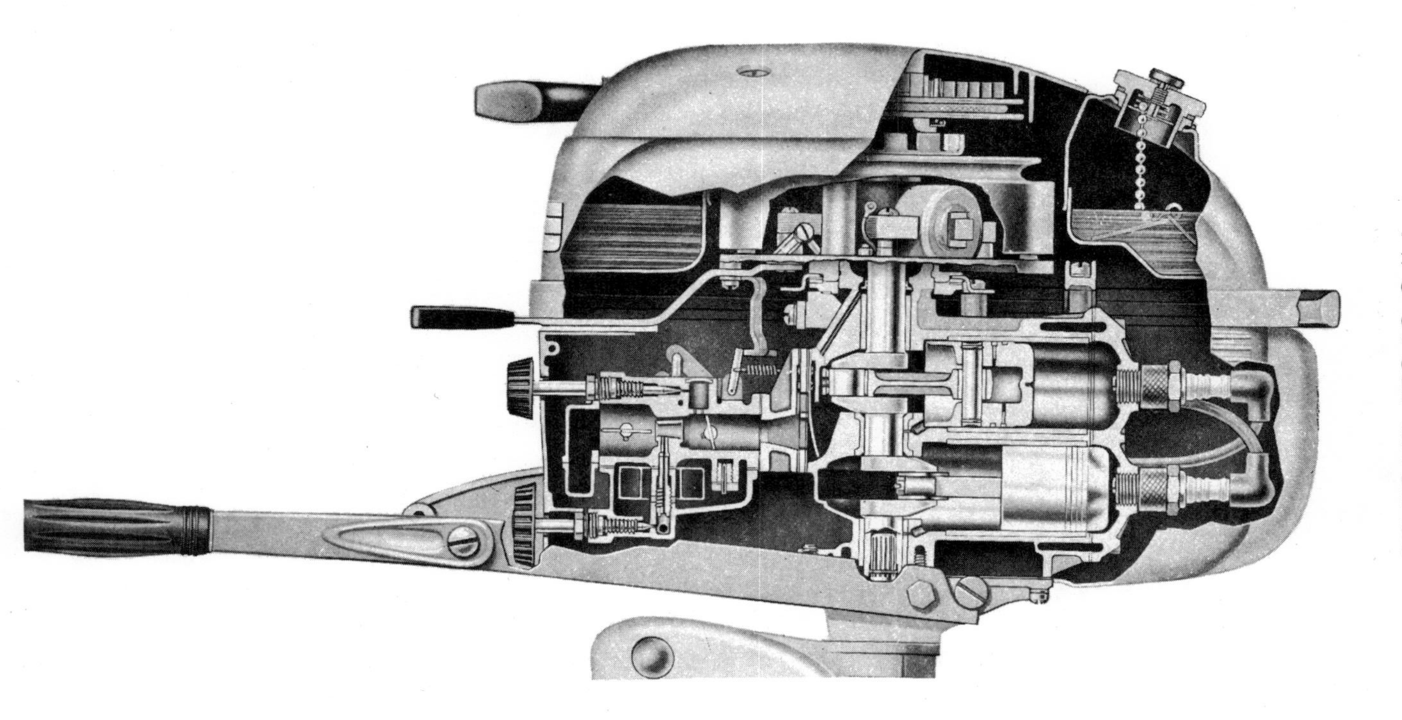

H-3. Cross section of Evinrude power head showing details of carburetor, magneto, starter and engine construction.

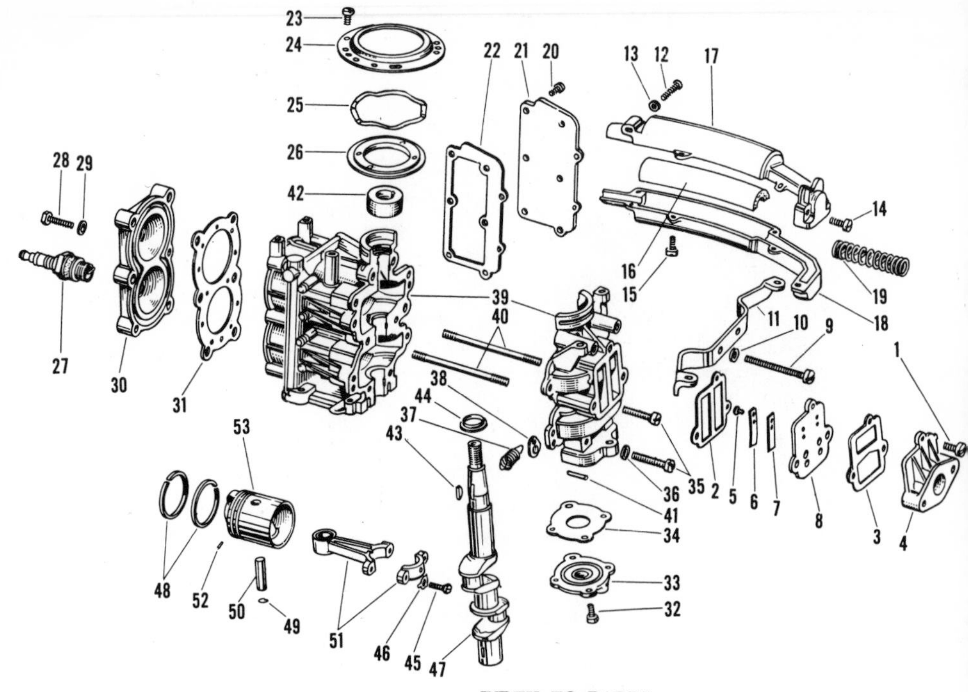

INDEX TO PARTS
(In order of disassembly)

1 Manifold to crankcase screw
2 Leaf plate to crankcase gasket
3 Leaf plate to manifold gasket
4 Carburetor manifold
5 Leaf mounting screw
6 Leaf back-up plate
7 Leaf
8 Leaf plate
9 Crankcase to cylinder screw, long
10 Crankcase to cylinder washer
11 Fuel tank mounting plate support
12 Silencer to cylinder screw
13 Silencer to cylinder screw washer
14 Silencer to carburetor screw
15 Silencer screw
16 Air silencer insert
17 Air silencer, upper half
18 Air silencer, lower half
19 Air silencer spring
20 Exhaust cover plate screw
21 Exhaust cover plate
22 Exhaust plate cover gasket
23 Armature plate support screw
24 Armature plate support
25 Armature plate wave washer
26 Armature plate retaining ring
27 Spark plug
28 Cylinder head screw
29 Cylinder head screw washer
30 Cylinder head
31 Cylinder head gasket
32 Inner flange mounting screw
33 Inner flange
34 Inner flange gasket
35 Crankcase to cylinder screw
36 Crankcase screw washer
37 High tension leads spring
38 Clamp
39 Cylinder and crankcase assembly
40 Cylinder and crankcase stud
41 Taper pin
42 Magneto cam
43 Flywheel key
44 Oil slinger
45 Connecting rod screw
46 Connecting rod screw lockplate
47 Crankshaft
48 Piston ring
49 Piston pin spring ring
50 Piston pin
51 Connecting rod assembly
52 Piston dowel pin
53 Piston, less rings

H-4. Lightweight Evinrude two cylinder engine in exploded form. This engine uses a plain crankshaft, plain bearings and two ring pistons.

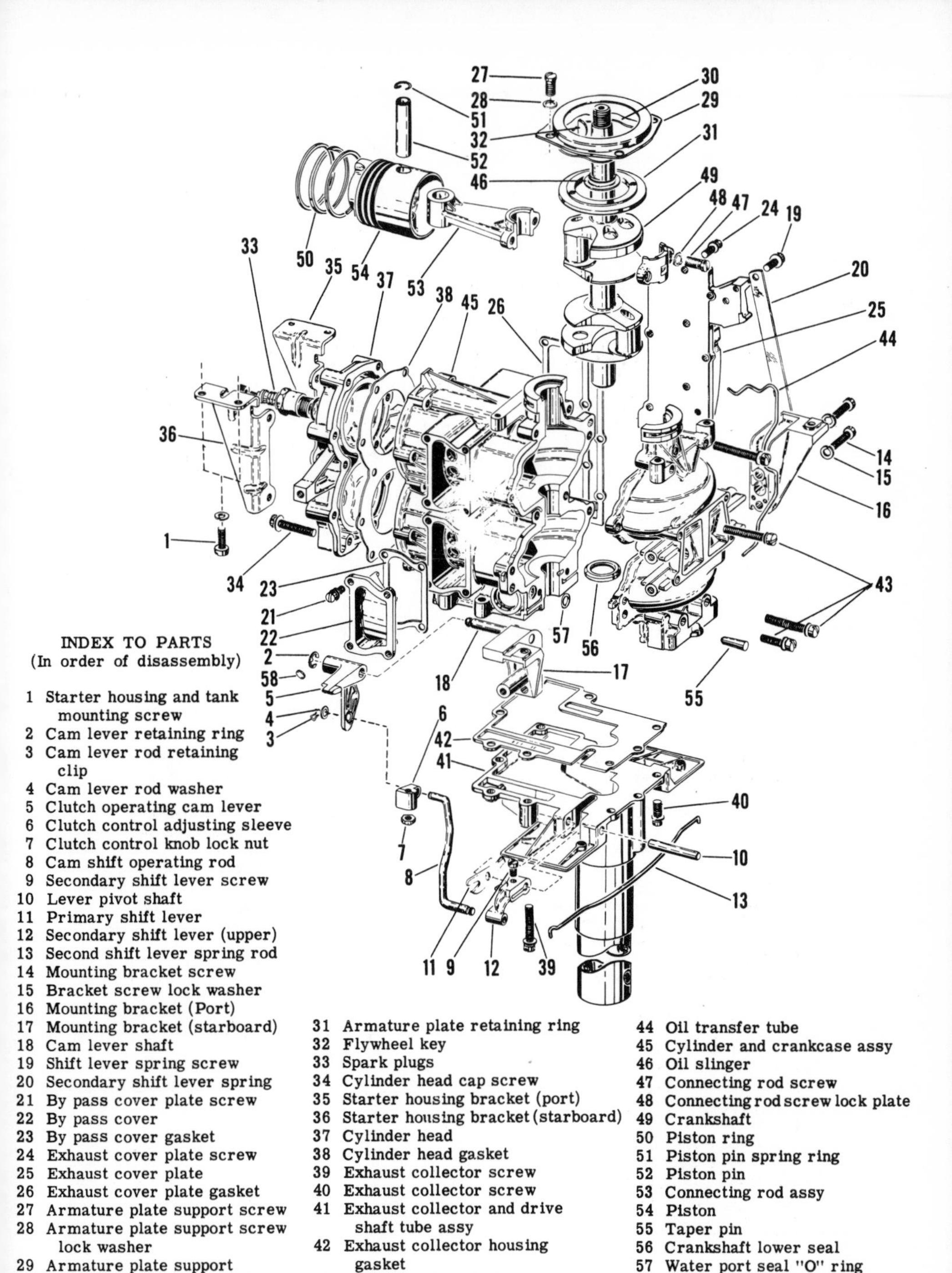

H-5. Heavier Evinrude two cylinder engine having a counterweighted crankshaft, plain bearings and three ring pistons.

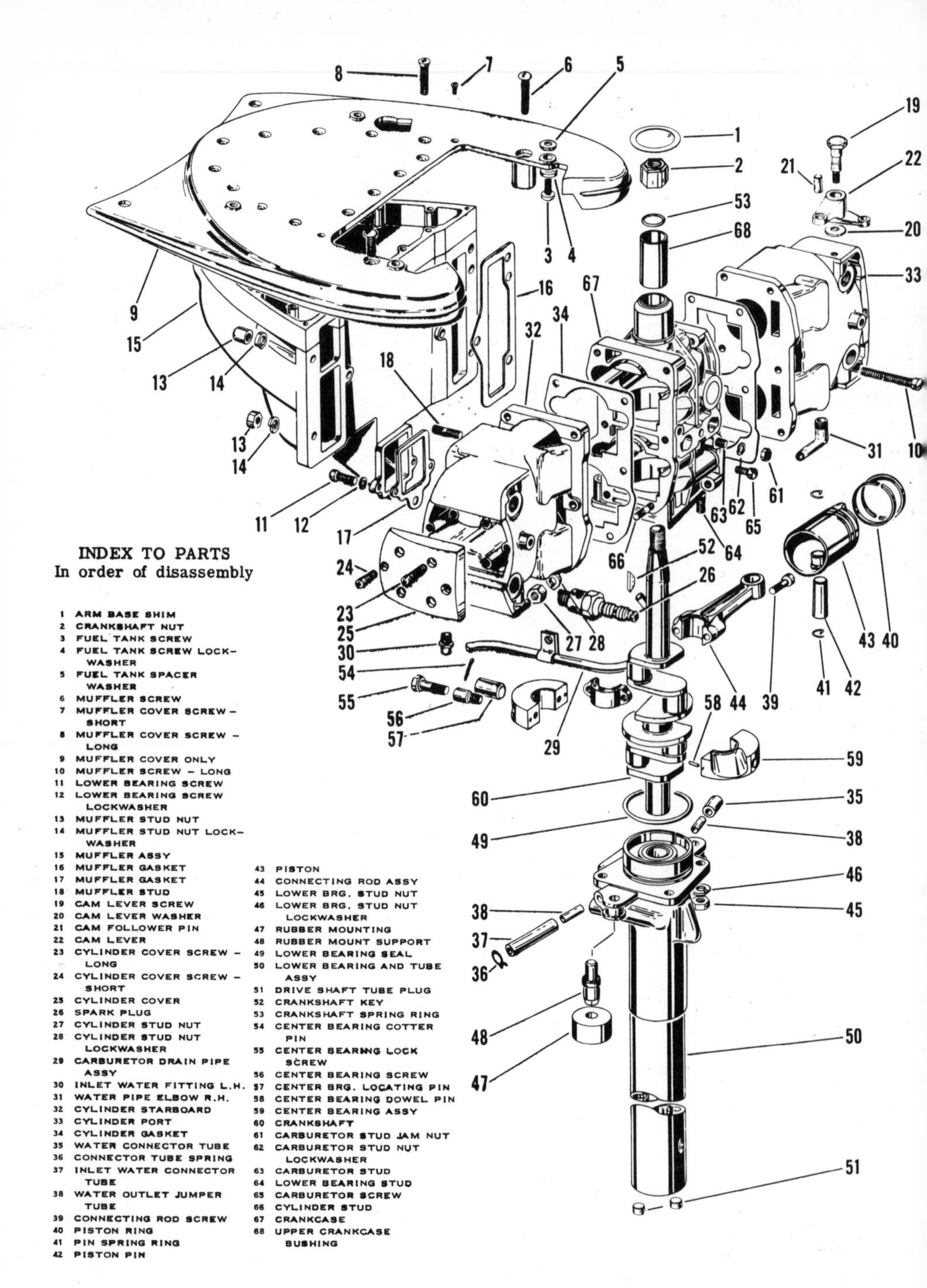

H-6. Four cylinder Evinrude outboard having two cylinder blocks; one "port" and the other "starboard."

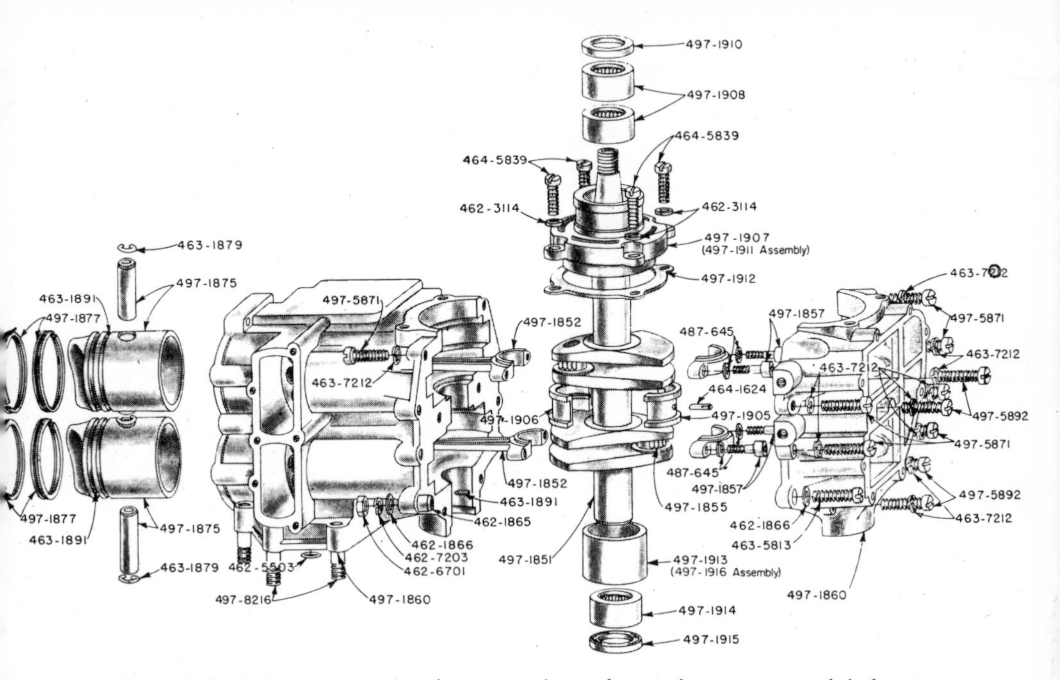

H-7. Two cylinder Scott-Atwater outboard engine with anti-friction bearings on crankshaft main and connecting rod bearings.

H-8. This V-four Evinrude outboard engine is similar in some constructional ways to V-type automobile engine.

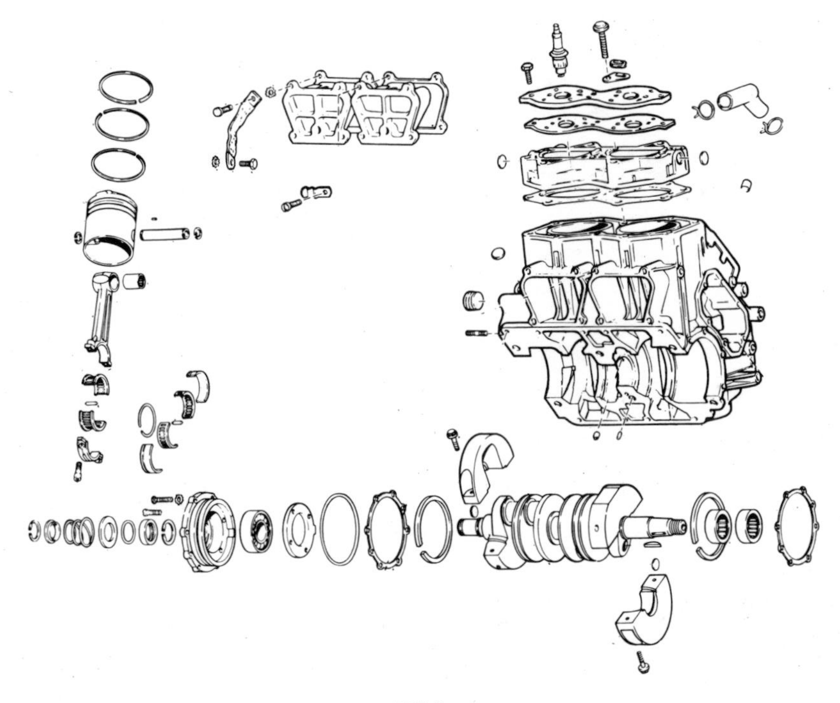

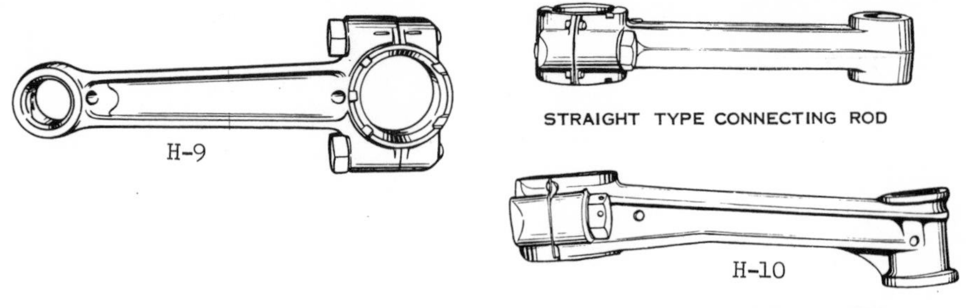

H-9. Typical plain bearing type of outboard engine connecting rod.

H-10. Outboard connecting rods may be either straight or of the offset type.

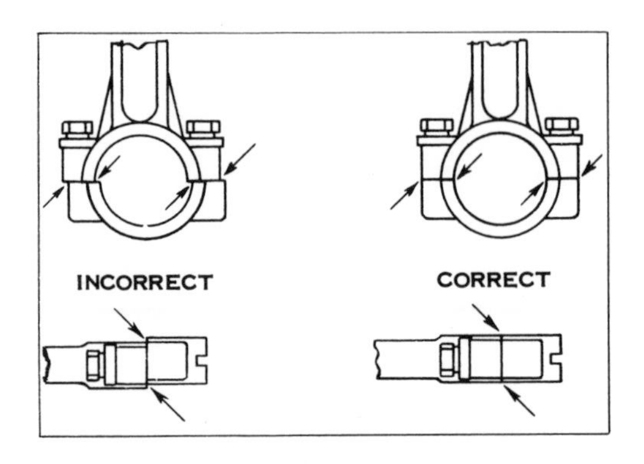

H-11. All split bearing caps should be marked before disassembly in order to avoid mis-mating.

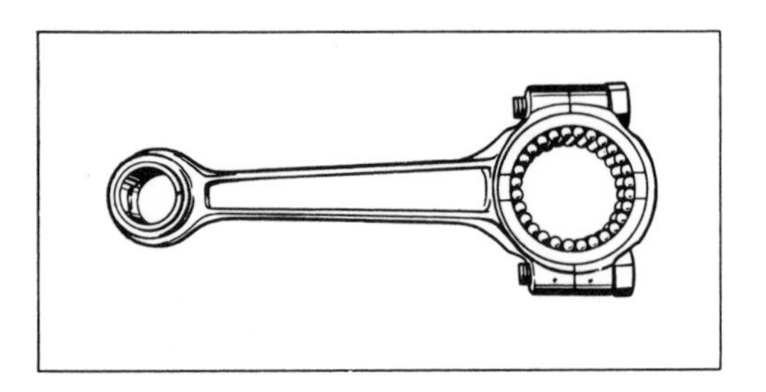

H-12. One type of anti-friction bearing used on outboard engine connecting rods.

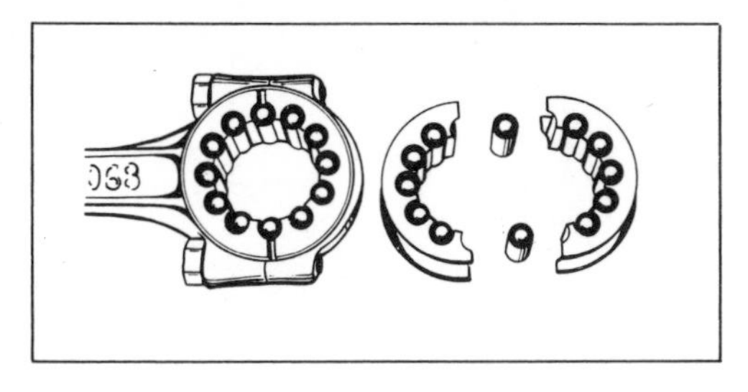

H-13. *Another type of outboard engine connecting rod anti-friction bearing.*

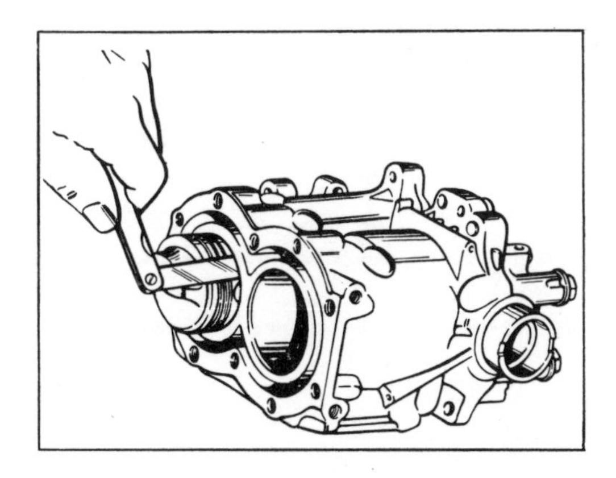

H-14. *One method of measuring clearance between piston skirt and cylinder wall using feeler gauge.*

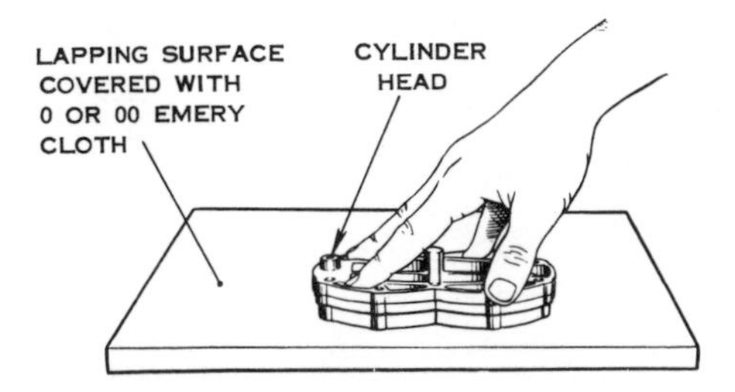

H-15. *Pump housings, cylinder heads and other flat parts can be trued up with lapping compound on a surface plate or with emery cloth on a piece of plate glass as shown here.*

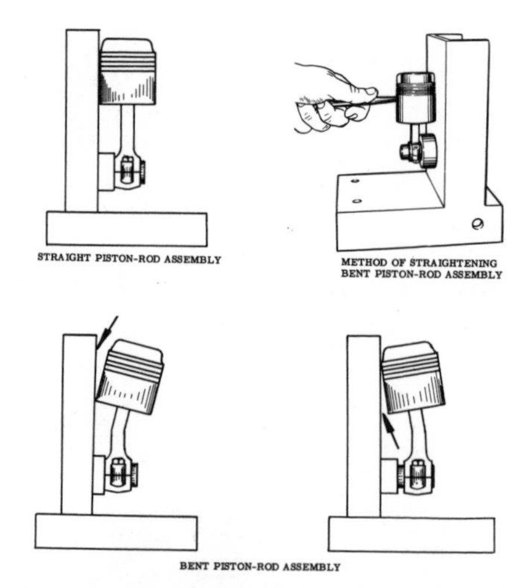

H-16. Every piston and rod assembly should be checked for bend or twist before assembly.

H-17. Evinrude lightweight gear housing using plain bearings on propeller shaft.

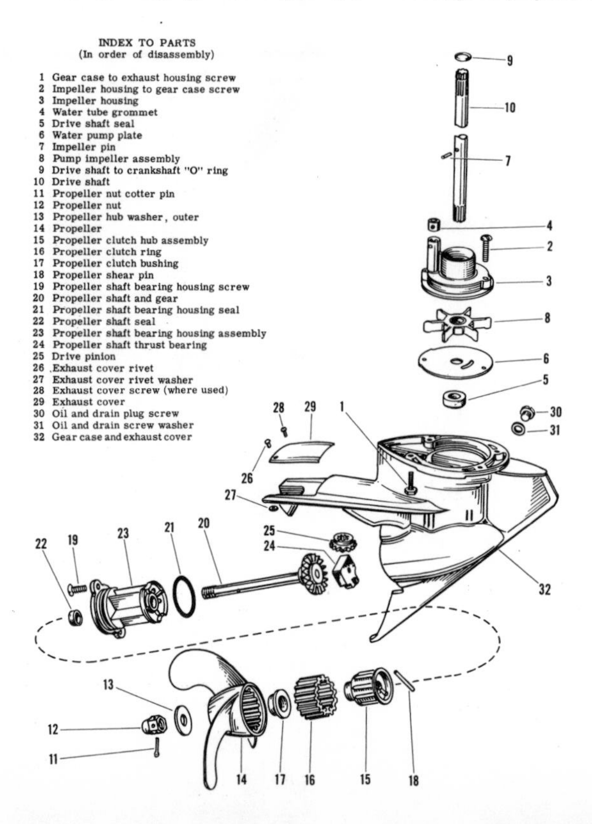

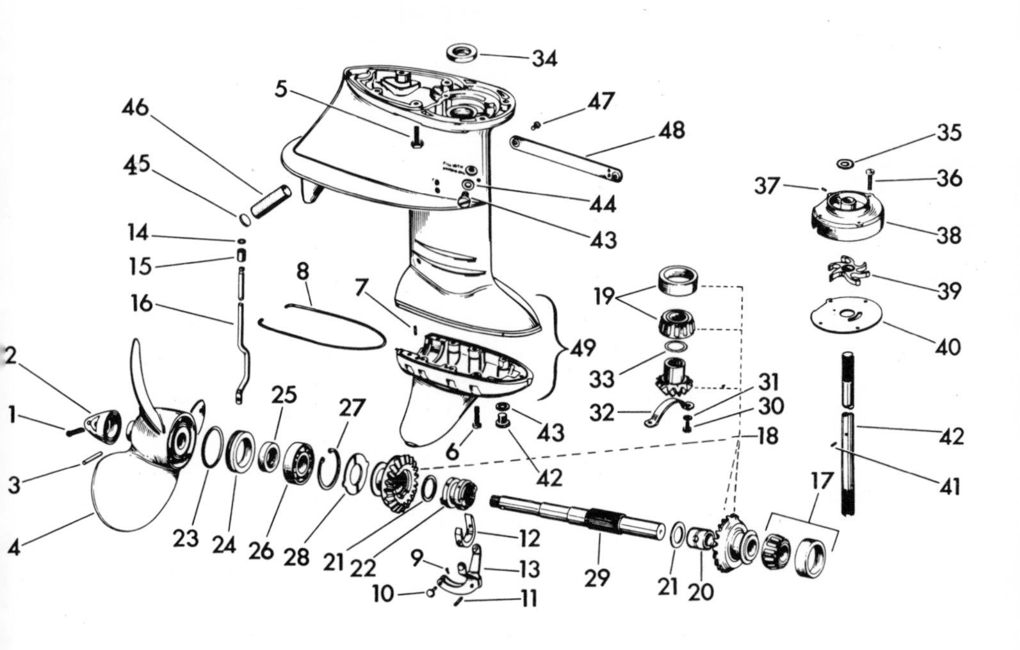

PARTS INDEX
(In order of disassembly)

1 Propeller nut cotter pin
2 Propeller nut
3 Propeller shear pin
4 Propeller & bushing
5 Gear case to exhaust tube screw
6 Gear case screw
7 Gear case to oil retainer dowel
8 Lower to upper gear case seal
9 Shift rod shifter lever cotter pin
10 Shift rod pin
11 Shift lever pin
12 Cradle
13 Shift lever & pin assembly
14 Lower shift rod "O" ring
15 Lower shift rod bushing
16 Shift rod lower
17 Propeller shaft roller bearing with cup
18 Matched set of gears with pinion bearing
19 Pinion roller bearing & cup assembly
20 Reverse gear bushing
21 Propeller shaft thrust washer
22 Shifter clutch dog assembly
23 Oil retainer housing "O" ring
24 Propeller shaft oil seal retainer housing
25 Propeller shaft oil seal
26 Propeller shaft ball bearing
27 Gear case retaining ring
28 Reverse gear thrust washer
29 Propeller shaft
30 Drive shaft support screw
31 Drive shaft support screw lock washer
32 Drive shaft support
33 Pinion bearing shim
34 Drive shaft oil retainer
35 Drive shaft to crankshaft seal
36 Impeller housing screw
37 Impeller housing plug
38 Water pump impeller housing
39 Impeller
40 Impeller housing plate
41 Impeller pin
42 Drive shaft
43 Drain and fill screw
44 Drain and fill screw washer
45 Water intake screen plug
46 Water intake screen
47 Water by-pass cover screw
48 Water by-pass cover
49 Gear case assembly, upper and lower

H-18. Another Evinrude design of gear housing which uses anti-friction bearings of both ball and roller type on driveshaft and propeller shaft.

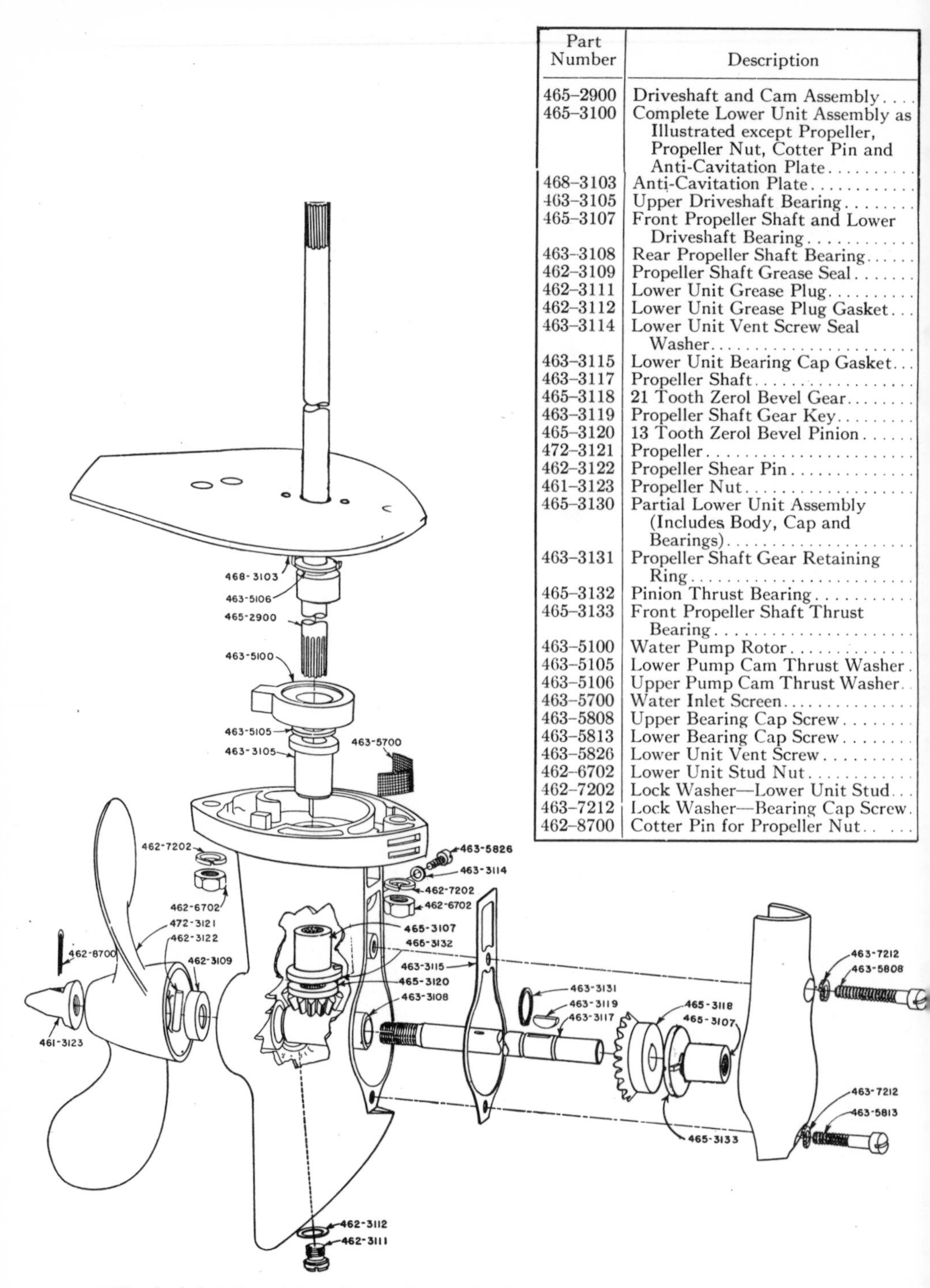

Part Number	Description
465–2900	Driveshaft and Cam Assembly....
465–3100	Complete Lower Unit Assembly as Illustrated except Propeller, Propeller Nut, Cotter Pin and Anti-Cavitation Plate..........
468–3103	Anti-Cavitation Plate............
463–3105	Upper Driveshaft Bearing........
465–3107	Front Propeller Shaft and Lower Driveshaft Bearing...........
463–3108	Rear Propeller Shaft Bearing......
462–3109	Propeller Shaft Grease Seal.......
462–3111	Lower Unit Grease Plug.........
462–3112	Lower Unit Grease Plug Gasket...
463–3114	Lower Unit Vent Screw Seal Washer.....................
463–3115	Lower Unit Bearing Cap Gasket...
463–3117	Propeller Shaft.................
465–3118	21 Tooth Zerol Bevel Gear.......
463–3119	Propeller Shaft Gear Key........
465–3120	13 Tooth Zerol Bevel Pinion......
472–3121	Propeller.......................
462–3122	Propeller Shear Pin.............
461–3123	Propeller Nut..................
465–3130	Partial Lower Unit Assembly (Includes Body, Cap and Bearings)...................
463–3131	Propeller Shaft Gear Retaining Ring......................
465–3132	Pinion Thrust Bearing..........
465–3133	Front Propeller Shaft Thrust Bearing.....................
463–5100	Water Pump Rotor.............
463–5105	Lower Pump Cam Thrust Washer.
463–5106	Upper Pump Cam Thrust Washer..
463–5700	Water Inlet Screen..............
463–5808	Upper Bearing Cap Screw........
463–5813	Lower Bearing Cap Screw........
463–5826	Lower Unit Vent Screw.........
462–6702	Lower Unit Stud Nut...........
462–7202	Lock Washer—Lower Unit Stud...
463–7212	Lock Washer—Bearing Cap Screw.
462–8700	Cotter Pin for Propeller Nut.. ...

H-19. Exploded view of Scott-Atwater lower unit showing location of driveshaft, propeller shaft and water pump.

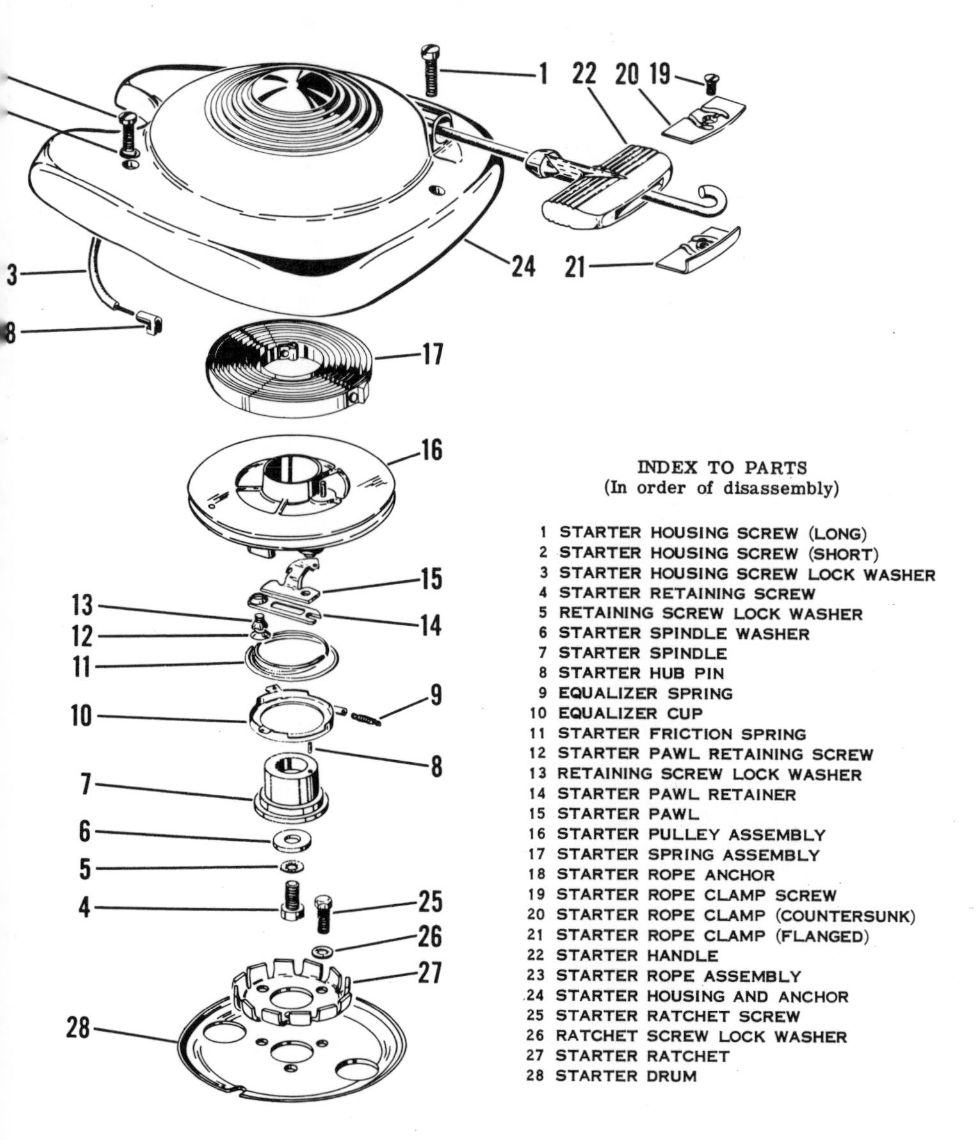

INDEX TO PARTS
(In order of disassembly)

1 STARTER HOUSING SCREW (LONG)
2 STARTER HOUSING SCREW (SHORT)
3 STARTER HOUSING SCREW LOCK WASHER
4 STARTER RETAINING SCREW
5 RETAINING SCREW LOCK WASHER
6 STARTER SPINDLE WASHER
7 STARTER SPINDLE
8 STARTER HUB PIN
9 EQUALIZER SPRING
10 EQUALIZER CUP
11 STARTER FRICTION SPRING
12 STARTER PAWL RETAINING SCREW
13 RETAINING SCREW LOCK WASHER
14 STARTER PAWL RETAINER
15 STARTER PAWL
16 STARTER PULLEY ASSEMBLY
17 STARTER SPRING ASSEMBLY
18 STARTER ROPE ANCHOR
19 STARTER ROPE CLAMP SCREW
20 STARTER ROPE CLAMP (COUNTERSUNK)
21 STARTER ROPE CLAMP (FLANGED)
22 STARTER HANDLE
23 STARTER ROPE ASSEMBLY
24 STARTER HOUSING AND ANCHOR
25 STARTER RATCHET SCREW
26 RATCHET SCREW LOCK WASHER
27 STARTER RATCHET
28 STARTER DRUM

H-20. Simplex mechanical starter as used on Evinrude outboard engine.

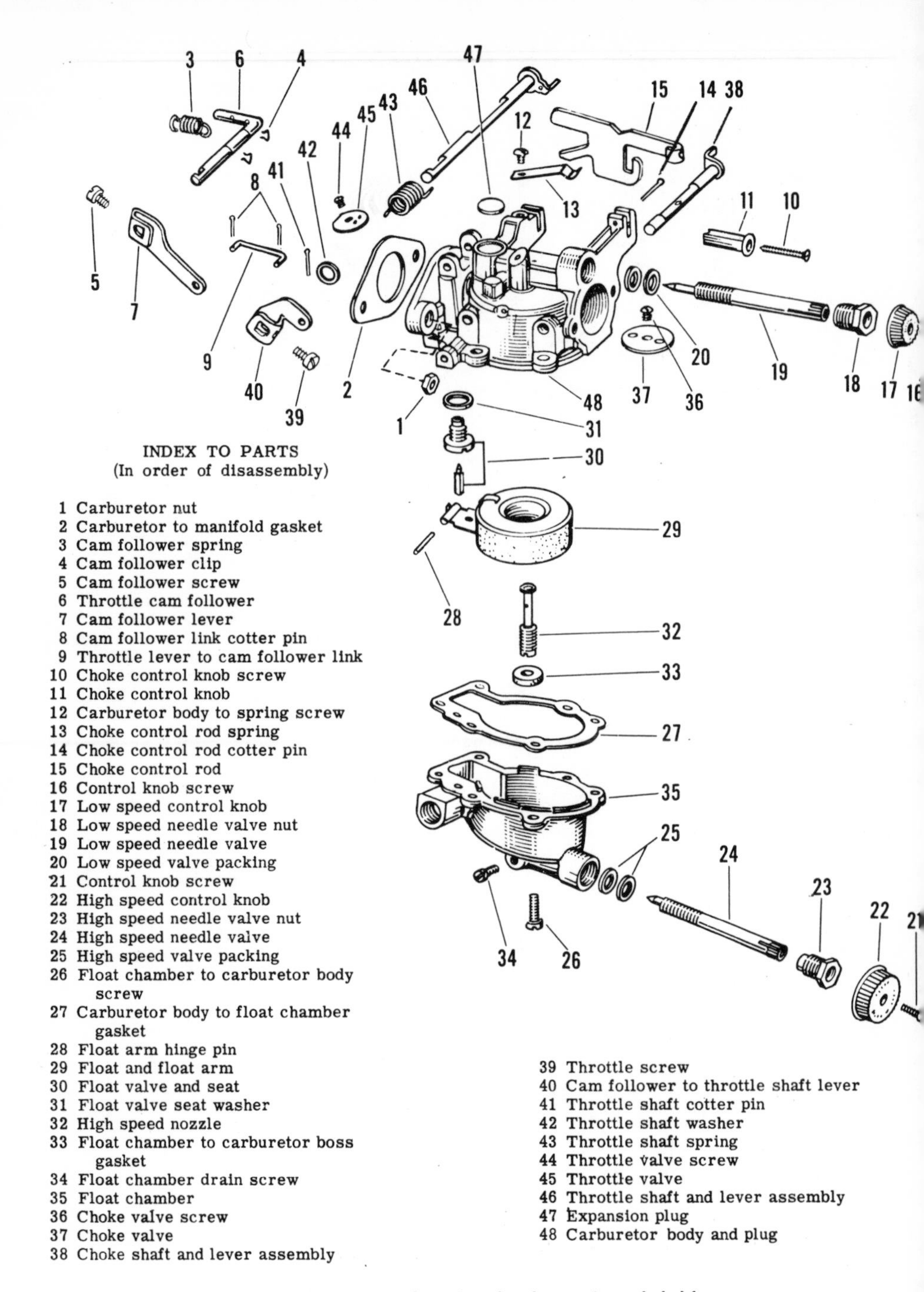

INDEX TO PARTS
(In order of disassembly)

1 Carburetor nut
2 Carburetor to manifold gasket
3 Cam follower spring
4 Cam follower clip
5 Cam follower screw
6 Throttle cam follower
7 Cam follower lever
8 Cam follower link cotter pin
9 Throttle lever to cam follower link
10 Choke control knob screw
11 Choke control knob
12 Carburetor body to spring screw
13 Choke control rod spring
14 Choke control rod cotter pin
15 Choke control rod
16 Control knob screw
17 Low speed control knob
18 Low speed needle valve nut
19 Low speed needle valve
20 Low speed valve packing
21 Control knob screw
22 High speed control knob
23 High speed needle valve nut
24 High speed needle valve
25 High speed valve packing
26 Float chamber to carburetor body screw
27 Carburetor body to float chamber gasket
28 Float arm hinge pin
29 Float and float arm
30 Float valve and seat
31 Float valve seat washer
32 High speed nozzle
33 Float chamber to carburetor boss gasket
34 Float chamber drain screw
35 Float chamber
36 Choke valve screw
37 Choke valve
38 Choke shaft and lever assembly
39 Throttle screw
40 Cam follower to throttle shaft lever
41 Throttle shaft cotter pin
42 Throttle shaft washer
43 Throttle shaft spring
44 Throttle valve screw
45 Throttle valve
46 Throttle shaft and lever assembly
47 Expansion plug
48 Carburetor body and plug

H-21. Evinrude outboard carburetor in exploded form.

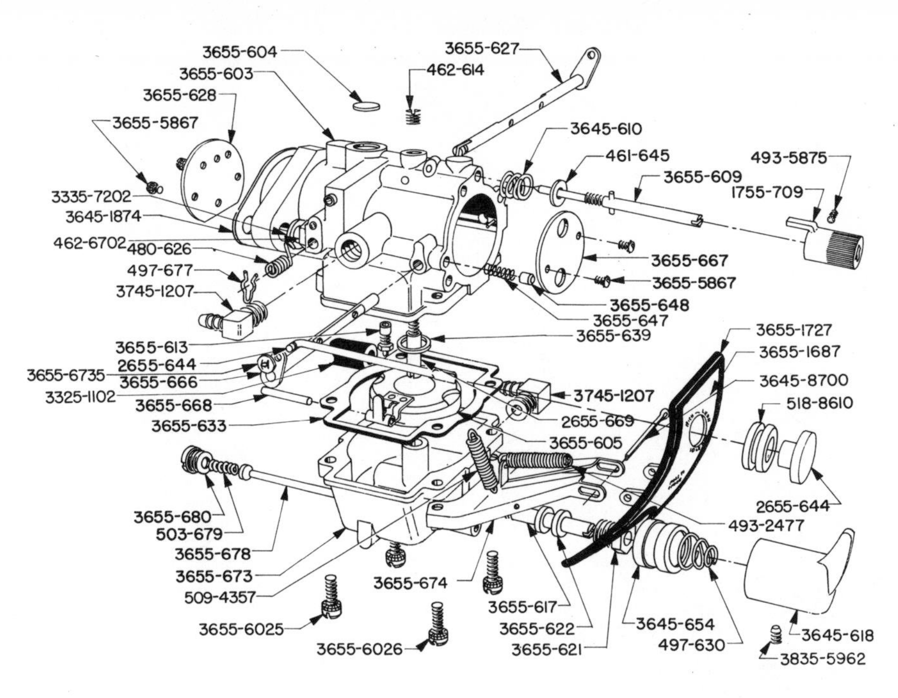

Part Number	*Description*
3655-671	Gasket and Packing Set
3655-672	Repair Kit
3655-673	Bowl
3655-674	Bracket and Stop Assembly
3655-676	Spring
497-677	Cotter Pin
3655-678	Drain Valve
503-679	Spring
3655-680	Plug—Drain Valve
1755-709	Knob—Idle Adj.
3325-1102	Tube—Bowl Drain
3745-1207	Fitting—Gas Line
3655-1687	Panel—Carb. Cont.
3655-1727	Grommet—Panel
3645-1874	Gasket—Carb. Flange
493-2477	Spring—Bkt. to Panel
509-4357	Spring
3655-5867	Screw—Shutter
493-5875	Screw—Idle Adj. Knob
3835-5962	Set Screw—Main Knob
3655-6025	Screw—Body
3655-6026	Screw—Body
462-6702	Nut
3655-6735	Speed Nut
3335-7202	Lockwasher
518-8610	Grommet—Choke Lever
3645-8700	Cotter Pin

Part Number	*Description*
3655-601	Carburetor Complete
3655-603	Body
3655-604	Welch Plug
3655-605	Float Assembly
3655-609	Screw—Idle Adj.
3645-610	Spring
3655-613	Inlet Needle Seat and Gasket
462-614	Plug Screw
3655-617	Screw—Main Adj.
3655-618	Knob—Main Adj.
3655-621	Nut—Packing Screw
3655-622	Packing
480-626	Return Spring
3655-627	Throttle Shaft and Lever
3655-628	Throttle Shutter
497-630	Spring
3655-633	Gasket
3655-639	Gasket—Nozzle Boss
2655-644	Shaft and Knob Assy.
461-645	Washer—Idle Adj. Sc.
3655-647	Spacer—Pick-up Lever
3655-648	Pick-up Lever
3645-654	Knob Body
3655-666	Choke Shaft Lever
3655-667	Choke Shutter
3655-668	Pin—Fulcrum
3655-669	Nozzle

H-22. Scott-Atwater outboard carburetor in exploded form.

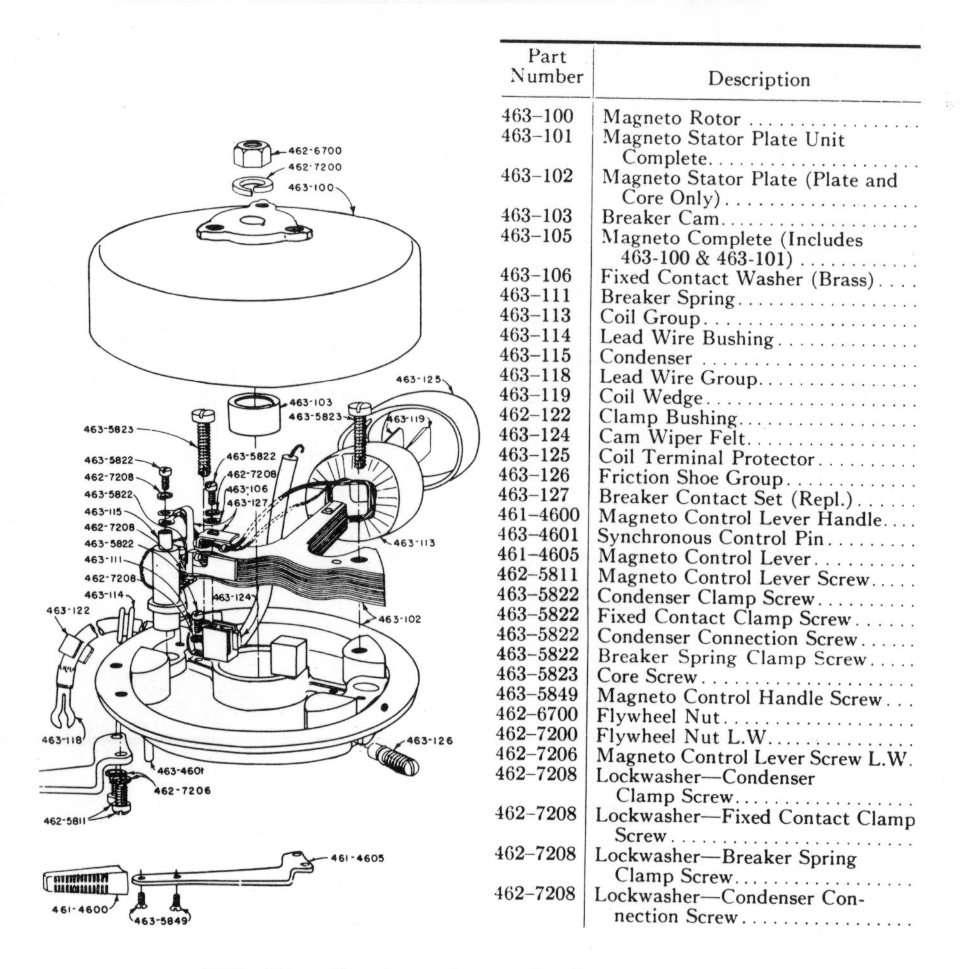

Part Number	Description
463–100	Magneto Rotor
463–101	Magneto Stator Plate Unit Complete
463–102	Magneto Stator Plate (Plate and Core Only)
463–103	Breaker Cam
463–105	Magneto Complete (Includes 463-100 & 463-101)
463–106	Fixed Contact Washer (Brass)
463–111	Breaker Spring
463–113	Coil Group
463–114	Lead Wire Bushing
463–115	Condenser
463–118	Lead Wire Group
463–119	Coil Wedge
462–122	Clamp Bushing
463–124	Cam Wiper Felt
463–125	Coil Terminal Protector
463–126	Friction Shoe Group
463–127	Breaker Contact Set (Repl.)
461–4600	Magneto Control Lever Handle
463–4601	Synchronous Control Pin
461–4605	Magneto Control Lever
462–5811	Magneto Control Lever Screw
463–5822	Condenser Clamp Screw
463–5822	Fixed Contact Clamp Screw
463–5822	Condenser Connection Screw
463–5822	Breaker Spring Clamp Screw
463–5823	Core Screw
463–5849	Magneto Control Handle Screw
462–6700	Flywheel Nut
462–7200	Flywheel Nut L.W.
462–7206	Magneto Control Lever Screw L.W.
462–7208	Lockwasher—Condenser Clamp Screw
462–7208	Lockwasher—Fixed Contact Clamp Screw
462–7208	Lockwasher—Breaker Spring Clamp Screw
462–7208	Lockwasher—Condenser Connection Screw

H-23. Wico outboard magneto as used on Scott-Atwater engine.

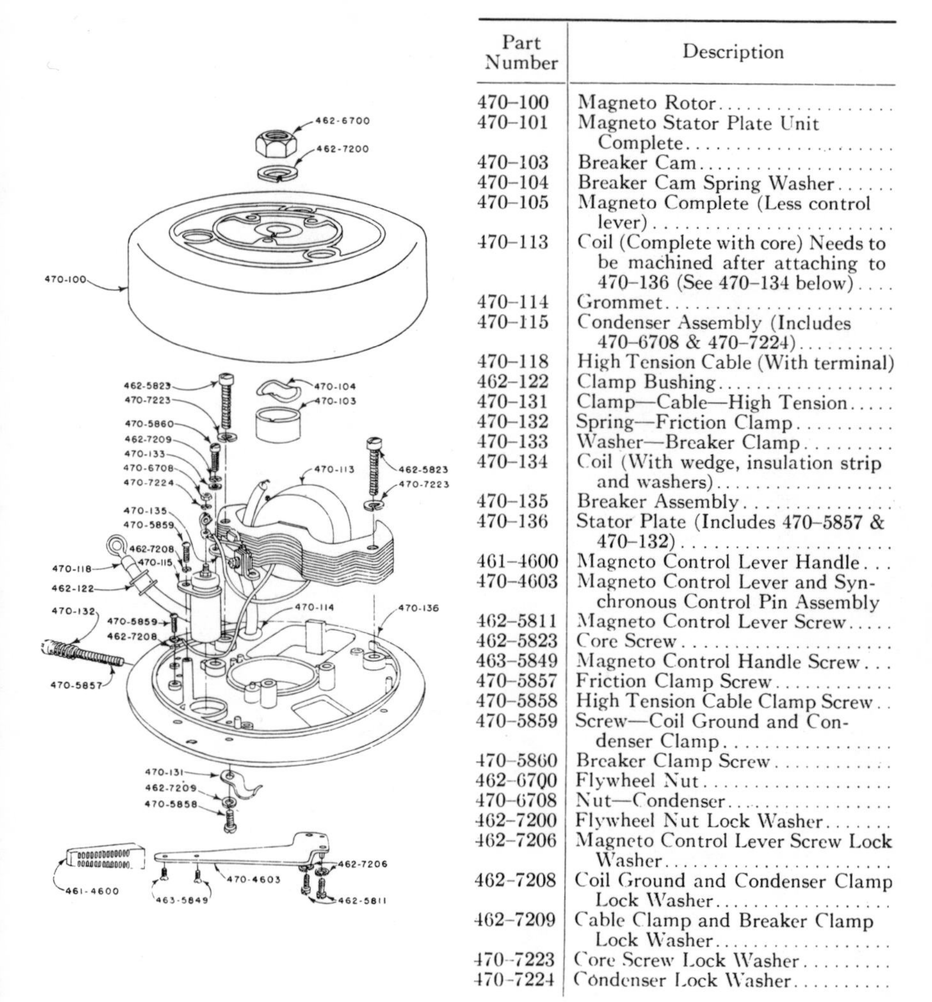

Part Number	Description
470–100	Magneto Rotor
470–101	Magneto Stator Plate Unit Complete
470–103	Breaker Cam
470–104	Breaker Cam Spring Washer
470–105	Magneto Complete (Less control lever)
470–113	Coil (Complete with core) Needs to be machined after attaching to 470–136 (See 470–134 below)
470–114	Grommet
470–115	Condenser Assembly (Includes 470–6708 & 470–7224)
470–118	High Tension Cable (With terminal)
462–122	Clamp Bushing
470–131	Clamp—Cable—High Tension
470–132	Spring—Friction Clamp
470–133	Washer—Breaker Clamp
470–134	Coil (With wedge, insulation strip and washers)
470–135	Breaker Assembly
470–136	Stator Plate (Includes 470–5857 & 470–132)
461–4600	Magneto Control Lever Handle
470–4603	Magneto Control Lever and Synchronous Control Pin Assembly
462–5811	Magneto Control Lever Screw
462–5823	Core Screw
463–5849	Magneto Control Handle Screw
470–5857	Friction Clamp Screw
470–5858	High Tension Cable Clamp Screw
470–5859	Screw—Coil Ground and Condenser Clamp
470–5860	Breaker Clamp Screw
462–6700	Flywheel Nut
470–6708	Nut—Condenser
462–7200	Flywheel Nut Lock Washer
462–7206	Magneto Control Lever Screw Lock Washer
462–7208	Coil Ground and Condenser Clamp Lock Washer
462–7209	Cable Clamp and Breaker Clamp Lock Washer
470–7223	Core Screw Lock Washer
470–7224	Condenser Lock Washer

H-24. *Eiseman magneto as used on Scott-Atwater outboard engine.*

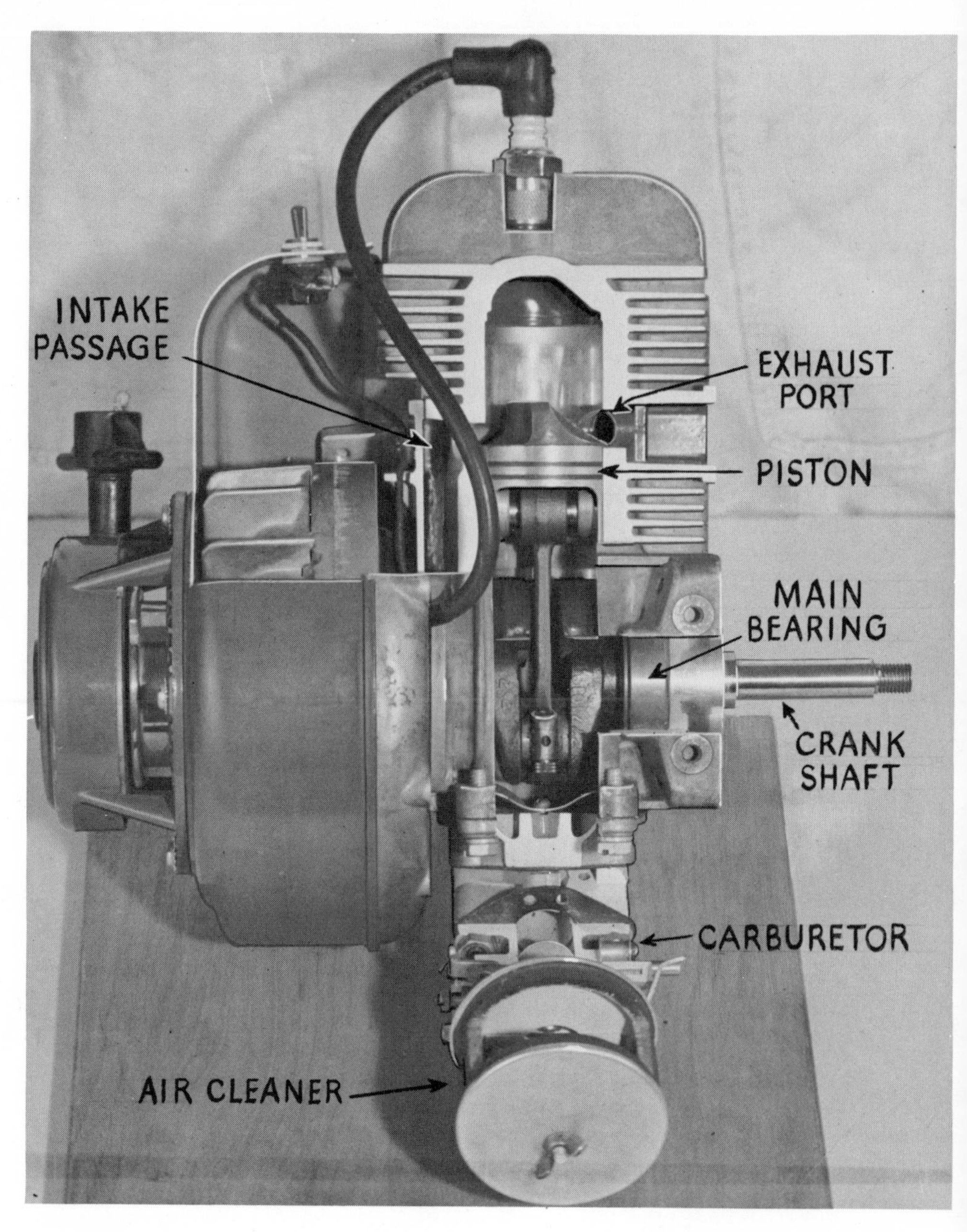

Partial cut-away showing construction of two cycle air cooled engine as made by West Bend Aluminum Co.

TWO-CYCLE ENGINES

TWO CYCLE AIR COOLED TYPES

Air cooled two cycle engines are used in many types of portable equipment such as chain saws, lawnmowers, snow plows, etc. They are popular for such purposes because they combine a high power output with low weight.

Due to their high power output they are somewhat sensitive to any loss of cooling ability or an undue accumulation of carbon.

For these reasons the surface of the cooling fins should be kept clean and a close check kept on the carburetor adjustment. The carbon should be cleaned from the cylinder ports rather frequently to avoid any restriction of the exhaust. At the same time, carbon is removed from the piston head.

Carbon removal is simple as shown in the illustrations as the ports are exposed by removal of the exhaust fitting. A wooden paddle is suggested for carbon removal rather than a metal tool. One reason for this is to avoid damage to the cylinder, particularly where aluminum cylinders with a chrome plate lining is used.

Much of the comment on water cooled two and four cycle and air cooled four cycle engines in preceding sections applies also to these engines.

J-1. Two views of typical single cylinder, two cycle, air cooled Clinton engine.

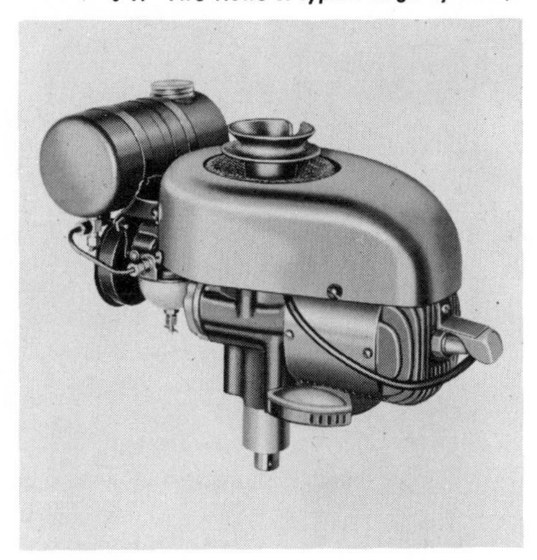

J-2. Air cooled, two cycle, single cylinder engine as made by Power Products.

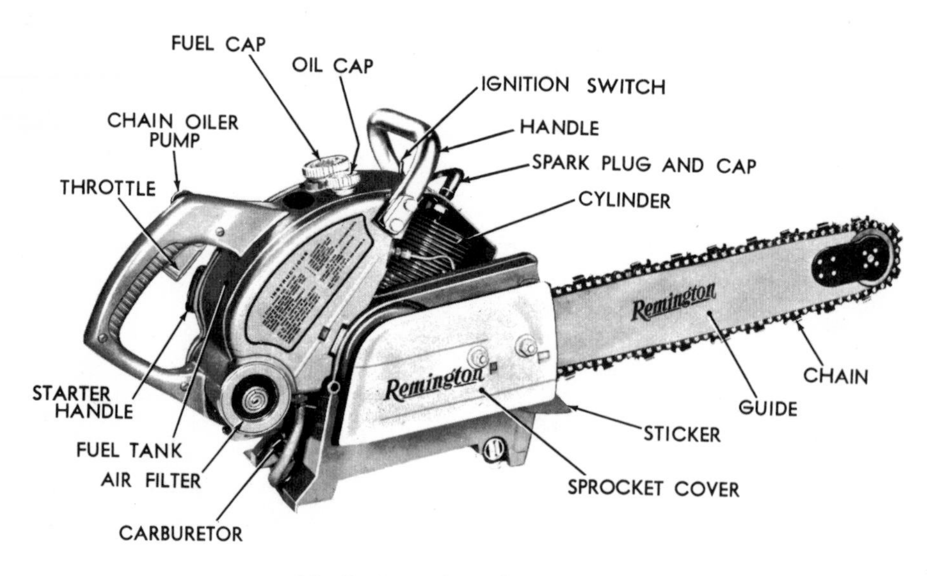

J-3. Remington direct drive chain saw.

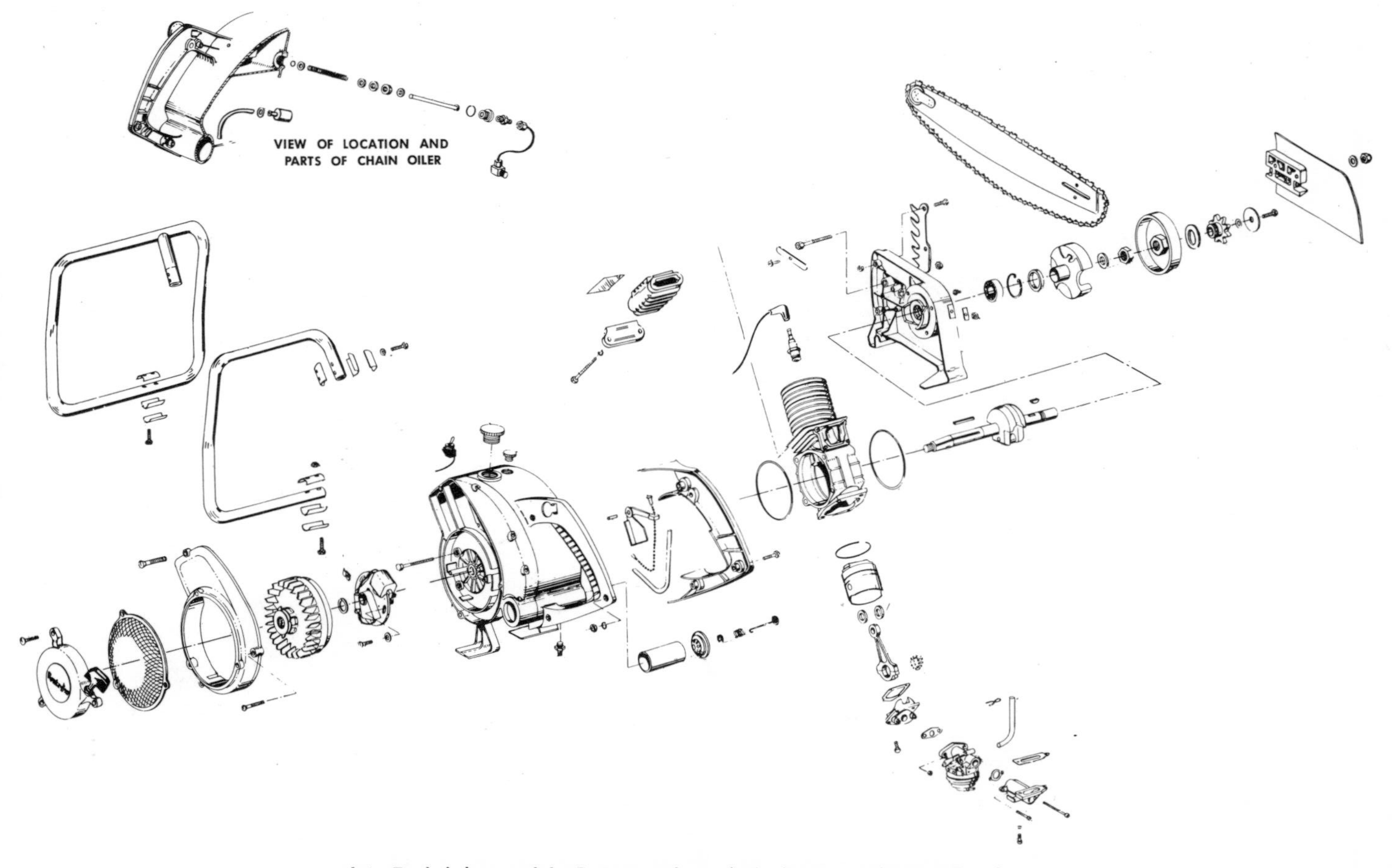

J-4. Exploded view of the Remington direct drive chain saw, shown in Fig. J-3.

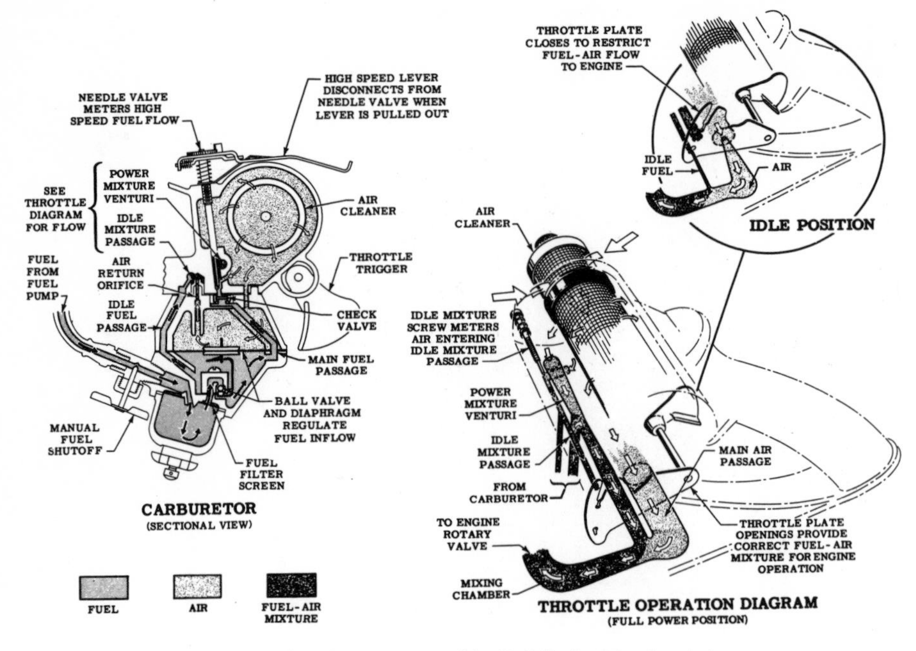

J-5. Diagram of fuel system as used by McCulloch engine for chain saw.

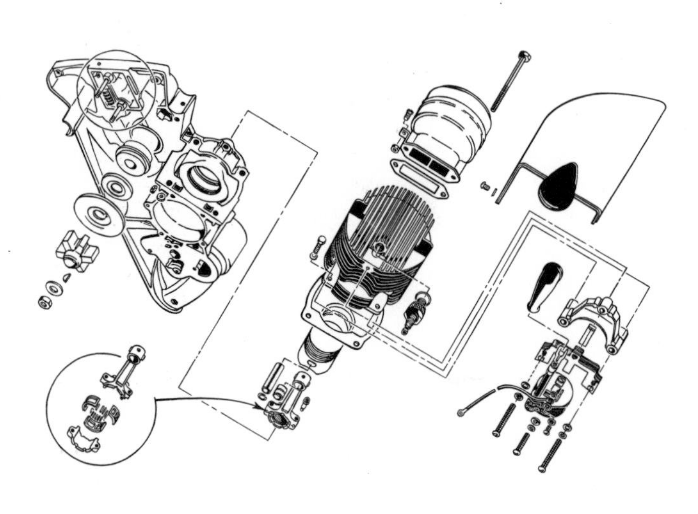

J-6. Exploded view of McCulloch crankcase and cylinder assembly.

J-7. Note that this McCulloch engine uses anti-friction bearings on piston pin and connecting rod as well as crankshaft.

J-8. *In working with small engines it is essential to use a torque wrench and follow the manufacturer's specifications which are usually given in inch-pounds.*

J-9. *In small engine work, hammers must be used with care and judgment as the parts are often small and fragile.*

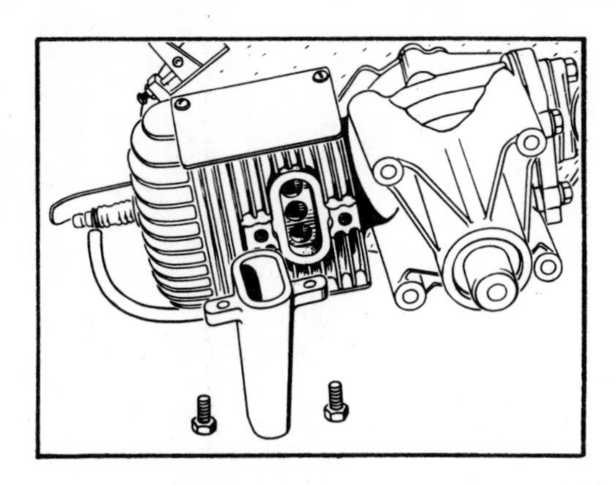

J-10. Carbon removal from piston head and exhaust ports is easily accomplished by removal of exhaust pipe.

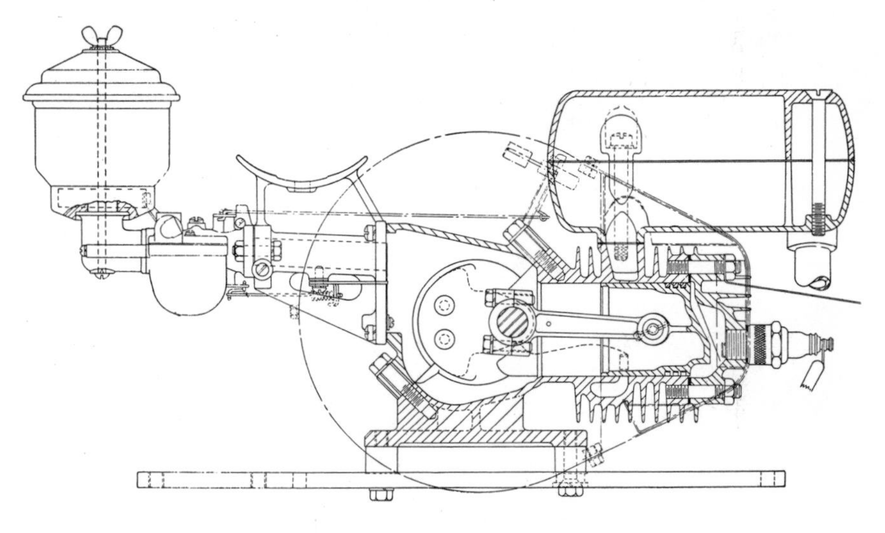

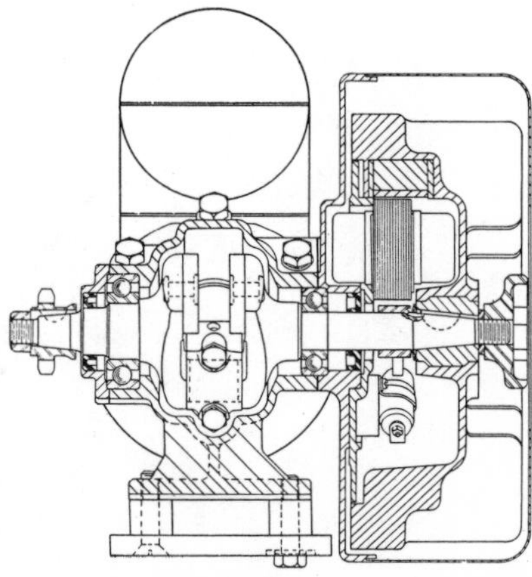

J-11. Cross sections of Jacobsen single cylinder, air cooled, two cycle engine.

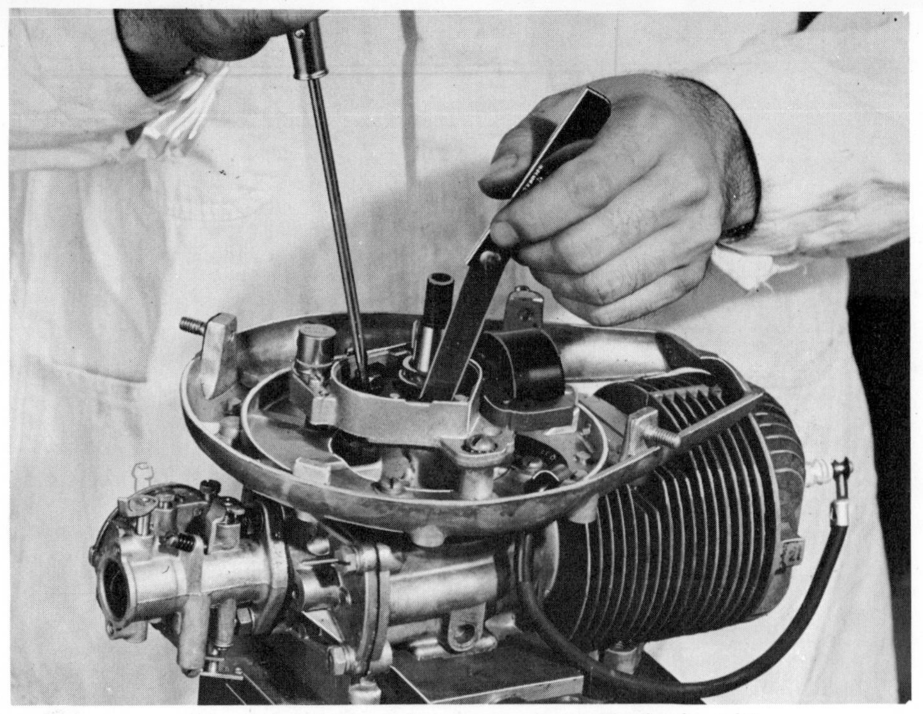

J-12. Method of using feeler gauge to adjust ignition breaker points.

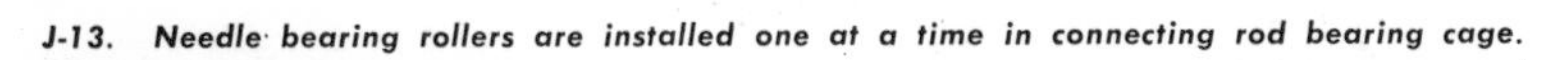

J-13. Needle bearing rollers are installed one at a time in connecting rod bearing cage.

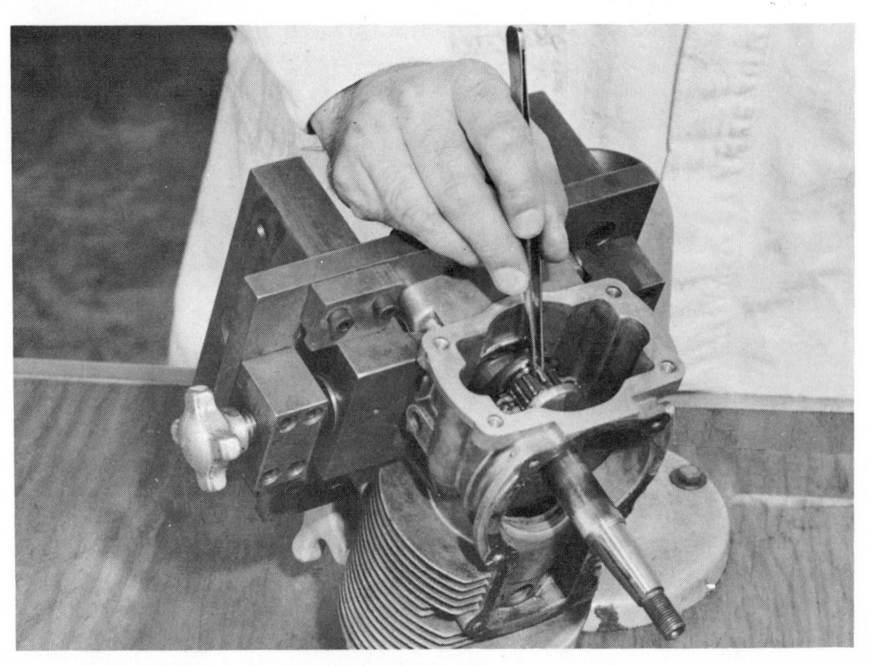

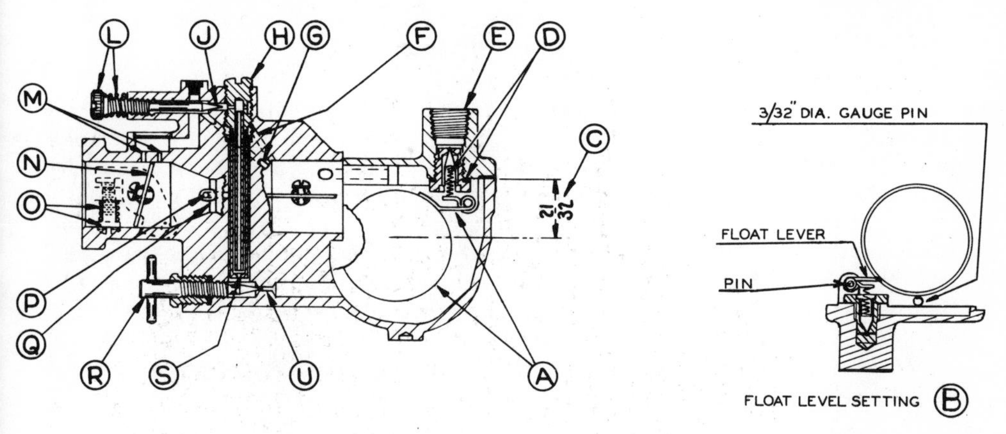

J-14. ***Cross section of carburetor and detail of float adjustment on carburetor used on Jacobsen engine.***

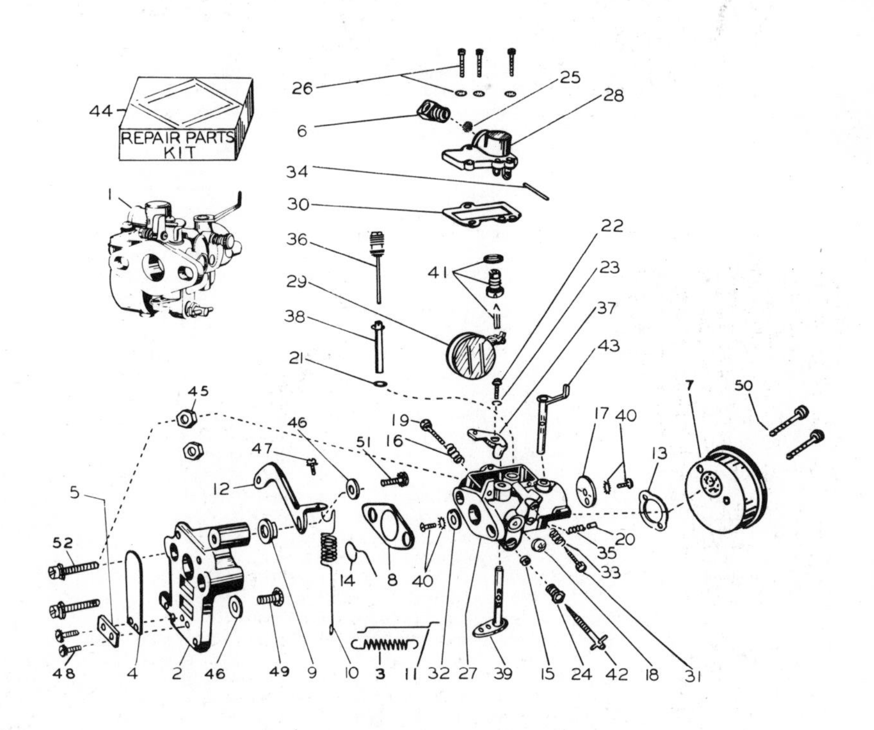

J-15. ***Carburetor used on Jacobsen engine in exploded form.***

ACKNOWLEDGMENTS

In the preparation of this textbook, almost every manufacturer in the industry was consulted. Without exception they extended to us the utmost in cooperation. Information, records and illustrations have been available to us. As a result, we have herein a complete library of service knowledge.

A list of every source of such assistance would result in a directory of the industry. The editors and publishers therefore wish to thank the industry and the individual companies for their valued assistance. It is our hope that this textbook will be helpful to the industry as a whole as well as students, teachers and automotive enthusiasts.

Some of the manufacturers who have been particularly cooperative are as follows:

AC Spark Plug Div. G. M. Corp., Airtex Products, Inc., Albertson & Co., American Bosch Corp., AMMCO Tools, Inc., AP Parts Corp., Atomized Materials Co., Bay State Abrasive Products Co., Behr-Manning Corp., Bendix Products Corp., Bingham-Herbrand Corp., Blackhawk Mfg. Co., Bonney Forge & Tool Works, Briggs & Stratton Corp., Buda Co., Buick Motor Div. G. M. Corp., Burd Piston Ring Co., Cadillac Motor Car Div. G. M. Corp., Carborundum Co., Carter Carburetor Corp., Cedar Rapids Engineering Co., Central Tool Co., Chevrolet Motor Div. G. M. Corp., Chrysler Corp., Clevite Service, Inc., Clinton Machine Co., Continental Engine Co., Cummins Engine Co., Delco-Products Div. G. M. Corp., Delco-Remy Div. G. M. Corp., DeSoto Div. Chrysler Corp., Detroit Diesel Engine Div. G. M. Corp., Dodge Div. Chrysler Corp., E. I. Du Pont de Nemours Co., Eaton Mfg. Co., E. Edelmann & Co., Thomas A. Edison, Inc., Electric Auto-Lite Co., Electric Storage Battery Co., Evinrude Motors, Fairbanks Morse & Co., Fairmount Tool & Forging Co., Federal-Mogul Corp., Ford Motor Co., Fox Products Co., General Electric Co., Gladden Products Corp., Grant & Grant, Harley-Davidson Motor Co., Hastings Mfg. Co., Hein-Warner Corp., Heller Brothers Co., Holley Carburetor Co., Hudson Motor Co., Imperial Brass Mfg. Co., International Harvester Co., J & S Carburetor Co., Jacobsen Mfg. Co., Johnson Lawn Mower Corp. Johnson Motors, Kiekhaefer Corp., King Electric Eqpt. Co., Kohler Co., Leece-Neville Co., Lempco Products, Inc., Lincoln Electric Co., Lincoln-Mercury Div. Ford Motor Co., Lisle Corp., Lucas Electric Services, Inc., Mall Tool Co., Mallory Electric Corp., Marvel-Schebler Carburetor Div., Borg-Warner Corp., McCulloch Motors Corp., McQuay-Norris Mfg. Co., Milwaukee Electric Tool Corp., Moog Industries, Inc., Oldsmobile Div. G. M. Corp., Outboard, Marine & Mfg. Co., Packard Motor Car Co., Perfect Circle Co., Plymouth Div. Chrysler Corp., Pontiac Motor Div. G. M. Corp., H. K. Porter, Inc., Power Products, Inc., Pruden Tool Co., Inc., Ramsey Corp., Reo Motors, Inc., Scott-Atwater Mfg. Co., Sealed Power Corp., Simplex Piston Ring Mfg. Co., Society of Automotive Engineers, South Bend Lathe Works, A. O. Smith Co., Snap-On Tools Corp., L. S. Starrett Mfg. Co., Studebaker Corp., Sun Electric Corp., Sunnen Products Co., Thompson Products, Inc., Tillotson Mfg. Co., United Motor Service Div. G. M. Corp., Universal Motor Co., Van Norman Co., Waukesha Motor Co., Westinghouse Electric Corp., Wico Electric Co., Wilkening Mfg. Co., Willard Storage Battery Co., Winona Tool Mfg. Co., Wisconsin Motor Corp., Zenith Carburetor Div. Bendix Products Corp.

GLOSSARY OF TERMS

AABM: Association of American Battery Manufacturers, Inc.

ABRASION: Wearing or rubbing away, such as sandpapering wood.

ACETYLENE OR OXY-ACETYLENE WELDING: The utilization of an acetylene flame to provide heat to bring metal to the fusion or melting point when uniting it.

ACTIVE MATERIAL: In a storage battery, this refers to the peroxide of lead (brown) in the positive plates and metallic lead (gray) in the negative plates upon which the sulphuric acid acts.

ADAPTOR CARBURETOR: A device attached to the gasoline carburetor when an internal combustion engine is to be run either on gasoline or on liquefied petroleum gas.

ADDITIVE: As used with reference to automotive oils, a material added to the oil to give it certain properties. For example, a material added to engine oil to lessen its tendency to congeal or thicken at low temperature.

AEA: Automotive Electric Association.

AERA: Automotive Engine Rebuilders Association.

AIR: A gas containing approximately 4/5 nitrogen, 1/5 oxygen and some carbonic gas.

AIR CLEANER: A device for filtering, cleaning, and removing dust from the air admitted to a unit, such as an engine or air compressor.

AIR-FUEL RATIO: The ratio by weight of the fuel as compared to the air of the carburetor mixture.

AIR GAP: The space between spark plug electrodes, motor and generator armatures, field shoes, etc.

AIR HORN: The air inlet of the carburetor to which the air cleaner is ordinarily attached.

AIR-LOCK: A bubble of air trapped in a fluid circuit which interferes with normal circulation of the fluid.

ALIGNMENT: An adjustment to a line or to bring into a line.

ALLEN WRENCH: A hexagonal wrench which fits into a recessed hexagonal hole. Ordinarily used in set screws.

ALLOY: A mixture of different metals such as solder which is an alloy consisting of lead and tin.

ALTERNATING CURRENT: An electrical current alternating back and forth in direction of flow.

ALUMINUM: A metal noted for its lightness and often alloyed with small quantities of other metals.

AMMETER: An instrument for measuring the flow of an electrical current.

AMPERE: The unit of measurement for the flow of electric current.

AMPERE-HOUR CAPACITY: A term used to indicate the capacity of a storage battery. For example, the delivery of a certain number of amperes for a certain number of hours.

ANNEALING: A process of softening metal. For example, the heating and slow cooling of a piece of iron.

ANNULAR BALL BEARING: A ball bearing with a non-adjustable inner and outer race or races.

ANODE: A positive pole of an electrical current.

ANTI-CLOCKWISE ROTATION: Rotating the opposite direction of the hands on a clock. The same as counter-clockwise rotation.

ANTI-FREEZE: A material such as alcohol, glycerin, etc., added to water to lower its freezing point.

ANTI-FRICTION BEARING: A bearing constructed with balls, rollers or the like between the journal and the bearing surface to provide rolling instead of sliding friction.

APERTURE: An opening, hole or port.

API: American Petroleum Institute.

ARC WELDING: A method of utilizing the heat of an electric current jumping an air gap to provide heat for welding metal.

ARMATURE: That part of an electrical machine which includes the main current-carrying winding. It is usually the core which rotates within the pole shoes which are surrounded by the field coils. See Electrical Section.

ASBESTOS: A natural fibrous mineral with great heat resisting ability.

ASME: American Society of Mechanical Engineers.

ATMOSPHERIC PRESSURE: The weight of the air at sea level; about 14.7 lbs. per square inch; less at higher altitudes.

B & S GAUGE: Brown and Sharpe gauge which is a standard measure of wire size. The smaller the number, the larger the wire.

BACK-FIRE: Ignition of the mixture in the intake manifold by flame from the cylinder such as might occur from a leaking inlet valve.

BACKLASH: The clearance or "play" between two parts, such as meshed gears.

BACK-PRESSURE: A resistance to free flow, such as a restriction in the exhaust line.

BAFFLE OR BAFFLE PLATE: An obstruction for checking or deflecting the flow of gases or sound.

BALL BEARING: An anti-friction bearing consisting of a hardened inner and outer race with hardened steel balls interposed between the two races.

BATTERY: Any number of complete electrical cells assembled in one housing or case.

B.D.C.: Bottom dead center.

BEARING: A part in which a journal, pivot or the like turns or moves.

BENZOL: A by-product of the manufacture of coke sometimes used as an engine fuel.

BEZEL: The groove in which a transparent instrument cover is placed.

B.H.P. (Brake Horsepower): A measurement of the power developed by an engine in actual operation.

GLOSSARY OF TERMS

BLOW-BY: A leakage or loss of pressure often used with reference to leakage of compression past the piston ring between the piston and the cylinder.

BOILING POINT: The temperature at atmospheric pressure at which bubbles or vapors rise to the surface and escape.

BORE: The diameter of a hole, such as a cylinder; also to enlarge a hole as distinguished from making a hole with a drill.

BORING BAR: A stiff bar equipped with multiple cutting bits which is used to bore a series of bearings or journals in proper alighment with each other.

BOSS: An extension or strengthened section, such as the projections within a piston which support the piston pin or piston pin bushings.

BOTTLED GAS: Liquefied petroleum gas compressed and contained in portable cylinders.

BRAZE: To join two pieces of metal with the use of a comparatively high melting point material. An example is to join two pieces of steel by using brass or bronze as a solder.

BREAKER ARM: The movable part of a pair of contact points in an electrical distributor or magneto.

BREAKER POINT: Also called contact points. Two separable points usually faced with silver, platinum or tungsten which interrupt the primary circuit in the distributor or magneto for the purpose of inducing a high tension current in the ignition system.

BREAK-IN: The process of wearing in to a desirable fit between the surfaces of two new or reconditioned parts.

BRINELL HARDNESS: A scale for designating the degree of hardness possessed by a substance.

BROACH: To finish the surface of metal by pushing or pulling a multiple edge cutting tool over or through it.

BRUSHES: The bars of carbon or other conducting material which contact the commutator of an electric motor or generator.

B.T.U. (British Thermal Unit): A measurement of the amount of heat required to raise the temperature of 1 lb. of water, 1 degree, Fahrenheit.

BUCKLED PLATES: Battery plates that have been bent or warped out of a flat plane.

BURNISH: To smooth or polish by the use of a sliding tool under pressure.

BUSHING: A removable liner for a bearing.

BUTANE: A petroleum hydrocarbon compound which has a boiling point of about 32 degs. F. which is used as engine fuel. Loosely referred to as Liquefied Petroleum Gas and often combined with Propane.

BY-PASS: An alternate path for a flowing substance.

CALIBRATE: To determine or adjust the graduation or scale of any instrument giving quantitative measurements.

CALIPERS (Inside and Outside): An adjustable tool for determining the inside or outside diameter by contact and retaining the dimension for measurement or comparison.

CALORIFIC VALUE: A measure of the heating value of fuel.

CALORIMETER: An instrument to measure the amount of heat given off by a substance when burned.

CALORY: The metric measurement of the amount of heat required to raise 1 gram of water from zero degrees to 1 degree Centigrade.

CAM OR BREAKER CAM: The lobed cam rotating in the ignition system which interrupts the primary circuit to induce a high tension spark for ignition.

CAM ANGLE: Also known as dwell period. Referring to an ignition distributor, the number of degrees of rotation of the ignition distributor shaft during which the contact points are closed.

CAM GROUND PISTON: A piston ground to a slightly oval shape which under the heat of operation becomes round.

CAMSHAFT: The shaft containing lobes or cams to operate the engine valves.

CAPE CHISEL: A metal cutting chisel shaped to cut or work in channels or grooves.

CARBON: A common non-metallic element which is an excellent conductor of electricity. It also forms in the combustion chamber of an engine during the burning of fuel and lubricating oil.

CARBON DIOXIDE: Compressed into solid form, this material is known as "dry ice" and remains at a temperature of -109 degs., F. It goes directly from a solid to a vapor state.

CARBONIZE: The process of carbon formation within an engine, such as on the spark plugs and within the combustion chamber.

CARBURETOR: A device for automatically mixing fuel in the proper proportion with air to produce a combustible gas.

CARBURETOR "ICING": A term used to describe the formation of ice on a carburetor throttle plate during the prevalence of certain atmospheric conditions.

CASE-HARDEN: To harden the surface of steel.

CASING HEAD GASOLINE: A term used to describe the lighter parts of petroleum products which were obtained as a natural gasoline by condensing natural gas from an oil well.

CASTELLATE: Formed to resemble a castle battlement as in a castellated nut.

CATHODE: The negative pole of an electric current.

CELL: An electrical cell is the unit of a battery containing a group of positive and negative plates along with electrolyte.

CELL CONNECTOR: The lead bar or link connecting the pole of one cell to the pole of another.

CELLULOID: A compound of gun cotton and camphor which is flexible and transparent.

CENTER OF GRAVITY: The point at which a mass of matter balances. For example, the center of gravity of a wheel is the center of the wheel hub.

CENTIGRADE: A measurement of temperature used principally in foreign countries, zero on the Centigrade scale being 32 degs. on the Fahrenheit scale.

CENTRIFUGAL FORCE: A force which tends to move a body away from its center of rotation. An example is supplied by whirling a weight attached to a string.

CHAMFER: A bevel or taper at the edge of a hole.

CHARGE (or Recharge): Passing an electrical current through a battery to restore it to activity.

CHASE: To straighten up or repair damaged threads.

CHECK-VALVE: A gate or valve which allows passage of gas or fluid in one direction only.

CHEMICAL COMPOUND: The combination of two or more chemical elements which can be a gas, a liquid or a solid.

CHEMICAL ELEMENT: Gaseous, liquid or solid matter which cannot be divided into simpler form.

CHILLED IRON: Cast iron on which the surface has been hardened.

CHIP: To cut with a chisel.

CHOKE: A reduced passage, such as a valve placed in a carburetor air inlet to restrict the volume of air admitted.

CHROMIUM STEEL: An alloy of steel with a small amount of chromium to produce a metal which is highly resistant to oxidation and corrosion.

CIRCUIT: The path of electrical current, fluids or gases. Examples: for electricity, a wire; for fluids and gases, a pipe.

CIRCUIT BREAKER: A device for interrupting an electrical circuit; often automatic and may be known as "contact breaker," "interrupter," "cut-out" or "relay."

CLEARANCE: The space allowed between two parts, such as between a journal and a bearing.

CLOCKWISE ROTATION: Rotation in the same direction as the hands of a clock.

COEFFICIENT OF FRICTION: A measurement of the amount of friction developed between two surfaces pressed together and moved one on the other.

"COLD" MANIFOLD: An intake manifold to which the exhaust gas is not applied for heating purposes.

COMBUSTION: The process of burning.

COMBUSTION SPACE OR CHAMBER: In automobile engines, the volume of the cylinder above the piston with the piston on top center.

COMMUTATOR: A ring of adjacent copper bars insulated from each other to which the wires of the armature or winding are attached.

COMPOUND: A mixture of two or more ingredients.

COMPOUND WINDING: Two electric windings, one in series and the other in shunt or parallel with other electric units or equipment. When applied to electric motors or generators, one winding is shunted across the armature while the other is in series with the armature.

COMPRESSION: The reduction in volume or the "squeezing" of a gas. As applied to metal, such as a coil spring, compression is the opposite of tension.

COMPRESSION RATIO: The volume of the combustion chamber at the end of the compression stroke as compared to the volume of the cylinder and chamber with the piston on bottom center.

CONCENTRIC: Two or more circles having a common center.

CONDENSATION: The process of a vapor becoming a liquid; the reverse of evaporation.

CONDENSER: A device for turning vapor into liquid form if applied to gas. If applied to an electric circuit, the condenser is a device for temporarily collecting and storing a surge of electrical current for later discharge.

CONDUCTOR: A material along or through which electricity will flow with slight resistance; silver, copper and carbon are good conductors.

CONNECTING ROD: Rod that connects the piston to the crankshaft.

CONTACT BREAKER: A device for interrupting an electrical circuit; often automatic and may be known as "circuit breaker," "interrupter," "cut-out" or "relay."

CONTACT POINTS: Also called breaker points. Two separable points usually faced with silver, platinum or tungsten which interrupt the primary circuit in the distributor or magneto for the purpose of inducing a high tension current in the ignition system.

CONTRACTION: A reduction in mass or dimension; the opposite of expansion.

CONVECTION: A transfer of heat by circulating heated air.

CONVERTER: As used in connection with liquefied petroleum gas, it is a device which converts or changes L.P.G. from liquid to vapor state for use in the engine.

CORRODE: To eat away gradually as if by gnawing, especially by chemical action, such as rust.

COUNTERBORE: To enlarge a hole to a given depth.

COUNTER-CLOCKWISE ROTATION: Rotating the opposite direction of the hands on a clock. The same as anti-clockwise rotation.

COUNTERSINK: To cut or form a depression to allow the head of a screw to go below the surface.

COUPLING: A connecting means for transferring movement from one part to another; may be mechanical, hydraulic or electrical.

CRANKCASE: The housing within which the crankshaft and many other parts of the engine operate.

CRANKCASE DILUTION: Under certain conditions of operation, unburned portions of the fuel find their way past the piston rings into the crankcase and oil reservoir where they dilute or "thin" the engine lubricating oil.

CRANKSHAFT: The main shaft of an engine which in conjunction with the connecting rods changes the reciprocating motion of the pistons into rotary motion.

CRANKSHAFT COUNTER-BALANCE: A series of weights attached to or forged integrally with the crankshaft so placed as to offset the reciprocating weight of each piston and rod assembly.

GLOSSARY OF TERMS

CRUDE OIL: Liquid oil as it comes from the ground.

CU. IN.: Cubic inch.

CURRENT: As used in automobiles, the flow of electricity.

CUT-OUT (Electric): A device for interrupting an electrical circuit; often automatic and may be known as "circuit breaker," "interrupter," "contact breaker," or "relay."

CUT-OUT (Muffler): A valve which can be used to divert the exhaust gases directly to the atmosphere instead of through the muffler.

CYLINDER: A round hole having some depth bored to receive a piston; also sometimes referred to as "bore" or "barrel."

CYLINDER BLOCK: The largest single part of an engine. The basic or main mass of metal in which the cylinders are bored or placed.

CYLINDER HEAD: A detachable portion of an engine fastened securely to the cylinder block which contains all or a portion of the combustion chamber.

CYLINDER SLEEVE: A liner or tube interposed between the piston and the cylinder wall or cylinder block to provide a readily renewable wearing surface for the cylinder.

DASH POT: A device consisting of a piston and cylinder with a restricted opening used to slow down or delay the operation of some moving part.

DEAD CENTER: The extreme upper or lower position of the crankshaft throw at which the piston is not moving in either direction.

DEGREE: Abbreviated deg. or indicated by a small "o" placed alongside of a figure; may be used to designate temperature readings or may be used to designate angularity, one degree being 1/360 part of a circle.

DEMAGNETIZE: To remove the magnetization of a pole which has previously been magnetized.

DENATURED ALCOHOL: Ethyl alcohol to which a denaturant has been added to make it unfit as a beverage.

DENSITY: Compactness; relative mass of matter in a given volume.

DEPOLARIZE: To remove polarity, such as to demagnetize a permanent magnet.

DETERGENT: A compound of a soap-like nature used in engine oil to remove engine deposits and hold them in suspension in the oil.

DETONATION: Indicates a too rapid burning or explosion of the mixture in the engine cylinders. It becomes audible through a vibration of the combustion chamber walls and is sometimes confused with a "ping" or spark knock.

DIAL GAUGE: A type of micrometer wherein the readings are indicated on a dial rather than on a thimble as in a micrometer.

DIAPHRAGM: A flexible partition or wall separating two cavities.

DIE: One of a pair of hardened metal blocks for forming metal into a desired shape or a thread die for cutting external threads.

DIE CASTING: An accurate and smooth casting made by pouring molten metal or composition into a metal mold or die under pressure.

DIESEL ENGINE: Named after its developer, Dr. Rudolph Diesel, the engine ignites the fuel in the cylinder from the heat generated by compression. The fuel is an oil rather than gasoline and no spark plug or carburetor is required.

DILUTION: See Crankcase Dilution.

DIRECT CURRENT: Electric current which flows continuously in one direction. An example is a storage battery.

DISCHARGE: With reference to a battery, the flow of electric current from the battery; the opposite of charge.

DISPLACEMENT: See Piston Displacement.

DISTORTION: A warpage or change in form from the original shape.

DOG CLUTCH: Mating collars or flanges with projecting lugs or fingers which interlock when engaged.

DOWEL PIN: A pin inserted in matching holes in two parts to maintain those parts in fixed relation one to the other.

DOWN-DRAFT: Used to describe a carburetor type wherein the mixture flows downward to the engine.

DRAW: To form by a stretching process or to soften hard metal.

DRAW-FILING: A method of filing wherein the file is drawn across the work while held at a right angle to the length of the file.

DRILL: A tool for making a hole or to sink a hole with a pointed cutting tool rotated under pressure.

DRIVE-FIT: Also known as a force-fit or press-fit. This term is used when the shaft is slightly larger than the hole and must be forced in place.

DROP FORGING: A piece of steel shaped between dies while hot.

DRY BATTERIES: Also called dry cell. A complete battery unit which does not contain liquid electrolyte.

DUAL-FUEL ENGINE: An engine equipped to operate on two different fuels, such as gasoline and L.P.G.

DWELL PERIOD: Also known as cam angle.

DYNAMO: A generator of electricity. See Generator.

DYNAMOMETER: A machine for measuring the actual power produced by an internal combustion engine.

EARTH CONNECTION: This term is sometimes used to designate a "ground" in the electrical system. See Ground.

ECCENTRIC: One circle within another circle wherein both circles do not have the same center An example of this is a cam on a camshaft.

ELECTRODE: Usually refers to the insulated center rod of a spark plug. It is also sometimes used to refer to the rods attached to the shell of the spark plug.

ELECTROLYTE: A mixture of sulphuric acid and distilled water used in storage batteries of the wet type.

ELECTRO-MAGNET: A coil of insulated wire wound around an iron rod or series of rods will magnetize the rod or rods and cause it to attract any other iron in the vicinity provided an electrical current is passed through the wire. An example of this is a solenoid magnet.

ELEMENT: One set of positive plates and one set of negative plates complete with separators assembled together.

E.M.F. (Electromotive Force or Voltage): See Electrical Section.

GLOSSARY OF TERMS

EMULSION: A milk-like viscous mixture of two liquids.

ENAMEL: A combination of varnish and coloring pigment. It is sometimes heated during or after application to provide a hard surface.

ENERGY: The capacity for doing work.

ENGINE: The term applies to the prime source of power generation.

ENGINE DISPLACEMENT: The sum of the displacement of all the engine cylinders. See Piston Displacement.

ETHYL GASOLINE: Gasoline to which Ethyl fluid has been added. Ethyl fluid is a compound of tetraethyl lead, ethylene dibromide and ethylene dichloride. The purpose of the material is to slow down and control the rate of burning of the fuel in the cylinder to produce an expansive force rather than an explosive force and thus reduce detonation or ''knocking'' in an engine.

EVAPORATION: The progress of changing from a liquid to a vapor, such as boiling water to produce steam; evaporation is the opposite of condensation.

EXCITER: Often used in referring to the third brush where this mode of regulation is used for a generator.

EXHAUST GAS ANALYZER: An instrument for determining the efficiency with which an engine is burning fuel.

EXHAUST PIPE: The pipe connecting the engine to the muffler to conduct the exhausted or spent gases away from the engine.

EXPANSION: An increase in size. For example, when a metal rod is heated it increases in length and perhaps also in diameter; expansion is the opposite of contraction.

FAHRENHEIT (F.): A scale of temperature measurement ordinarily used in English speaking countries. The boiling point of water is 212 degrees, Fahrenheit, as compared to 100 degrees Centigrade.

FEELER GAUGE: A metal strip or blade finished accurately with regard to thickness used for measuring the clearance between two parts; such gauges ordinarily come in a set of different blades graduated in thickness by increments of .001 in.

FERROUS METAL: Metals which contain iron or steel and are therefore subject to rust.

F-HEAD ENGINE: An engine designed with one valve in the cylinder block at the side of the piston and the other valve in the cylinder head above the piston.

FIELD: In a generator or electric motor the area in which magnetic flow occurs.

FIELD COIL: A coil of insulated wire surrounding the field pole.

FILE: To finish or trim with a hardened rasp or file.

FILLET: A rounded filling between two parts joined at an angle.

FILTER (Oil, Water, Gasoline, Etc.): A unit containing an element, such as a screen of varying degrees of fineness. The screen or filtering element is made of various materials depending upon the size of the foreign particles to be eliminated from the fluid being filtered.

FIT: A kind of contact between two machined surfaces.

FLANGE: A projecting rim or collar on an object for keeping it in place.

FLASH POINT: The temperature at which an oil when heated will flash and burn.

FLOAT: A hollow tank which is lighter than the fluid in which it rests and which is ordinarily used to operate automatically a valve controlling the entrance of the fluid.

FLOATING PISTON PIN: A piston pin which is not locked in the connecting rod or the piston, but is free to turn or oscillate in both the connecting rod and the piston.

FLOAT LEVEL: The pre-determined height of the fuel in the carburetor bowl, usually regulated by means of a suitable valve.

"FLUTTER" OR "BOUNCE": As applied to engine valves, refers to a condition wherein the valve is not held tightly on its seat during the time the cam is not lifting it.

FLUX, ELECTRIC OR MAGNETIC: Lines of magnetic force passing or flowing in a magnetic field.

FLUX, SOLDERING, WELDING, BRAZING: The material used to cause the joining metal to adhere to both parts to be joined.

FLYWHEEL: A heavy wheel in which energy is absorbed and stored by means of momentum.

FOOT POUND (or lbs. ft.): This is a measure of the amount of energy or work required to lift 1 lb. 1 ft.

FORCE-FIT: Also known as a press-fit or drive-fit. This term is used when the shaft is slightly larger than the hole and must be forced in place.

FORGE: To shape metal while hot and plastic by hammering.

FOUR CYCLE ENGINE: Also known as Otto cycle, wherein an explosion occurs every other revolution of the crankshaft; a cycle being considered as 1/2 revolution of the crankshaft. These strokes are (1) suction stroke; (2) compression stroke; (3) power stroke; (4) exhaust stroke.

FUEL KNOCK: Same as detonation.

FULCRUM: The support on which a lever turns in moving a body.

FUSE: A fuse consists of a piece of wire which will carry a limited amount of current only. It is placed in an electrical circuit as a safety measure to avoid damage and is designed to melt and open the circuit in case of excessive current flow.

GAL.: Gallon.

GALVANIZE: To coat with a molten alloy of lead and tin to prevent rusting.

GALVANOMETER: An instrument used for the location, measurement and direction of an electric current.

GAS: A substance which can be changed in volume and shape according to the temperature and pressure applied to it. For example, air is a gas which can be compressed into smaller volume and into any shape desired by pressure. It can also be expanded by the application of heat.

GASKET: Anything used as a packing, such as a non-metallic substance placed between two metal surfaces to act as a seal.

GASSING: The bubbling of the battery electrolyte which occurs during the process of charging a battery.

GEAR RATIO: The number of revolutions made by a driving gear as compared to the number of revolutions made by a driven gear of different size. For example, if one gear makes three revolutions while the other gear makes one revolution, the gear ratio would be 3 to 1.

GENERATOR: A device consisting of an armature, field coils and other parts which when rotated will generate electricity. It is usually driven by a belt from the engine crankshaft.

GLAZE: As used to describe the surface of the cylinder, an extremely smooth or glossy surface such as a cylinder wall highly polished over a long period of time by the friction of the piston rings.

GLAZE BREAKER: A tool for removing the glossy surface finish in an engine cylinder.

GOVERNOR: A device to control and regulate speed. May be mechanical, hydraulic or electrical.

GRAM: A metric unit of weight which is equal to 1/454th part of a pound.

GRID: The metal framework of an individual battery plate in which the active material is placed.

GRIND: To finish or polish a surface by means of an abrasive wheel.

GROUP: In a battery a set of plates either positive or negative joined together but not assembled with separators.

GROWLER: An electrical device for testing electric motor or generator armatures.

GUDGEON PIN: Also known as "wrist pin" and piston pin. This is the pin that connects the connecting rod to the piston and piston pin is the preferred term.

GUM: In automotive fuels, this refers to oxidized petroleum products which accumulate in the fuel system, carburetor or engine parts.

HARD SOLDER: Uniting two pieces of metal with a material having a melting point higher than "soft" solder. An example is silver soldering wherein silver is used instead of lead-tin alloy.

HARMONIC BALANCER: A device to reduce the torsional or twisting vibration which occurs along the length of the crankshaft used in multiple cylinder engines. Also known as a vibration damper.

H.C.: High compression.

HEAT EXCHANGER: Sometimes used to describe a vaporizer.

HEAT RISER: The passage in the manifold between the exhaust and intake manifold.

HEAT TREATMENT: A combination of heating and cooling operations timed and applied to a metal in a solid state in a way that will produce desired properties.

HEEL: The outside or larger half of the gear tooth.

HELICAL: Shaped like a coil of wire or a screw thread.

HELICAL GEAR: A gear design wherein the gear teeth are cut at an angle to the shaft.

HERRINGBONE GEAR: A pair of helical gears designed to operate together in which the angle of the pair of gears forms a V.

HIGH TENSION: As used in electricity, it refers to the secondary or induced high voltage electrical current; includes the wiring from the cap of the ignition distributor to the coil and to each of the spark plugs.

HONE: An abrasive tool for correcting small irregularities or differences in diameter in a cylinder, such as an engine cylinder.

HOT SPOT: Refers to a comparatively thin section or area of the wall between the inlet and exhaust manifold of an engine, the purpose being to allow the hot exhaust gases to heat the comparatively cool incoming mixture. Also used to designate local areas of the cooling system which have attained above average temperatures.

HP: Horsepower, the energy required to lift 550 lbs. 1 ft. in 1 second.

HUNTING LINK: A section of thin leaves used in a timing chain with an odd number of links. Can be removed to shorten the chain.

HYDROCARBON: Any compound composed entirely of carbon and hydrogen, such as petroleum products.

HYDROCARBON ENGINE: An engine using petroleum products, such as gas, liquefied gas, gasoline, kerosene or fuel oil as a fuel.

HYDROMETER: An instrument for determining the state of charge in a battery by finding specific gravity of the electrolyte.

ICEI: Internal Combustion Engine Institute, Inc.

I.D.: Inside Diameter.

IDLE: Refers to the engine operating at its slowest speed.

IGNITION DISTRIBUTOR: An electrical unit usually containing the circuit breaker for the primary circuit and providing a means for conveying the secondary or high tension current to the spark plug wires as required.

IGNITION SYSTEM: The means for igniting the fuel in the cylinders; includes spark plugs, wiring, ignition distributor, ignition coil and source of electrical current supply.

I.H.P.: Indicated horsepower developed by an engine and a measurement of the pressure of the explosion within the cylinder expressed in pounds per square inch.

IN.: One inch.

INDUCTION: The influence of magnetic fields of different strength not electrically connected to one another.

INDUCTION COIL: Essentially a transformer which through the action of induction creates a high tension current by means of an increase in voltage.

INERTIA: A physical law which tends to keep a motionless body at rest or also tends to keep a moving body in motion; effort is thus required to start a mass moving or to retard or stop it once it is in motion.

INHIBITOR: A material to restrain or hinder some unwanted action, such as a rust inhibitor which is a chemical added to cooling systems to retard the formation of rust.

INLET VALVE OR INTAKE VALVE: A valve which permits a fluid or gas to enter a chamber and seals against exit.

INSULATION: Any material which does not conduct electricity; used to prevent the flow or leakage of current from a conductor. Also used to describe a material which does not conduct heat readily.

INSULATOR: An electrical conductor covered or shielded with a non-conducting material, such as a copper wire within a rubber tube.

INTAKE MANIFOLD OR INLET PIPE: The tube used to conduct the gasoline and air mixture from the carburetor to the engine cylinders.

INTEGRAL: The whole made up of parts.

INTENSIFY: To increase or concentrate, such as to increase the voltage of an electrical current.

INTERMITTENT: Motion or action that is not constant but occurs at intervals.

INTERNAL COMBUSTION: The burning of a fuel within an enclosed space.

INTERRUPTER: A device for interrupting an electrical circuit; often automatic and may be known as "contact breaker," "circuit breaker," "cut-out" or "relay."

JAR: In a battery the rubber or composition container for a battery cell.

JOURNAL: A bearing within which a shaft operates.

JUMP SPARK: A high tension electrical current which jumps through the air from one terminal to the other.

KEY: A small block inserted between the shaft and hub to prevent circumferential movement.

KEYWAY OR KEYSEAT: A groove or slot cut to permit the insertion of a key.

KILOWATT: A measure of electrical energy consisting of 1,000 watts; it is equal to 1 1/3 horsepower.

KNURL: To indent or roughen a finished surface.

KNOCK: A general term used to describe various noises occurring in an engine; may be used to describe noises made by loose or worn mechanical parts, pre-ignition, detonation, etc.

LACQUER: Lacquer is a solution of solids in solvents which evaporate with great rapidity.

LAMINATE: To build up or construct out of a number of thin sheets. An example is the laminated core in an electric motor or generator.

LAPPING: The process of fitting one surface to another by rubbing them together with an abrasive material between the two surfaces.

LB.: One pound.

L.C.: Low compression.

LEAD BURNING: Joining two pieces of lead by melting or fusing the metal.

L-HEAD ENGINE: An engine design in which both valves are located on one side of the engine cylinder.

LINER: Usually a thin section placed between two parts, such as a replaceable cylinder liner in an engine.

LINKAGE: Any series of rods, yokes, and levers, etc., used to transmit motion from one unit to another.

LIQUID: Any substance which assumes the shape of the vessel in which it is placed without changing volume.

LIQUID WITHDRAWAL SYSTEM: A method of piping and connecting whereby liquid is taken from the bottom of an L.P.G. tank and converted into gas by a vaporizer.

LITER: A metric measure equal to 2.11 pints.

LITHARGE: Lead monoxide, a yellow earthy substance which when mixed with glycerin forms a hard-setting cement for metal seals.

LIVE: Electrical parts connected to the insulated side of the electrical system, such as an insulated wire connected to the battery and often referred to as the "hot" wire.

LOST MOTION: Motion between a driving part and a driven part which does not cause actuation of the driven part. Also see Backlash.

L.P.G., LIQUEFIED PETROLEUM GAS: Made usable as a fuel for internal combustion engines by compressing volatile petroleum gases to liquid form. When so used, must be kept under pressure or at low temperature in order to remain in liquid form.

LUG: The extension of the plate grid of a battery for connecting the plate to the strap.

MAGNET (Permanent): A piece of hard steel often bent into a "U" shape so as to have opposite poles and which can be charged with and retain magnetic power.

MAGNETIC FIELD: The flow of magnetic force or magnetism between the opposite poles of a magnet.

MAGNETO: An electrical device which generates current when rotated by an outside source of power; may be used for the generation of either low tension or high tension current.

MALLEABLE CASTING: A casting which has been toughened by annealing.

MANIFOLD: A pipe with multiple openings used to connect various cylinders to one inlet or outlet.

MANGANESE BRONZE: An alloy of copper, zinc and manganese.

MANOMETER: A device for measuring a vacuum consisting of a "U" shaped tube partially filled with fluid. One end of the tube is open to the air and the other is connected to the chamber in which the vacuum is to be measured. A column of Mercury 30 in. high equals 14.7 lbs. per square in. which is atmospheric pressure at sea level. Readings are given in terms of inches of Mercury.

MECHANICAL EFFICIENCY (Engine): The ratio between the indicated horsepower and the brake horsepower of an engine.

MEMA: Motor and Equipment Manufacturers Association.

MERCURY COLUMN: A reference term used in connection with a Manometer.

METHANOL OR WOOD ALCOHOL: A poisonous alcohol made from distillation of wood; can also be made synthetically.

MEWA: Motor and Equipment Wholesalers Association.

MICROMETER: A measuring instrument for either external or internal measurement in thousandths and sometimes tenths of thousandths of inches.

GLOSSARY OF TERMS

MILL: To cut or machine with rotating tooth cutters.

MILLIMETER (mm.): One millimeter is the metric equivalent of .039370 of an inch or one inch being the equivalent of 25.4 mm.

MISFIRING: Failure of an explosion to occur in one or more cylinders while the engine is running; may be continuous or intermittent failure.

MONO-BLOCK: Meaning that all cylinders of an engine are contained in one casting; the same as en-bloc or in-block.

MOTOR: Actually this term should be used in connection with an electric motor and should not be used when referring to the engine.

MUFFLER: A chamber attached to the end of the exhaust pipe which allows the exhaust gases to expand and cool. It is usually fitted with baffles or porous plates and serves to subdue much of the noise created by the exhaust.

NBFU: National Board of Fire Underwriters.

NEEDLE BEARING: An anti-friction bearing using a great number of small diameter rollers of greater length; also known as a quill type bearing.

NEGATIVE POLE: The point to which an electrical current returns after passing through the circuit. It is designated by a minus sign (-).

NEON GAS: A rare element of the air which has low electrical resistance and is therefore a good conductor for electricity. When placed in a closed glass tube and connected to a high tension electric current, the gas gives off a bright glow.

NICKEL STEEL: Nickel is alloyed with steel to form a heat and corrosion resistant metal.

NON-FERROUS METALS: This designation includes practically all metals which contain no iron or very little iron and are therefore not subject to rusting.

NORTH POLE: The pole of a magnet from whence the lines of force start; the opposite of south pole.

NSPA: National Standard Parts Association.

OCTANE NUMBER: A unit of measurement on a scale intended to indicate the tendency of a fuel to detonate or knock.

OCTANE SELECTOR: A calibrated device for adjusting the timing of the ignition distributor in accordance with the characteristics of the fuel in use.

O.D.: Outside diameter.

OHM: A measurement of the resistance to the flow of an electrical current through a conductor.

OIL PUMPING: A term used to describe an engine which is using an excessive amount of lubricating oil.

OPEN CIRCUIT: A break or opening in an electrical circuit which interferes with the passage of the current.

OSCILLATE: To swing back and forth like a pendulum.

OTTO CYCLE: Also called four stroke cycle. Named after the man who adopted the principle of four cycles of operation for each explosion in an engine cylinder. They are (1) suction stroke, (2) compression stroke,

(3) power stroke, (4) exhaust stroke.

OVERDRIVE: Any arrangement of gearing which produces more revolutions of the driven shaft than of the driving shaft.

OVERHEAD VALVE OR VALVE-IN-HEAD ENGINE: An engine design having valves located in the cylinder head directly above the pistons.

OVERRUN COUPLING: A device to permit rotation in one direction but not in the other.

OXIDIZE: To combine an element with oxygen or convert into its oxide. The process is often accomplished by combination; for example, when carbon burns, it combines with oxygen to form carbon dioxide or carbon monoxide. An example is rusted iron wherein the iron has combined with the oxygen in the air to form an oxide of iron or in other words rust.

PAWL: A pivoted bar adapted to engage with the teeth of a ratchet or the like used either to prevent or impart motion.

PEEN: To stretch or clinch over by pounding with the rounded end of a hammer.

PERIPHERY: The circumference of a circle such as the tread of a tire.

PETCOCK: A small valve placed at various points in a fluid circuit usually for draining purposes.

PETROL: European name for gasoline.

PETROLEUM: A group of liquid and gaseous compounds composed of carbon and hydrogen which are removed from the earth.

PHILLIPS SCREW OR SCREWDRIVER: A type of screw head having a cross instead of a slot for a corresponding type of screwdriver.

PHOSPHOR-BRONZE: An alloy consisting of copper, tin and lead sometimes used in heavy duty bearings.

PILOT VALVE: A small valve used to control the action of a larger valve, such as a main valve.

PINION: A small gear having the teeth formed in the hub.

PINION CARRIER: The mounting or bracket which retains the bearings supporting a pinion shaft.

PISTON: A cylindrical part closed at one end which is connected to the crankshaft by the connecting rod. The force of the explosion in the cylinder is exerted against the closed end of the piston causing the connecting rod to move the crankshaft.

PISTON COLLAPSE: A condition describing a collapse or a reduction in diameter of the piston skirt due to heat or stress.

PISTON DISPLACEMENT: The volume of air moved or displaced by moving the piston from one end of its stroke to the other.

PISTON HEAD: That part of the piston above the rings.

PISTON LANDS: Those parts of a piston between the piston rings.

PISTON PIN: The journal for the bearing in the small end of an engine connecting rod which also passes through piston walls; also known as a wrist pin.

PISTON RING: An expanding ring placed in the grooves of the piston to provide a seal to prevent the passage of fluid or gas past the piston.

PISTON RING EXPANDER: A spring placed behind the piston ring in the

groove to increase the pressure of the ring against the cylinder wall.
PISTON RING GAP: The clearance between the ends of the piston ring.
PISTON RING GROOVE: The channel or slots in the piston in which the piston rings are placed.
PISTON SKIRT: That part of the piston below the rings.
PISTON SKIRT EXPANDER: A spring or other device inserted in the piston skirt to compensate for collapse or decrease in diameter.
PITOT TUBE: An instrument for measuring fluid velocity by means of the difference in pressure between the tip and side openings.
PIVOT: A pin or short shaft upon which another part rests or turns or upon and about which another part rotates or oscillates.
PLATINUM: An expensive metal having an extremely high melting point and good electrical conductivity. Often used in magneto breaker points.
POLARITY: Refers to the positive or negative terminal of a battery or an electric circuit; also the north or south pole of a magnet.
POPPET VALVE: A valve structure consisting of a circular head with an elongated stem attached in the center which is designed to open and close a circular hole or port.
PORCELAIN: General term applied to the material or element used for insulating the center electrode of a spark plug.
PORT: In engines, the openings in the cylinder block for valves, exhaust and inlet pipes, or water connections. In two-cycle engines the openings for inlet and exhaust purposes.
"PORTING": As applied to racing engines, the enlarging, matching, streamlining and polishing of the inside of the manifolds and valve ports to reduce the friction of the flow of gases.
POSITIVE POLE: The point from whence the current flows to the circuit. This is designated by a plus sign (+).
POST: The heavy circular part to which the group of plates is attached and which extends through the cell cover to provide a means of attachment to the adjacent cell or battery cable.
POTENTIAL: An indication of the amount of energy available.
POTENTIAL DIFFERENCE: A difference of electrical pressure which sets up a flow of electric current.
POTENTIAL DROP: A loss of electrical pressure due to resistance or leakage.
PRE-HEATING: The application of heat as a preliminary step to some further thermal or mechanical treatment.
PRE-IGNITION: Ignition occurring earlier than intended. For example, the explosive mixture being fired in a cylinder as by a flake of incandescent carbon before the electric spark occurs.
PRE-LOADING: To place a small amount of pressure or tension on an anti-friction bearing by adjustment to eliminate any semblance of looseness.
PRESS-FIT: Also known as a force-fit or drive-fit. This term is used when the shaft is slightly larger than the hole and must be forced in place.
PRIMARY WINDING: In an ignition coil or magneto armature is a wire

which conducts the low tension current which is to be transformed by induction into high tension current in the secondary winding.

PRIMARY WIRES: The wiring circuit used for conducting the low tension or primary current to the points where it is to be used.

PRONY BRAKE: A machine for testing the power of an engine while running against a friction brake.

PROPANE: A petroleum hydrocarbon compound which has a boiling point about -44 degrees, F. and which is used as an engine fuel; loosely referred to as L.P.G. and often combined with Butane.

P.S.I.: A measurement of pressure in pounds per square inch.

PUSH ROD: A connecting link in an operating mechanism, such as the rod interposed between the valve lifter and rocker arm on an overhead valve engine.

QUENCHING: A process of rapid cooling of hot metal by contact with liquid, gases or solids.

QUILL BEARING: See Needle Bearing.

RACE: As used with reference to bearings, a finished inner and outer surface in which or on which balls or rollers operate.

"RACE-CAM": A type of camshaft which increases the lift of the valve, increases the speed of valve opening and closing, increases the length of time the valve is held open, etc. Also known as "Full," "Three-quarter" or "Semi-race cams," depending upon design.

RADIAL ENGINE: An engine construction wherein the cylinders are mounted in a row or circle around the crankcase.

RADIATION: The transfer of heat by rays, such as heat from the sun.

RATIO: The relation or proportion that one number bears to another.

REAM: To finish a hole accurately with a rotating fluted tool.

RECIPROCATING: A back and forth movement, such as the action of a piston in a cylinder.

RECTIFIER: An electrical device for transforming or changing alternating current into direct current.

REGULATOR: An automatic pressure reducing or regulating valve.

RELAY: A device for interrupting an electrical circuit; often automatic and may be known as "circuit breaker," "interrupter," "contact breaker," or "cut-out."

RELIEF: The amount one surface is set below or above another surface.

"RELIEVING": As applied to racing engines, the removal of some metal from around the valves and between the cylinder and valves to facilitate flow of the gases.

RESISTOR: A current consuming piece of metal wire or carbon inserted into an electrical circuit to decrease the flow.

RETARD: When used with reference to an ignition distributor, means to cause the spark to occur at a later time in the cycle of engine operation; opposite of spark advance.

RIVET: To attach with rivets or to batter or upset the end of a pin.

ROCKER ARM: In an engine a lever located on a fulcrum or shaft, one end of the lever being on the valve stem; the other being on the push rod.

ROCKWELL HARDNESS: A scale for designating the degree of hardness possessed by a substance.

ROLLER BEARING: An inner and outer race upon which hardened steel rollers operate.

ROTARY VALVE: A valve construction in which ported holes come into and out of register with each other to allow entrance and exit of fluids or gases.

ROTOR: Rotating valve or conductor for carrying fluid or electrical current from a central source to the individual outlets as required.

R.P.M.: Revolutions per minute.

RUBBER: An elastic vibration absorbing material of either natural or synthetic origin.

RUNNING-FIT: Where sufficient clearance has been allowed between the shaft and journal to allow free running without overheating.

SAE: Society of Automotive Engineers.

SAE STEELS: A numberical index system used to identify composition of SAE steel. Basically the first digit indicating the type to which the steel belongs; thus (1) indicates a carbon steel, (2) a nickel steel, etc. The second digit generally indicates the approximate percentage of the predominant alloying element. Usually the last two or three digits indicates the approximate average carbon content in points or hundredths of 1 per cent. Thus (SAE 2340 steel) indicates a nickel steel of approximately 3 per cent nickel and 0.40 per cent carbon.

SAE THREAD: Refers to a table of threads set up by the Society of Automotive Engineers and determines the number of threads per inch. For example, a quarter inch diameter rod with an SAE thread would have 28 threads per inch.

SAFETY FACTOR: The degree of surplus strength over and above normal requirements which serves as insurance against failure.

SAFETY RELIEF VALVE: A spring loaded valve designed to open and thus relieve excessive pressure in a vessel when it exceeds a pre-determined safe point.

SAND BLAST: To clean a surface by means of sand propelled by compressed air.

SAYBOLT TEST: A method of measuring the viscosity of oil with the use of a viscosimeter.

SCALE: A flaky deposit occurring on steel or iron. Ordinarily used to describe the accumulation of minerals and metals accumulating in a cooling system.

SCORE: A scratch, ridge or groove marring a finished surface.

SEALING COMPOUND: A readily melted acid-proof non-conducting material used in sealing the battery cover in the jar. Similar to asphalt.

SEAT: A surface, usually machined, upon which another part rests or seats; for example, the surface upon which a valve face rests.

SECONDARY WINDING: In an ignition coil or magneto armature, a wire in which a secondary or high tension current is created by induction due to the interruption of the current in the adjacent primary winding.

SEDIMENT: In a battery this refers to the active material of the plates which is gradually shed and accumulates in a space provided below the plates.

SEIZE: When one surface moving upon another scratches, it is said to seize. An example is a piston score or abrasion in a cylinder due to lack of lubrication or over-expansion.

SEMI-DIESEL: A semi-Diesel engine operates on comparatively high compression and utilizes solid injection of the fuel. However, it does use an electrical ignition system rather than depend solely upon the heat generated by compression to furnish ignition.

SEPARATORS: Sheets of rubber or wood inserted between the positive and negative plates of a cell to keep them out of contact with each other.

SERIES WINDING: An electric winding or coil of wire in series with other electrical equipment. When applied to electric generators or motors, the field coil is connected in series with the armature.

SHEAR: To cut between two blades.

SHIM: Thin sheets used as spacers between two parts, such as the two halves of a journal bearing.

SHORT CIRCUIT: To provide a shorter path; often used to indicate an accidental ground in an electrical device or conductor.

SHRINK-FIT: Where the shaft or part is slightly larger than the hole in which it is to be inserted. The outer part is heated above its normal operating temperature or the inner part chilled below its normal operating temperature or both and assembled in this condition; upon cooling an exceptionally tight fit is obtained.

SHUNT: To by-pass around or turn aside; in electrical apparatus an alternate path for the current.

SHUNT WINDING: An electric winding or coil of wire, which forms a by-pass or alternate path for electric current. When applied to electric generators or motors, each end of the field winding is connected to an armature brush.

SHUTTLE VALVE: A valve for diverting pressure from one channel to another.

SILENCER: Same as Muffler.

SILICON STEEL: An alloy of silicon and chromium with steel. As this alloy resists burning and oxidation and does not warp readily, it is often used for exhaust valves of internal combustion engines.

SILVER SOLDERING: Same as Hard Soldering.

SLEEVE VALVE: A reciprocating sleeve or sleeves with ported openings placed between the piston and cylinders of an engine to serve as valves.

SLIDING-FIT: Where sufficient clearance has been allowed between the shaft and journal to allow free running without overheating.

SLIP-IN BEARING: A liner made to extremely accurate measurements which can be used for replacement purposes without additional fitting.

SLUDGE: As used in connection with engines, indicates a composition of oxidized petroleum products along with an emulsion formed by the mixture of oil and water. This forms a pasty substance and clogs oil lines and passages and interferes with engine lubrication.

SOLDER: An alloy of lead and tin used to unite two metal parts.
SOLDERING: To unite two pieces of metal with a material, such as solder having a comparatively low melting point.
SOLENOID: An iron core surrounded by a coil of wire which moves due to magnetic attraction when an electrical current is fed to the coil; often used to actuate mechanisms by electrical means.
SOLID INJECTION: The system used in full Diesel and semi-Diesel, wherein fuel in the fluid state is injected into the cylinder rather than a mixture of air and fuel drawn from a carburetor.
SOLVENT: A solution which dissolves some other material. For example, water is a solvent for sugar.
SOUTH POLE: The pole of a magnet to which the lines of force flow; the opposite of north pole.
SPARK: An electrical current possessing sufficient pressure to jump through the air from one conductor to another.
SPARK ADVANCE: When used with reference to an ignition distributor, means to cause the spark to occur at an earlier time in the cycle of engine operation; opposite of retard.
SPARK GAP: The space between the electrodes of a spark plug through which the spark jumps. Also a safety device in a magneto to provide an alternate path for the current when it exceeds a safe value.
SPARK KNOCK: Same as Pre-ignition.
SPARK PLUG: A device inserted into the combustion chamber of an engine containing an insulated central electrode for conducting the high tension current from the ignition distributor or magneto. This insulated electrode is spaced a pre-determined distance from the shell or side electrode in order to control the dimensions of the gap for the spark to jump across.
SPECIFIC GRAVITY: The relative weight of a substance as compared to water. For example, if a cubic inch of acid weighs twice as much as a cubic inch of water, the specific gravity of the substance would be 2.
SPIN: As applied to metal work, to shape sheet metal by forcing it against a form as it revolves.
SPIRAL BEVEL GEAR: A gear and pinion wherein the mating teeth are curved and placed at an angle with the pinion shaft.
SPLINE: A long keyway.
SPLINE JOINT: Two mating parts each with a series of splines around their circumference, one inner and one outer in order to provide a longitudinally movable joint without circumferential motion.
SPOT WELD: To attach in spots by localized fusion of the metal parts with the aid of an electric current.
SPUR GEAR: A gear in which the teeth are cut parallel to the shaft.
SPURT-HOLE: A hole drilled through a connecting rod and bearing which allows oil under pressure to be squirted out of the bearing for additional lubrication of the cylinder walls.
SQ. FT.: Square feet.
SQ. IN.: Square inch.

STAMPING: A piece of sheet metal cut and formed into the desired shape with the use of dies.

STANDARD THREAD: Refers to the U.S.S. table of the number of threads per inch. For example, a quarter inch diameter standard thread would have 20 threads per inch.

STATIC ELECTRICITY: Atmospheric electricity as distinguished from electricity as produced by a mechanical device. Usually has extremely high tension.

STEEL CASTING: Cast iron to which varying amounts of scrap steel have been added.

STELLITE: An alloy of cobalt, chrome and tungsten which is often used for exhaust valve seat inserts. It has a high melting point, good corrosion resistance and unusual hardness when hot.

STRAP: In a battery, refers to a lead section to which the plates of a group are joined.

STRESS: The force or strain to which a material is subjected.

STROBOSCOPE: A term applied to an ignition timing light which by being attached to the distributor points gives the effect of making a marking on a rapidly rotating wheel, such as a flywheel, appear to stand still for observation.

STROKE: In an engine, the distance moved by the piston.

"STROKING": As applied to racing engines, re-machining the crankshaft throws off center to alter the stroke.

STUDS: A rod with threads cut on both ends, such as a cylinder stud which screws into the cylinder block on one end and has a nut placed on the other end to hold the cylinder head in place.

SUCTION: Suction exists in a vessel when the pressure is lower than the atmospheric pressure; also see Vacuum.

SULPHATED: When a battery is improperly charged or allowed to remain in a discharged condition for some length of time, the plates will have an abnormal amount of lead sulphate. The battery is then said to be "sulphated."

SUPERCHARGER: A blower or pump which forces air into the cylinders at higher than atmospheric pressure. In an engine the increased pressure forces more air into the cylinder, thus enabling more gasoline to be burned and more power produced.

SWEAT: To join metal pieces by clamping together with solder between them and applying heat.

SYNCHRONIZE: To cause two events to occur in unison or at the same time.

TACHOMETER: A device for measuring and indicating the rotative speed of an engine.

TAP: To cut threads in a hole with a tapered, fluted, threaded tool.

TAPPET: The adjusting screw for varying the clearance between the valve stem and the cam. May be built into the valve lifter in an engine or may be installed in the rocker arm on an overhead valve engine.

T.D.C.: Top dead center.

TEMPER: To change the physical characteristics of metal by the application of heat.

TENSION: Effort devoted towards elongation or "stretching" of a material.

TERMINAL: In electrical work, a junction point whereat connections are made, such as the terminal fitting on the end of a wire.

T-HEAD ENGINE: An engine design wherein the inlet valves are placed on one side of the cylinder and the exhaust valves placed on the other.

THERMAL EFFICIENCY: A gallon of fuel contains a certain amount of potential energy in the form of heat when burned in the combustion chamber. Some of this heat is lost and some is converted into power. The thermal efficiency is the ratio of work accomplished compared to the total quantity of heat contained in the fuel.

THERMOSTAT: A heat controlled valve used in the cooling system of an engine to regulate the flow of water or used in the electrical circuit to control the current.

THERMO-SYPHON: A method of cooling an engine which utilizes the difference in specific gravity of hot and cold water. No pump is used, but the water passages are larger than in the pump circulation system.

THIRD BRUSH: As used on generators, this is an auxiliary brush placed on the commutator in such relation to the main brushes that it serves to control the current output of the generator.

THROW: With reference to an engine, usually the distance from the center of the crankshaft main bearing to the center of the connecting rod journal.

TIMER: Refers to the ignition distributor which times or supplies a spark to the spark plugs at the proper instant.

TIMING CHAIN: Chain used to drive camshaft and accessory shafts of an engine.

TIMING GEARS: Any group of gears which are driven from the engine crankshaft to cause the valves, ignition and other engine driven apparatus to operate at the desired time during the engine cycle.

TOLERANCE: A permissible variation between the two extremes of a specification of dimensions.

TORQUE: An effort devoted toward twisting or turning.

TORQUE WRENCH: A special wrench with a built-in indicator to measure the applied force.

TRANSFORMER: An electrical device, such as a high tension coil which transforms or changes the characteristics of an electrical current.

TROUBLE SHOOTING: Refers to a process of diagnosing or deducing the source of the trouble or troubles from observation and testing.

TUNE-UP: With reference to an engine, a process of accurate and careful adjustments to obtain the utmost in performance.

TURBINE: A series of blades located on a wheel at an angle with the shaft against which fluids or gases are impelled to impart rotary motion to the shaft.

TURBULENCE: A disturbed or disordered, irregular motion of fluids or gases.

TWO CYCLE ENGINE: An engine design permitting a power stroke once for each revolution of the crankshaft.

UNIVERSAL JOINT: A connection for transmitting power from a driving to a driven shaft through an angle.

UP-DRAFT: Used to describe a carburetor type wherein the mixture flows upward to the engine.

UPPER CYLINDER LUBRICATION: A method of introducing a lubricant into the fuel or intake manifold in order to permit lubrication of the upper cylinder, valve guides, etc.

UPSET: To compress endwise causing an increase in diameter.

VACUUM: A perfect vacuum has not been created as this would involve an absolute lack of pressure. The term is ordinarily used to describe a partial vacuum, that is, a pressure less than atmospheric pressure; in other words a suction.

VACUUM GAUGE: An instrument designed to measure the degree of vacuum existing in a chamber.

VALVE: Used in great variety and of many types. A valve is a device for opening and sealing an aperture.

VALVE CLEARANCE: The air gap allowed between the end of the valve stem and the valve lifter or rocker arm to compensate for expansion due to heat.

VALVE FACE: That part of a valve which mates with and rests upon a seating surface.

VALVE GRINDING: Also called valve lapping. A process of lapping or mating the valve seat and valve face usually performed with the aid of an abrasive.

VALVE HEAD: The portion of the valve upon which the valve face is machined.

VALVE-IN-HEAD ENGINE: Same as overhead valve engine.

VALVE KEY OR VALVE LOCK: The key, washer, or other device which holds the valve spring cup or washer in place on the valve stem.

VALVE LIFTER: A push rod or plunger placed between the cam and the valve on an engine; is often adjustable to vary the length of the unit.

VALVE MARGIN: On a poppet valve the space or rim between the surface of the head and the surface of the valve face.

VALVE OVERLAP: An interval expressed in degrees where both valves of an engine cylinder are open at the same time.

VALVE SEAT: The matched surface upon which the valve face rests.

VALVE SPRING: A spring attached to a valve to return it to the seat after it has been released from the lifting or opening means.

VALVE STEM: That portion of a valve which rests within a guide.

VALVE STEM GUIDE: A bushing or hole in which the valve stem is placed which allows lateral motion only.

VANES: Any plate, blade or the like attached to an axis and moved by or in air or a liquid.

VAPORIZER: A device for transforming or helping to transform a liquid into a vapor; often includes the application of heat.

VAPOR LOCK: A condition wherein the fuel boils in the fuel system forming bubbles which retard or stop the flow of fuel to the carburetor.

VAPOR PRESSURE: The pressure developed over a liquid in a closed vessel depending upon the liquid and the temperature.

VAPOR WITHDRAWAL: A system of piping and connections to operate an engine directly on the vapor taken from the top of an L.P.G. tank.

VENTURI: Two tapering streamlined tubes joined at their small ends so as to reduce the internal diameter.

VIBRATION DAMPER: A device to reduce the torsional or twisting vibration which occurs along the length of the crankshaft used in multiple cylinder engines; also known as a harmonic balancer.

VISCOSITY: The resistance to flow or adhesiveness characteristics of an oil.

VOLATILITY: The tendency for a fluid to evaporate rapidly or pass off in the form of vapor. For example, gasoline is more volatile than kerosene as it evaporates at a lower temperature.

VOLT: A unit of electrical force which will cause a current of one ampere to flow through a resistance of one ohm.

VOLTAGE REGULATOR: An electrical device for controlling or regulating voltage.

VOLTMETER: An instrument for measuring the voltage in an electrical circuit.

VOLUME: The measure of space expressed as cubic inches, cubic feet, etc.

VOLUMETRIC EFFICIENCY: A combination between the ideal and actual efficiency of an internal combustion engine. If the engine completely filled each cylinder on each induction stroke the volumetric efficiency of the engine would be 100 per cent. In actual operation, however, volumetric efficiency is lowered by the inertia of the gases, the friction between the gases and the manifolds, the temperature of the gases and the pressure of the air entering the carburetor. Volumetric efficiency is ordinarily increased by the use of large valves, ports and manifolds and can be further increased with the aid of a supercharger.

VORTEX: A whirling movement or mass of liquid or air.

WATER COLUMN: A reference term used in connection with a Manometer.

WATT: A measuring unit of electrical power. It is obtained by multiplying amperes by volts.

WELDING: To join two pieces of metal by heating them to the fusion or melting point.

WHITE METAL: An alloy of tin, lead and antimony having a low melting point and a low co-efficient of friction.

WIRING DIAGRAM: A detailed drawing of all wiring, connections and units connected together in an electrical circuit.

WORM GEAR: A shaft having an extremely coarse thread which is designed to operate in engagement with a toothed wheel, as a pair of gears.

WRIST PIN: The journal for the bearing in the small end of an engine connecting rod which also passes through piston walls; also known as a piston pin.

INDEX

INDEX

SILVER
BROWN
RICHARDSON

(ALBASENYA)